UNDER THE EDITORSHIP OF

Herold C. Hunt

Charles William Eliot
Professor of Education
Harvard University

Working with

 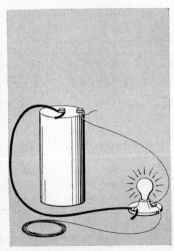 

HOUGHTON MIFFLIN COMPANY   BOSTON

Children in Science

Clark Hubler   Wheelock College

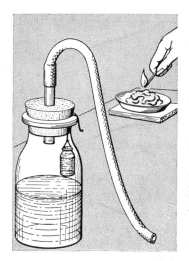

The Riverside Press   Cambridge

Cover photo by Ed Fitzgerald.   Courtesy, The Children's Museum, Boston

The Riverside Press   Cambridge, Massachusetts.   Printed in the U.S.A.

Editor's Introduction

Today's world reflects an interest in science never known before. Books and magazine articles predict the wonder age of a tomorrow not far distant while newspapers, radio and television bring into our homes a realization of the impact of science upon mankind everywhere. The satisfaction of our needs and wants through the utilization of scientific discoveries, inventions and methods offers tangible testimony to the comforts and conveniences of modern living while the combination of improved standards of health, of miracle drugs and automation gives promise of both greater longevity and heretofore unrealized leisure to enjoy it. Truly this is the scientific age.

Increasingly since the mid-point of the twentieth century, with the growing appreciation of the importance of science in peace and survival, has there developed a concern not only for greater competency and skill in the scientific method but, more fundamentally, for basic literacy in science itself.

Such a concern suggests, surely, the need for increased familiarity with the scientific world by all of us. Such a familiarity should begin in the elementary grades, where lifetime interests and habits are developed. Here, for the first time, girls and boys seek the answers to questions that spring from normal and natural curiosity growing out of new and meaningful experiences.

It is to this area of interest and concern that Dr. Clark Hubler, an able scientist and an outstanding teacher, has directed *Working with Children in Science,* a new book which strongly supports the author's belief that reading about science is not enough and that the child must investigate and experiment to receive maximum benefit from his study. Demonstrations and experiments already successfully employed in the classroom are utilized to build confidence in the elementary school teacher who may be either uncertain or skeptical of his ability to teach science through such techniques. A convincing and reassuring approach, a multiplicity and richness of practical helps, a clarity and simplicity of presentation, style and treatment all enhance a basically sound and authoritative treatment.

Herold C. Hunt

Preface

Working with Children in Science is designed for teachers and prospective teachers in the elementary and junior high schools. Its usefulness also should extend to nursery-school and kindergarten teachers. The book contains numerous practical suggestions for classroom procedures to aid the student teacher, and if kept at hand as a source of reference should continue to be helpful in the classroom for many years. It is hoped that this volume will also be of assistance to administrators, supervisors, and consultants interested in promoting science programs in their schools.

Working with Children in Science is concerned with realities — with opportunities and problems that arise in actual teaching situations. It considers ways of getting a science program started, of answering children's questions, of conducting experiments, and of improvising equipment, as well as numerous other practical questions. Experience indicates that teachers prefer and find most useful the kind of assistance which fills an immediate need in their work. The suggestions offered here fit together in a coherent pattern designed to encourage continuing growth of understanding. The classroom incidents described show what can be accomplished in work with children of various ages and learning experiences.

The procedures recommended are simple yet sound. Overly complex or misleading experiments have been omitted. Stressed throughout is the value of firsthand experience motivated by the child's natural curiosity about the world in which he lives. The subject matter is presented in such a way that the teacher can learn with the children, no matter how limited his own scientific background.

It will be apparent throughout *Working with Children in Science* that the educational point of view is in substantial agreement with that of the *Forty-Sixth Yearbook* of the National Society for the Study of Education. There are, however, features which have been developed further. In fact, there is scarcely anything in the text that has not been modified, adapted, or developed as the direct result of experience and a constant search for better methods of work. It is hoped that this publication will help in the general effort to promote science instruction in the schools so that science will become as prominent in education as it is in society.

The teaching illustrations cited are authentic. Many are derived from the author's own experience as a teacher. Some were reported by fellow teachers, some by the author's wife, Reta Allinson Hubler, and some by students in undergraduate, graduate, and in-service classes. Except where credit is otherwise given, the photographs were prepared by the author and his wife. The line drawings were made by John V. Morris from rough sketches by the author.

Clark Hubler

Contents

Working with Children in Science

1

Science for Children

Science plays a prominent and essential part in life today; it should have a prominent role also in the education of children. Through science children can gain a better understanding of themselves and of the world about them. Everyone today should have some understanding and appreciation of science. Because the teaching of science at the elementary level often has been neglected in the past — and advanced courses have been highly technical — many teachers need help in preparing for their work with children in science. The suggestions and illustrations that follow are derived from practical experience in teaching and helping others to teach science in elementary schools.

IS SCIENCE SUITABLE FOR CHILDREN?

Although scientific research may be highly technical and may seem remote from the daily experiences of most people, the science advocated for elementary schools today is concerned with commonplace things and events. Science appeals to the persistent curiosity of children. It helps children see how exposure to the weather has caused rocks by the roadside to crumble, how seed are spread from the weeds in the empty lot next door, how a toy harmonica makes notes of different pitch. Science helps answer countless other questions of interest to children. Many people are beginning to realize that no area of the curriculum can be more appropriate for children, and none more profitable.

Science based upon active investigation is easy to conduct in the classroom, for the teacher need not know all the answers in advance, but can help children find out for themselves. Science for children is apt to be more like the investigations children carry on of their own volition, in their own free time, than like the traditional courses of high school or college. Science can be fascinating and highly rewarding for even the youngest child in school; and if the teacher is willing to begin, an effective program can develop. Given the opportunity, the children themselves will point the way.

Science is active investigation

Science in the schools should help children understand and appreciate their natural environment. In accord with the methods of science itself, the most effective way to learn science is through direct investigation. Perhaps a few accounts of actual teaching situations will help to depict the kind of science experiences considered desirable:

Examples of investigations in the first and second grades. When a first-grade boy came to school one morning with a caterpillar in a jar, the teacher asked him to show it to the class. Among the ensuing comments and questions, someone asked what a caterpillar eats. Several children thought it would eat flies and bugs; others thought it should be fed leaves. So an experiment was performed. A leaf and a dead fly were placed in the jar with the caterpillar. There was much excitement in the classroom; the children could hardly wait to see what would happen.

The next morning, when the children arrived at school, they found that part of the leaf was gone but the fly remained. The class decided the caterpillar had eaten the leaf; nevertheless, to be sure the caterpillar preferred leaves, more leaves and flies were added to the jar.

Later in the day, however, the investigation took a surprising turn, for it was discovered that the caterpillar had begun to spin a cocoon. The children were puzzled at first and asked many questions: What was he doing? Where did the threads come from? Was the caterpillar going to die?

The teacher found a book about caterpillars and butterflies. She read it to the children, and afterwards wrote their conclusions on the blackboard:

We have a caterpillar.
It eats leaves.
It is weaving a cocoon.

At the first opportunity the teacher printed the "story" on a sheet of tagboard and placed it on the table beside the jar with the caterpillar. The caterpillar was the center of interest for a while, and more books were found that contained pictures and information concerning caterpillars. Then one morning, after a number of weeks had passed, the class found a butterfly on the inside of the classroom window. After examining the butterfly they hurried over to the jar and found the cocoon empty.

New lines were added to the story about the caterpillar:

Our caterpillar changed into a butterfly.
The butterfly will lay eggs.
The eggs will hatch into caterpillars.

In another case a seven-year-old child asked the teacher why there were drops of water on the under side of the aquarium cover. Instead of giving a direct verbal answer, the teacher asked him what he thought was the reason. The child was not sure, but several other children suggested possible explanations. To help solve the problem, the teacher placed a kettle of water on an electric hot plate, and when the water began to boil she asked one of the children to hold a drinking glass above the kettle. Everybody watched the glass grow misty as little drops formed. The drops grew larger, and soon water was dripping from the glass. The children concluded that water from the aquarium had gathered on the aquarium cover much as water from the kettle had collected on the drinking glass, and that what had happened must be the same thing that sometimes occurs on schoolroom windows on cold days.

An example of investigation in the fifth grade. While a class in New Hampshire was studying the New England states in geography, it was brought out that much of the land is not good for farming, largely because of the many steep hillsides and many rocks. Someone asked where all the rocks had come from in the first place, and the class was well on its way to a study of rocks and the changing surface in New England. A large stone had been brought in previously, and the conversation turned to it. The teacher was familiar with that type of rock, which was common locally, and knew it was schist, a metamorphic rock, and that high mountains once existed where it is found as bedrock, as in New Hampshire.

"How could a mountain be washed away?" someone wanted to know.

"How old is the world, really?" someone else inquired.

The answers varied from 1954 years (1954 being the date at that time) to a million years — all much less than the three billion years or more estimated by geologists.

After the geography lesson that turned into a science lesson, Patty came to

Fig. 1

Children are natural investigators.

the teacher and with shining eyes said, "Oh, Mrs. M——, I usually hate geography, but I loved the lesson we had today!"

As the teacher made her plans for the next day, she decided to take the children outside to gather rocks from the grounds. But before the plan could be put into practice the children came to school laden with bags of stones, and they employed their recesses and noon hour scouring the grounds for more rocks — all as a result of enthusiasm generated by the previous day's work.

After the children had acquired a large collection of stones they began to sort them, putting together the ones that were alike in some respect. Later they listed what they had observed about rocks:

Some are sharp and pointed.
Some are smooth and rounded.
Some are hard, many so hard we can't break them.
Some are easy to break.
The different colors are from the minerals in them.
Some have mica that sparkles.
Some are heavier than others.
Some seem to be in layers, but others are in a mass.

In their reading the children learned that rocks can be grouped into three great classes according to the way they were formed: *igneous, sedimentary,* and *metamorphic.* Reporting what he had read, one child said that *igneous rocks* were at one time hot like lava, although not all were poured out onto the surface from volcanoes. Many igneous rocks are exposed only after the rocks above them have been worn away. Granite, common in New Hampshire, served as an example familiar to the class. Someone reported he had found in his reading that the size of the crystal depends largely on how rapidly the molten rock cooled. The specimen he showed the class had large crystals and thus probably had been deep in the earth at the time it cooled. The three minerals, mica, feldspar, and quartz, were noted in the rock and compared to the descriptions in the books.

Speaking of the *sedimentary rocks,* John said, "Yes, but how can sand get to be rock? What makes it stick together?"

Mary agreed: "Even if you wet sand and press it hard, it doesn't stick together the way mud does."

An experiment found in a book helped to clarify the point. Following the directions, the children mixed sand with slaked lime, then moistened the mixture and set it aside to harden. The lime served as cementing material to hold the sand together and form an artificial stone. Other suitable experiments were located in books. One child demonstrated stratification by stirring sand and clay in a jar and pointing out how the particles settled in layers, and then the class visited a nearby bank by the roadside where the strata were visible. Some shale brought back to class was compared with the clay already on hand. One of the girls found in her reading that shale is formed from clay and that shale and clay can be differentiated by putting water on them. The children did so, placing each in a pan of water. The clay began to dissolve, but the shale remained firm; both smelled like mud. Because there was so much sedimentary rock near the school, the class decided that the land there must have been flooded, perhaps long ago.

Mary Ann read that limestone may still contain some of the shells from which it was formed. The limestone the class had collected was examined for evidence of shells, but none was found. The rock was identified, however, by the odor of lime that could be detected when the rock was scratched with a nail, and by the fact that the rock was soft enough to be scratched by the nail. Further evidence was obtained when bubbles formed where acid was dropped onto the rock. The class was intrigued when they found that their specimen of marble reacted to the acid in the same way. The books said that marble is made from limestone, and that rocks which have undergone such changes are called *metamorphic*. In their collection of stones the class also had slate as another example of metamorphic rock. In addition to learning of the vast changes undergone by the rocks and soil of New Hampshire, and of the forces involved in such changes, these children began to develop some conception of the great expanse of time and the enduring stability of the earth upon which we live.

The preceding illustrations and others that follow will help show what can be accomplished while working with children in science. Actual examples and definite suggestions are stressed in the belief that such will provide the greatest help for teachers who wish to begin work in science or to improve their teaching in this area of the curriculum. It will be obvious that in one way or another most really successful experiences in science deal with everyday realities and rely heavily upon the natural curiosity of the children.

Children are natural investigators

Children of elementary-school age normally have great curiosity concerning whatever is real and vital about them. The child's natural impulse to investigate is in accord with the spirit of scientific research. As parents well know, children are constantly asking questions and forever "getting into things," with hands perpetually fingering whatever may be within reach. The proprietors of stores become nervous, and parents become exasperated, for fragile articles and hazardous equipment are not excepted from the restless inspection. Such activity is the child's means of learning about his surroundings. Even an adult in unfamiliar surroundings is likely to run his hand along a strange surface, is inclined to touch material of unusual texture, is impelled to handle new devices on the counter at the store, and may have difficulty resisting a temptation to manipulate a new tool in his neighbor's kitchen or workshop. The child encounters much that is novel to him; hence he continues to explore and to learn.

Children have persistent curiosity. In one second-grade room a child was observed looking at some stones that had become worn and rounded, probably somewhere in the bed of a stream. She took from the table a smooth, brightly colored pebble, rubbed it with her hands, put it against her face, smelled it, and then licked it — not exactly a hygienic process, but in this way she discovered the texture of the pebble and tasted the saltiness. Through such means, involving first-hand contacts, children acquire an understanding of the world about them.

When an animal, such as a rabbit, is placed in an unfamiliar situation, it at once begins to investigate by nosing about, sniffing at the walls, the floor, and the feeding devices, or whatever may be near. Apparently the child's curiosity is similar to that of the lower animals. In a world that is new to the child there is much which is strange, and the natural impulse is to investigate.

A teacher can help children with their investigations. In one case, while the first-grade teacher was watering some potted plants, one of the girls asked if the plants would grow without water. Rather than simply answering *no*, the teacher asked if Sally would like to work with the plants each morning to see for herself what would happen to them without water. Sally was willing, and she decided to water some of the plants but let others go without for a while. After about a week the plants without water began to turn brown, and Sally had the answer to her question.

Fig. 2

The child's curiosity is much like that of the lower animals.

Children ask many questions about their surroundings that science can help to answer. The following are a few recorded questions of early childhood asked in teaching situations and indicative of an interest in the environment; not all served as the impetus for study, but a teacher can make use of whatever concerns seem profitable and practicable at the time:

Why did the lights go out? What made the horn on Daddy's car keep blowing? How did he make it stop? Why does the fishbowl make a rainbow? Why do the leaves fall off the trees? Then why don't the pine needles fall? If those are seed [maple], why do they have wings? How do boats float? What makes night? Where was the moon last night? Do you think it was shining on Cape Cod? It wasn't here. Where does the sun go at night? Can a river go uphill? Where did the turtle go [hibernating in the sod of the terrarium]? Why did he do that? Do birds have tongues? What made the car at the service station go up and down [on the grease-rack lift]? What is that greenish stuff on the paste? What are atoms made of? How did the fish get into the water? How do we make airplanes go? How does a bear find her home? How does the telephone work? What makes a hurricane?

Such a list could go on indefinitely. There seems to be no end to children's questions. In a study of the questions asked by pre-school children, M. E. Smith found that ninety-four per cent were concerned with the immediate environment. The kind of questions and the number asked depend upon the maturity of the child and upon the environment which stimulates the questioning, but there is ample evidence that the healthy child is an investigator concerned with learning about his surroundings.[1]

Curiosity is not always expressed in words. The child who is constantly "into things" may be investigating, and his behavior can reveal his curiosity more eloquently than words. The child quietly absorbed in watching a squirrel bury a nut may have little to say at the time; and the boy who spends class time dismantling an automatic pencil instead of reading the assigned lesson may become so absorbed in learning how the pencil works that he has little time for talk. The inquisitiveness of childhood is proverbial and need not be stressed further here, except to point out that this common trait has educational value. Through such means the child becomes acquainted with his environment and the adult is given a clue to his interests and capabilities.

Even small children are capable of direct investigation. The urge to investigate emerges at an early age. The infant in his crib is investigating when he discovers his toes and pulls them down to his mouth, as he is likely to do with

---

[1] Reported in Dorothea McCarthy, "Language Development in Children," *Manual of Child Psychology*, edited by Leonard Carmichael, John Wiley & Sons, New York, 1954, pp. 572–574.

anything else in reach. When he begins to crawl, his range is increased and parents must scurry about to the rescue, for the child is already a persistent investigator. That such endeavors are basically scientific has been pointed out by Gesell:

> Adults take time and space for granted; not so the growing baby. The infant is not a scientist, yet he must master the very first principles on which all physical science is based. His mind is constantly taking first steps into the physical universe from the moment of birth . . . he acquires his command of these elements by slow degrees, first through his muscles of manipulation and locomotion, through eyes, hands, and feet. In this motor experience he lays the foundation for his later judgments and concepts. . . . There comes a time when the child asks many questions . . . words will not be assimilated unless the child's mental maturity and previous experience give them meaning.[2]

Even the youngest can be helped with their investigations. On a rainy day the nursery-school teacher opened her wet umbrella and set it in a corner to dry. Asked why she had opened it, she explained that it would dry sooner that way, and she suggested an experiment. An old piece of cloth was torn in two. Both parts were dipped into water and then wrung as dry as possible. One was left in a tight ball, the other spread out and left so the children could see for themselves which would dry first. Direct investigation has no age limits.

There is no substitute for the child's own observation and experimentation. When Bobby noticed a magnet lying on the kindergarten table he became curious, picked it up, and looked at it carefully. Another child rushed over and told him that it was a magnet and it would pick up things. Bobby, plainly skeptical about this information, went about the room experimenting for himself, touching the magnet to all sorts of articles, finding out just what the magnet would do. At any age such direct experience is basic to science and to learning.

Science has been variously defined as knowledge, as an interpretation of the environment, as an inductive method of investigation, and, in its broader aspects, as a way of life. By any definition, science within the realm of the child's maturity and experience is in accord with the child's own impulse to investigate, to gain knowledge of his surroundings. The child's spontaneous activities suggest that he is eager to learn and capable of doing so. Children can and will investigate of their own accord and need only to be encouraged, guided, and assisted to make the work profitable.

[2] Arnold Gesell and Frances L. Ilg, *Infant and Child in the Culture of Today,* Harper, New York, 1943, pp. 21, 26.

Fig. 3

Even small children are capable of direct investigation.

Opportunity for investigation is all about the child

Because of his youth the young person encounters much that is still unfamiliar and hence arouses his curiosity. He is fascinated by the doorbell that rings when he presses a button, and he will flip the light switch on and off incessantly. On the child's level there is much that requires interpretation through investigation. Children are concerned with the concrete and the immediate. It is the function of science in the elementary school to encourage interest in the environment and channel such concerns into worthwhile learning. A basic policy of education in the elementary school is to begin with the immediate environment and broaden the field of study as the child matures.[3] Accordingly,

[3] Hollis L. Caswell and A. Wellesley Foshay, *Education in the Elementary School*, American Book, New York, 1950, pp. 139–40.

many activities are centered upon themes involving the home and the community.

Potential learnings are plentiful in the home and the community. Appropriate to the maturity of the child, there are many potential learnings in science which are concerned with experiences in the home. Our houses are equipped with electric lamps, wires, heaters, toasters, and countless other devices, such as the vacuum cleaner, lawn mower, refrigerator, and telephone — all capable of rousing a child's curiosity. Biological principles are well represented in our pets, the plants in the garden, and the insects as well, but most prominently in the child himself. Many of the adult activities in a home hold the attention of children and can be the basis of worthwhile learnings. Children are fascinated

Fig. 4

Opportunity for investigation is all about the child.

by fire and matches, for example. Caution based on understanding is more desirable than blind fear or surreptitious investigations without adult guidance.

In their play children have many experiences which can serve to inculcate scientific concepts. They play with mechanical toys, chemistry sets, toys that float in water, magnetic and electrical toys. Many other playthings, including those that children improvise for themselves, embody scientific principles. A child simply may place a board between two large stones and pry against them; in the process he may acquire the basis for understanding certain forces and simple machines. The roller skates he uses have ball bearings to reduce friction, just as does the machinery in the factory where someday he may work.

Many community agencies provide potential science experiences. Included in such a list are the fire department, the water department, with its reservoirs and purification plants, the city park department or county agricultural agency, the museum and zoo, the electric power plant, the air fields and weather stations — even a not too complex factory that may demonstrate chemical or physical processes.

Local events, perhaps commonplace to an adult, may be of interest to a child and stimulate his learning. A thunderstorm creates excitement and wonder. In fact, any abrupt change in the weather is likely to attract attention that can result in learning. Even such a lowly event as maggots appearing in the neighbor's garbage may excite a child's curiosity and become the basis for understanding how insects go through changes in their development — a knowledge that is essential in the control of insect pests. The normal child has great curiosity, and his environment is potentially rich in the materials and experiences of science. Innumerable questions can be asked in even the most unpromising surroundings.

Much that happens in and about the school requires interpretation. Occurrences at school, some of them deliberately planned by the teacher, may prompt worthwhile questions and stimulate learning. The pattern of sunlight in the room, it may be noted, shifts as the day progresses. Many children are inclined to think at first that a magnet has something sticky on it. How does it happen that a bar of metal left in the sunshine gets hotter than one left in the shade? And what are bees doing in the flowers on the school grounds? A learning situation arises when the hamsters in the cage or the snails in the aquarium bear young, when seedlings wilt for lack of water, or when a spider is discovered spinning a web. The child is making numerous conceptual adjustments: Do spiders cause rain, or meteors bring death, as some people say? Smoke and clouds are likely to be confused. Did water disappear from the aquarium because of a leak? Or how did the pattern of frost get onto the cold windowpanes? The child may become engrossed in watching the fish in the aquarium, or in finding out how a friend's new toy works. There is much to be learned.

On his way to school the child may discover a bird feeding its young, a mole-hill beside the path, new growth on the trees and bushes, and seed forming at the base of the flowers; or at another season the seed may be scattering in the wind, or burs may cling to the child's clothing. The child may see a squirrel scampering about in the trees, or he may become absorbed in making a grass-hopper jump. And if by chance he comes upon a line of ants busily scurrying along a narrow path, he ordinarily will have time to stop for a few moments of observation. Machinery is always of interest, and if the child should pass an unusual piece of equipment, such as a derrick lifting a telephone pole into place or a power shovel digging a ditch, he can wait a little longer to see how it works — and in this mechanical age the child needs some understanding and appreciation of such activities. The school should encourage such observations and help with the interpretations.

The child needs guidance in his investigations. Without adult help many of the questions children ask will remain unanswered, and many of the interpreta-tions they make will be false. With appropriate suggestions and assistance children will find safer, more profitable explorations, and new possibilities for learning will become apparent. Through proper guidance science can help children to understand what is going on about them.

However, unless children have capable guidance the materials and phenom-ena which represent potential science learnings may instead become the basis of superstition and misunderstanding, of bias and needless apprehension. The stars of the sky, for example, can be a source of superstition as readily as a source of insight. Not infrequently a child will show by his actions that he believes the button switch on the front porch is really the bell itself, for when it is pressed a bell rings. The same person who is violently afraid of touching the terminals of a dry cell for fear of getting a shock, at the next moment may blunder into something actually dangerous. The mere existence of potential science learnings in the environment is no guarantee of adequate adjustment without the help of adults, and the schools should be one source of such help.

HOW CAN WORK IN SCIENCE BE INITIATED?

In professional publications, in college courses, in conferences and faculty meetings, teachers are told they should include science in their work. Very likely also provision is made for science in the course of study. Today the failure to teach science is an admission of weakness. Yet teachers who recognize the importance of instruction in this area sometimes hesitate to begin, for there are obstacles to be overcome. One of the obstacles is uncertainty about where and how to begin.

For those who have not taught science, contemplation of the new experience can be challenging and exciting, or discouraging and overwhelming even before starting, depending upon the attitude of the individual concerned. Although a background of courses in science and the teaching of science is helpful, learning need not end with college, and the teacher who is willing can find the work as interesting as do the children. For some people the situation is complicated by a belief that science is a complex, technical field, plainly unsuitable for children. But there is no need to overwhelm children with cold facts. Just as the complex symbols and equations of advanced calculus need not inhibit the development of number concepts in the first grade, the marvelous achievements of technical research should be no obstacle to the investigations of children. Science for children should help to explain the common objects and occurrences with which children come in contact; because the objects and occurrences are common the teacher will have some familiarity with them even before beginning, and as the work progresses will gain further understanding. The first plans should be simple, and the work should never become complex, although some very interesting programs develop from simple beginnings. Once the work has begun and the teacher has seen how the children respond, the way will become clear, and further plans can be shaped accordingly. Those who have not worked with children in science are apt to think of it as difficult, but in a way it is far easier to teach children science than most other subjects, simply because they respond so well to an active program of investigation.

There are many good ways to introduce work in science. The introduction should raise questions and stimulate interest, should help the children see that the work is not only interesting but worthwhile, and should develop plans for conducting the study. The investigations may begin with some interest the children already have, or the teacher may introduce something new.

An interest already apparent can be developed

Classroom procedures should be flexible enough to be influenced by the aspirations of the children themselves. There are many possible routes to the desired ends of education, and there is no good reason for changing directions if the children are already on the way. When children ask significant questions, when they bring to school something of interest, or their behavior otherwise indicates that they have become engrossed in a worthwhile topic, the subject already has been introduced, and the task of the teacher is simplified. A learning situation then exists. Newer educational policies commonly seek to give children as much opportunity as possible to exercise their own initiative, yet channel their efforts toward acceptable goals.

Instruction can begin with the worthwhile questions children ask. Seeking solutions to their own questions can lead children to valuable learnings — learnings that are meaningful, timely, and applicable in the real situations of the child's own life. Each of the following questions, asked by children in the first grade, could have yielded information as significant as anything the teacher might have proposed: "Where does the sun go when it rains?" "What makes it rain?" "Why do the leaves turn brown?" "How do the fish breathe?" These questions lacked only a teacher who could see their worth and a daily schedule flexible enough to take advantage of them.

Other cases have turned out better. One fourth-grade girl wanted to know how the fish in the classroom aquarium were able to breathe under water. The query prompted additional questions about how fish swim, eat, and sleep. Through reading followed by further direct observation, the questions were answered. As the children watched the aquarium they could see for themselves how the fish got their food, how the gills moved in breathing, how the fins were used for swimming. Patricia read that fish do not sleep as people do but get their rest while motionless. Carol wanted to know if a snail has a tongue; so for a few days the children watched carefully through a reading glass until several had observed the snail in the aquarium moving its tongue in and out. As the work continued, the interest in living things broadened, and soon the children were investigating problems that had not occurred to them earlier. The natural curiosity of the children had been directed toward the goals of education in science.

Instruction can begin with some of the articles children bring to class. When children bring objects to class, their actions are evidence of an interest which, if promising, may be used to introduce a new topic. A third grade, for example, began working with magnets shortly after Christmas when one child came in with a magnetic fishing game she had received and another brought a toy car that could be moved about by a magnet held in the child's hand.

Sometimes the children themselves will initiate just what the teacher had in mind. An interesting sequence developed when Douglas came to school with a note from his mother asking if he might bring to school a wasp's nest he had found. The note explained that several of the wasps were dead but still in the nest. The teacher left the decision up to the class, and of course they were eager to have the nest brought to school. The next day Douglas arrived with his nest, and when the time came for him to tell about it, the class listened intently while he recounted where he had located it and what he had learned about the wasps that had built it. Later some of the children made a sign to place beside the nest. The sign read: "See the bee nest." But Douglas objected. He insisted it was a wasp's nest, not a bee's nest. After a portion of the nest was cut away to show the cells inside, the nest was compared with nests shown and described in the books and thus was identified as that of a paper wasp, not that of a bee. Eventually another placard was prepared and displayed with the nest on a table in the hall. Because the wasp's nest was welcomed, other contributions followed, and the class continued with their study of living things. In this case the teacher had been looking for an effective and natural way to introduce some work in science, and so the wasp's nest arrived at a most opportune time.

Some occurrence may stimulate inquiry. In addition to the questions asked and the articles brought in, something that happens, some occurrence which seems important to the children, may stimulate further inquiry and serve to introduce new experiences in science. The event may be of major significance, or it may seem important only to the children themselves, yet serve as the impetus for learning. If outside the classroom windows squirrels are seen romping in the trees, or a skunk is sighted in a nearby field, the class may decide to study animals, how they protect themselves, get their food, care for their young. In one second grade a discussion of animals began when Patricia told about an animal she had seen on television, and the other children began asking questions. Arthur wanted to bring in his rabbit, and Dick volunteered to bring his big new picture dictionary with "lots of animals in it!" Barbara suggested they all look up and read about animals and then tell the class about them the next day. And thus a study of animal life was launched by the children themselves.

In the first grade one morning a child volunteered his impressions of an eclipse that had occurred the evening before. He said, "An eclipse is when a black cloud goes over the moon and takes away half the moon. When the eclipse breaks, there is a flash of light. Then there is thunder." Obviously he had confused an eclipse with a thunderstorm, but his report raised significant questions and served to initiate a study of the sky. With the questions raised, the teacher simply helped the children to find the information they already were seeking. It is always more pleasant and more effective to work with people when they really want to learn.

The enthusiasm of one child may stimulate others to learn. On some occasions the enthusiasm of one child may be contagious so that others become engrossed in the situation that has developed. In one case it was the enthusiasm of a sixth-grade girl for flowers that led to a study of plant growth. In another class, a third grade, during a language lesson one of the boys gave an interesting report of his experiences with a tin-can telephone. He and a friend had prepared the apparatus, set it up in his father's barn, and had been able to talk over it. After the report the class agreed that the tin-can arrangement did not work the way a real telephone does, but the boy had reported his experience with so much pleasure that the others caught his enthusiasm and decided that the class should build a real telephone. One boy said he could bring his brother's receiver, and it was planned to construct a transmitter as described in the textbooks. Dry cells would be needed, and a cigar box and some wire. The next morning without fail all that was needed had arrived. The children not only prepared a telephone circuit that worked, with moderate success and frequent adjustments, but also performed related experiments and reported them. The enthusiasm carried over into the history lesson, which included the story of Alexander Graham Bell and his invention of the telephone. The language work stressed telephone conversations, enunciation, and politeness. One child's enthusiasm had developed into a major project.

The child's initiative has both advantages and limitations. If directed toward acceptable goals, experiences that children help to initiate have some marked advantages. Facts gained through such experiences can be used to interpret real situations. Instructional problems that arise from the child's own circumstances are more likely to be timely and meaningful, the learnings more real and functional. The child becomes a more constructive, responsible individual when his wishes are respected, when his concerns stimulate a like response in others and when his ideas are accepted, or at least considered. Responding to the child gives the child greater opportunity to develop initiative and permits greater self-direction and individualization of instruction. A child can learn to weigh values and make decisions when his choice does not lie merely between compliance and rebellion. In short, some of the initiative must be left with the child if learning is to be effective and education democratic.

No teacher should feel obligated to follow all the tangents suggested by the children. Moreover, teachers should be cautious about overestimating the degree and quality of a child's interest and should not assume interest where no real interest exists. Nevertheless, instruction that develops from the real concerns of the children and is directed toward desirable goals is work well begun.

New undertakings can be introduced

Where the work undertaken is introduced by the teacher, the genuine interest of the children must be won if the effort is to be effective. In science this usually is not difficult, for science instruction which deals actively with reality appeals to children. A field trip can be used to rouse interest and at the same time provide a basis for understanding work which follows in the classroom. One teacher used a motion picture for a similar purpose. The film showed common animals of the woods and was used to introduce a study of living things.

Material placed on a work table will stimulate investigation. A highly successful way of stimulating interest in something new — a way quite commonly used in the younger grades but effective at any level — is to place some appropriate materials on a work table for the children to examine. The equipment should catch the attention of the children and stimulate worthwhile observation and experimentation. As a result, the children make their own discoveries and initiate the work for themselves, in accord with the teacher's plans. Resources suitable for stimulating an interest in living things might include a salamander from the woods, some fish obtained by the teacher at a pet shop, or perhaps some flower bulbs and a package of seed. A dry cell, an electric bell, and some wire may be placed on the table to initiate an interest in electricity. A magnifying glass, a mirror, and a prism will stimulate experimentation with light and suggest many questions for continued study. By selecting what is to be displayed on the table, the teacher can direct the natural curiosity of the children toward work in the desired field.

Demonstrations can be used to stimulate interest and raise problems for investigation. Having the real thing on hand for direct observation can stimulate interest and help launch a new undertaking in science. Even though everyone is to some extent familiar with rocks, for example, having one on hand can help the teacher initiate a discussion of the earth's surface. The rock will hold attention, and if it is a good specimen will help to convey the desired meanings.

Secondary-school science teachers frequently use demonstrations to motivate a discussion or to introduce a new topic. On some occasions a similar approach is effective in the elementary school. In fact, demonstrations are so effective in stimulating interest that some teachers rely too heavily upon them, and the classes merely watch exciting displays. Nevertheless, a demonstration that is pertinent can provide a very successful introduction to a new topic or problem. A demonstration of spontaneous combustion served very well to stimulate a second-grade discussion of Fire-Prevention Week, and a demonstration of how to make ink from two chemicals was an appropriate introduction to the study of chemical changes by a sixth grade. Demonstrations are vivid and more likely to be meaningful than mere descriptions.

A discussion can be an effective way to begin. Even though the teacher has some plans already in mind, a discussion with the children of what is to be

taken will be known in advance; hence in effect the beginner will be able to keep one foot on shore while venturing into the water with the other. A teacher trained in the social studies, for example, may feel more at home if the topic selected is closely related to life on the farm, the Industrial Revolution, the culture of the American Indian, or the Fire Department — areas previously studied or taught and already familiar.

One teacher who chose the social applications of science as a familiar yet worthwhile area for investigation began by suggesting that the children of his sixth grade might like to experiment with some of the phenomena being studied in their history and then demonstrate and explain the principles involved, as well as report the historical circumstances. The children worked individually, or where the individuals had a common interest they worked in small groups. The members of this class studied the work of Watt, Franklin, Bell, Edison, Morse, Faraday, Burbank, Pasteur, Leeuwenhoek, Harvey, Galileo, and the Wright brothers. One of the boys, a refugee from Occupied France, chose to study Pasteur and the influence of his achievements. In addition to extensive reference work, the boy prepared bacteria cultures in flasks of beef broth, much as the biographies he had read reported that Pasteur had done. The girls who studied Franklin's accomplishments experimented with static electricity and then demonstrated it to the class when making their reports. In like manner the achievements of other historical figures were explained and their influence on our lives described. Work in science can well be an outgrowth of work in related fields.

Whatever the source or degree of familiarity with the subject, both the insight and the assurance that goes with it can be helpful in venturing into a new field. Largely because the teacher was familiar with music and many in the class were studying it, the teacher of a fifth- and sixth-grade class proposed that they begin with a study of sound, and the proposal was greeted with enthusiasm. Another teacher who had taught geography for many years used her knowledge of this field to begin work in science. In September, when the newspapers began running articles about the change of seasons, she brought the articles to the attention of the class. The cause of seasonal changes and the meaning of words such as *equinox* and *solstice* were considered. As the work continued, it broadened to include a variety of activities and eventually progressed into related areas of science.

Available resources may suggest a way to begin. Familiar resources in or about the school may provide a means of initiating work in science. A nearby stream, animals in the zoo, or the changing autumn foliage about the school grounds may serve such a purpose. One teacher borrowed her neighbor's baby

61615

chicks in the spring; another went to a chick hatchery. In one case a bank of rock in a nearby park was used to introduce a study of the earth. In the same park were many trees, and one of the teachers found some of the large seed pods that had fallen to the ground from a Kentucky coffee tree. A few of the pods were shown to the class, and a discussion followed; then the class was taken to the park to see for themselves the seed pods that remained on the tree. In the park other related observations were made, and the class was launched on a study of how plants grow and reproduce themselves. The electricity for this school was generated in a nearby steam plant. One teacher began work in science by visiting the power house and having the engineer in charge explain how the electricity is generated. Many questions were raised, and the class went back to their books seeking answers. The fact that magnets, electric bells, dry cells, and similar items were on hand has been the stimulus, in many cases, for a study of magnetism and electricity. The New England Dairy Council provides laboratory rats for dietary experiments in the classrooms, and as a result many teachers in New England have undertaken a study of nutrition. The facilities available can suggest worthwhile investigations. Once such studies are begun, it is not hard to find other areas of science in which to work.

Books can be used as a point of departure. A teacher who is unfamiliar with science and hesitant about teaching it may well follow a textbook for a time, until familiarity makes possible a more versatile approach. Most textbooks and their teaching manuals suggest experiments and other activities to accompany the reading; the activities which seem appropriate to the circumstances may be carried out. Following a book with nothing but more reading can be a dull business, lacking in significance for the children and the teacher as well; but if new ideas are welcomed and tried, the book will be but a starting point, and the work can be challenging for both teacher and students.

In using elementary-science books, ordinarily it will not be necessary to begin with the first chapter and follow through the book in routine fashion. In most elementary texts each chapter or unit is concerned with a different area of the environment, rather than being a continuation of what has preceded; hence the topics can be studied independently and made to fit the class program. If for some reason a class is interested in a particular problem and circumstances at the time help to make it meaningful, that is the time for effective study, regardless of where a chapter may be located in a book. If there has been a violent storm recently, for example, a study of the weather at that time is likely to be stimulating and effective.

Should it happen that the topic chosen from a book is based upon an earlier chapter of the book, the class can turn back to the earlier section for reference as needed. One seventh-grade text begins with a topic entitled "The Air Around Us," whereas the topic "Effects of the Weather and Climate" comes late in the book. The latter topic obviously is based upon the first. But that presents no problem, for a class studying the weather can readily use both references at the same time.

In beginning with a book, it often is helpful to call attention to some point of especial interest in the book, something that will catch attention and lead the children to seek further information. In one fourth-grade book, for example, the teacher referred the children to a story of how people once thought the noise of thunder was made by huge stones rolling over the roof of the sky.

The children themselves often find suggestions and stimulating ideas in books. In one combined first-, second-, and third-grade room, work with electricity began when one of the girls came across a statement in a book that electricity can be made by rubbing; when the statement was discussed all the children in the class were moved to try the suggestion. One child told how while he was combing his hair it cracked and snapped:

"It was getting dark, and my sister said she could see the sparks," he explained.

Another told how his father walked across the room, sliding his feet along the carpet: "Then he touched my nose, and I jumped. Dad said that was electricity."

One child said his father makes electricity in his home from a gasoline motor, the motor being used to turn a generator. Continued discussion of electricity in homes prompted the bringing to class of dry cells and wire, a socket and flashlight bulb, and several other items; and with these work began.

In their reading children can find the stimulus for many profitable experiences in science, provided that the teacher is receptive to new ideas and willing to encourage initiative.

Confidence can be acquired

Progress in science has come from solving one problem at a time, gaining a limited understanding at each step, rather than attempting to explain everything at once. In the classroom, too, achievement comes from undertaking whatever experiences seem worthwhile, rather than waiting to know all the answers even before the questions are asked. The teacher who sees some worthwhile possibilities for children in science can learn from experience; but the teacher who hesitates until the whole field is understood will never begin.

A teacher who wishes to extend his understanding of some topic may obtain reference books from a public library, or it may be more convenient to have a

Fig. 6

Teachers too can enjoy working in science.

personal copy of some especially useful book or books, so that information will be at hand when needed. The biology and physical-science books used in high school or college will serve the purpose well. Good reference books which are readily available can do much to bolster a teacher's confidence.

No teacher should fear science or be anxious because questions may be asked that he cannot answer. Unanswered questions are the essence of science. If all the answers were known in advance there would be no research, nothing left to investigate. Such a situation is inconceivable. When the teacher, like the scientist, accepts the view that no one can know all the answers, the fear will be gone, making room for the natural delight in exploring new situations.

Even though no teacher need be embarrassed by inability to answer all the questions that may arise while working with children in science, there is no doubt that familiarity with the subject can help a teacher in planning the work and in guiding children toward worthwhile experiences and understandings. It is helpful to be familiar enough with the field to see a few of the possibilities and to understand the suggestions made in books. However, there are some important compensations for the teacher unfamiliar with science but willing and eager to explore. Children enjoy making discoveries, especially if the knowledge gained surprises even the teacher. The feeling that the investigations are new and vital to everyone concerned, not just a pedagogic routine, is a real stimulus to learning. A teacher need be no more disturbed by unanswered questions than is the reader of a novel by not knowing the plot in advance.

Children commonly delight in science when the program is one of active investigation. Many teachers who have begun their work with misgivings have continued with assurance after seeing how well the children respond.

STUDY GUIDE

The functional value of any teaching suggestion is dependent upon the extent to which the suggestion is made applicable to the individual teacher's own classroom and pupils. Each of the questions and suggestions which follow this chapter and subsequent chapters should be considered in terms of an actual classroom. In-service teachers and student teachers should apply what they read to their own situations, accepting what seems reasonable and modifying and adapting the suggestions to their own circumstances. Other students likewise should think and speak in terms of actual children and the grade in which the student hopes eventually to teach. Plans that are clear and definite can be adjusted later, but vague generalities leave a gap between theory and practice.

1. What kind of science instruction is suitable for the children with whom you work, or expect to work? What are the children able to do and understand? What knowledge do they already have?
2. How do the principles of child development apply to the preceding question? How can the children in your situation interpret their experiences through science? Give examples you have observed.
3. Record the questions a child asks upon some occasion and note what scientific knowledge would be necessary for answering these questions.
4. What are some actual observations of children's responses to natural objects and phenomena? What potential science learnings are involved in the daily experiences of the children with whom you are associated?
5. What background of understanding in science should the teacher have? What can be done to gain confidence in teaching science? Where can the teacher find references? How technical should the work be?
6. Select one area of science as an example and explain how you could begin working with children in that area.
7. Use Underhill's *The Origins and Development of Elementary-School Science* as a reference and report orally to your class regarding the beginnings of science in elementary schools. With the preface of Comstock's *Handbook of Nature Study* as a reference, explain the origin of nature study and its purpose. How did the original purpose of nature study differ from the objectives of science in the elementary schools today? What are the weaknesses and strengths of typical elementary-school science programs today? [4]

[4] See Theresa J. Lammers, "One Hundred Interviews with Elementary School Teachers Concerning Science Education," *Science Education*, 33:292–295, October, 1949. See also New York State Association of Elementary School Principals, *Science for Our Children*, Bulletin XII, January, 1949.

Examine recent issues of *Science Education* for additional studies regarding the status of elementary-school science.

Harriet Weil

2

Planning for Science

The foresight that goes into planning helps insure pleasant and profitable learning situations. Well-prepared plans give a teacher confidence, and rightly so, for the plans enable the teacher to see ahead and to make essential preparations for the anticipated undertakings. Depending entirely on spur-of-the-moment decisions can lead to confusion; following a fixed routine day after day can be dull and uninspiring. Especially for the beginning teacher or a teacher unfamiliar with science, adequate planning is most important.

HOW ARE SCIENTIFIC CONCEPTS DEVELOPED?

When Eric explained that the leaves on the trees move and make the wind blow, his statement revealed the extent of his concept of the wind. When another child asked how an airplane can fly through a cloud, it was obvious that his concept of a cloud was vague. The term *concept* may be applied to something as specific as a cloud or to a broad generalization. Developing a broad concept of the vast distances in the universe, for example, is considered one of the goals of science instruction. The child who asked if clouds are as high as the moon had but a limited concept of space or distance. In seeking to develop the concepts of children, teachers face many problems, such as: What

26

are the children able to do and understand? What knowledge do they already have? How can understanding be developed logically if we follow the interests of the children? The basic purpose of science instruction is to help children interpret their surroundings adequately; therefore problems concerned with the development of concepts are fundamental.

Insight is based upon experience

We are all dependent upon our senses for understanding. For example, no amount of explaining will make clear to a color-blind person the color he never has seen. A boy of eight waited with his father in a Seattle department store while his mother shopped for a dress. At the end of one of the nearest racks was a placard in attractive pastel browns and greens giving the price of the garments. The boy studied the sign for a time and then asked why the store had a sign with no writing on it. He was unable to see those particular colors, and no explanation could give him a reliable impression of what he was unable to see; likewise, the father, who had normal vision, was unable to comprehend fully how the world of color appeared to the child.

First-hand experience is essential. Understanding is based upon experience and the interpretation of that experience. If the experience is lacking, or lacking in some of the necessary elements, to that extent the understanding will be incomplete. Even the more abstract concepts can be traced back to their bases in sensory perception. Comenius recognized this principle long ago in his *Orbis Pictus*, where he advocated the study of "things, not words."

The nursery-school child who held snow in her hand, watching the snow turn to water, was gaining understanding through experience. A second-grader was using the same approach when she held her hand by the damp blackboard, trying to feel the water leaving as the blackboard dried. That such experiences are the basis of a child's concepts was indicated by the nursery tot who explained what the different kinds of rock are: "Some are fun to suck on; some aren't."

In the words of John Dewey:

Education in order to accomplish its ends both for the individual learner and for society must be based upon experience — which is always the actual life-experience of some individual.[1]

Not all experience is manual activity. To observe a violent thunderstorm may be a vivid experience; quietly observing a snowflake through a magnifying glass

[1] John Dewey, *Experience and Education*, Macmillan, New York, 1938, p. 113.

Fig. 7

An understanding of life is based upon direct experience with living things.

may be less exciting but also a valuable experience. To read a book is a real experience — but real only in the sense of sitting in a chair contemplating printed words. Even though the words may describe a snowstorm, the experience is not the experience one has while outside during a real storm.

Concrete experiences are basic to reading and discussion. Words themselves are but symbols, and their meaning is dependent upon previous experience. A word may have various meanings or none at all, depending upon the previous experiences with which it has become associated. Commonly we expect too much of words. Developing a vocabulary and the ability to use it — oral and written expression — is one of the goals of education; but before words can be used effectively, experience must give the words meaning; and where previous experience is not adequate the experience can be gained in school through some form of active participation.

Experience requires interpretation. Where direct experience is lacking, some degree of understanding can be developed from more or less related experiences. The Easterner can visualize to some extent the mountains of the West by thinking of them as even more rugged than the most precipitous heights he has known in the Appalachians. A child can understand somewhat the way primitive people live by thinking in terms of his own camping experience — provided he has had such experience. The situation is well illustrated by the Hawaiian girl who explained how her concept of a snow storm was developed. As a child she had seen snow only upon a mountain top, packed and hard. Her teachers had demonstrated how snow falls, likening it to soap flakes falling from a box. Her first real snow storm, upon her arrival in Boston to attend college, was a revelation to her. She had thought the particles of snow would be harder, fall more violently, much as hail in a thunderstorm — which had been within her experience. Thus her concept, not entirely erroneous, was built from experiences with hail, rain, snow on a mountain top, frost in a refrigerator, and falling soap flakes. In other respects, too, her concept of a snow storm had been incomplete. She had not experienced the cold, the feel of the wind, the crunching of snow beneath her feet. Vicarious experience is primarily a reconstruction of previous experiences, not a substitute for them.

Interpretation of experiences, using one idea to explain another, is essential. The workman who has spent years at a particular machine or industrial process without comprehending it has had experience without making the essential interpretations. The housewife whose home is equipped with electrical and mechanical devices that she uses regularly yet fails to understand, likewise could profit by an explanation.

Creative thinking and the solution of complex, abstract problems are dependent upon ability to derive new relationships, new meanings from experience. Unless understanding is to be limited by the horizon, some interpretation of the remote in terms of the familiar must be made. The amount and variety of firsthand experience that is possible for one individual is limited. Schools are properly concerned with the development of abstract meanings. Although all thinking is derived from sensory experiences, the meanings assembled need not be limited to the concrete and the immediate. In fact, the firmer the foundation, the taller the structure that can be erected.

A child's background is limited. The experiences that children can recall are limited. In one kindergarten class of twenty-five in a Boston suburb, when the class began working with boats, the teacher found that two-thirds of the class never had seen a boat, although Boston is a port city. Of the remaining one-third, most had seen rowboats, sailboats, Harvard's racing shells on the Charles River, and the swan boats in Boston's Public Garden. Three had taken a steamer trip across Boston Harbor. None could recall seeing an ocean-going passenger or cargo ship.

In another suburb of Boston, while the first-grade class prepared for a trip to the museum, the teacher found that of the twenty-eight children six had never ridden in a bus, fifteen had never been to a museum of any kind, and twenty-three had never seen a snake. Yet these children and those in the preceding case were from definitely privileged homes with well-educated parents. In contrast, one of the first-graders, Jimmie, had been to the museum three times and was able to explain to the others in great detail how he had stroked the back of the snake, Black Beauty, touched the porcupine, heard his own voice come back to him on the telephone, and had seen "lightning" jump across the spark gap.

Children in less favorable circumstances may have even narrower backgrounds. In one such class of fifteen children, aged ten to fourteen, in New York City, when the class entered a room in which the teacher had a White Leghorn cockerel, about half the class had no idea what it was. The other half thought perhaps it might be a chicken. Not one of the children was sure the animal was a chicken.

Small children have only a few years of conscious memories, and such memories are ordinarily limited to the home and the immediate neighborhood. It is true also that children fail to notice much of what they encounter, for at the time it may have little significance for them. Experiences at school, under the guidance of the teacher, have the advantages of being immediate and of taking place under circumstances in which emphasis can be given to significant points; the teacher is more likely to know what understanding the child has gained; and when so desired, the experience can be common to all. For effective learning the school must supply experience that is basic to the particular concept being taught.

Meanings should be developed in some logical order

Complex understandings are built of many meanings, many experiences and interpretations. The mechanic's knowledge of an automobile includes his understanding of the generator, the distributor, and the wiring system and of the relationship of these to many other parts. For a child to understand how sound is transmitted through the air, he should know that there is air, should know that sound is vibration, and also should have some acquaintance with waves, such as the ripples which spread across a pond. Likewise some knowledge of sound is requisite to understanding the telephone, and the principles involved in the telephone are basic to an understanding of radio, radio in turn being the foundation of television. To begin a study of television without developing the preceding concepts would be to undertake an overwhelming task. It seems apparent that some logical development of concepts is essential for efficient learning.

Logic may be confused with tradition. Customarily those who stress the logical development of subject matter have been prone to overlook the learning situation — the child's reactions — yet this consideration is fundamental. Teachers who have placed their emphasis on the child, rather than on the subject matter, have often erred in the opposite direction by not ensuring a logical sequence in the development of concepts, so that experiences have been to some extent a jumble of unrelated activities. Is it possible to profit by the modern emphasis on the child without losing the values inherent in logical planning? Can children's concepts expand and develop logically without a prearranged sequence imposed by the school?

The traditional sequence in electricity begins with a study of magnetism. A person well acquainted with the subject probably has learned it in the usual order and therefore is likely to assume that the traditional sequence is the only logical one possible. Yet the subject is also developed logically in books which do not follow the usual sequence but begin with static electricity, or with electric circuits. Courses of study also begin in various ways. In the New Hampshire syllabus for elementary schools [2] the first concepts introduced are that electricity does all kinds of work for us, that it comes from a power house or is produced in dry cells, and that we must be careful in using it. Electricity is introduced at the second grade in New Hampshire, whereas Oregon introduces the topic at the sixth-grade level, beginning with conductors and non-conductors, the electromagnet, and light and heat from electricity.[3] The familiar way may seem the only correct one, but the number of variations, each a logical development, is almost unlimited.

An understanding of the telephone involves a knowledge of sounds, electric circuits, electromagnets, resistance, and the source of current. Ordinarily the telephone is introduced after some understanding of the more basic concepts has been gained. What should the teacher do if the children in a particular class become genuinely interested in the telephone, stimulated perhaps by some occurrence, such as a telephone repairman coming to the school building, or a repair crew working in the street and on the poles outside the classroom windows? What should be done if interest is keen and a basis for understanding is provided, but the children have not acquired the prerequisite information?

As far as the logic of the subject is concerned, instruction can very well begin with the telephone to take advantage of a meaningful situation. Just as children are able to use a dry cell and understand its function without knowledge of the chemistry of cells, the telephone can be used before it is fully understood, and the use of the instrument can be the first step in learning the basic concepts involved. For example, a telephone receiver can be connected to one terminal of a dry cell. Whenever the other terminal is touched momentarily to complete

[2] New Hampshire State Board of Education, *Program of Studies Recommended for the Elementary Schools of New Hampshire: Science, Grades One–Six*, The Board, Concord, 1944.

[3] Oregon State Department of Education, *Science for Oregon Schools*, Part I, The Board, Salem, 1948.

the circuit, a click will be heard at the receiver. What makes the sound? Removing the end of the receiver will reveal a magnet and a metal diaphragm. If no other materials are available, there is no hazard involved in examining the receiver of the telephone in the school office, or wherever one can be found. A telephone also can be borrowed from the telephone company. It can be shown that the magnet inside a receiver will attract a nail, a knife blade, a paper clip, or other objects of iron. Such an examination will raise questions about magnets, and can lead to a study of magnetism. In a similar way, using a receiver will make a complete circuit necessary. A short circuit in the line will furnish a natural learning situation, and the insulation must be removed to make connections; so why have insulation? Does the sound of a voice actually go along the wire? All the basic questions can be raised through use of the telephone, in which the children are already interested, and those questions can be studied as thoroughly as the maturity of the children and other pertinent factors make advisable.

Inasmuch as the traditional approach, or the one used in a particular text or syllabus, is not the only logical development possible, the teacher and the class can devise their own sequence, adapted to the circumstances yet in a logical order, building one idea upon another with increasing comprehension. Inasmuch as science for children is all quite elementary and all very much interrelated, it is possible to begin with the interests children have and yet build concepts logically.

Incidental and prearranged plans can be complementary. To what extent should the teacher follow a prearranged plan and to what extent should he take advantage of learning opportunities as they arise? For example, a little girl brought a milkweed pod to her second-grade teacher. To encourage the child's interest in plants and to help her understand that some plants produce seed which are scattered in the wind, the teacher opened the pod and showed the seed and the silk inside. She blew some of the seed into the air and watched them drift across the room. The child then went on with her previously scheduled work.

In another second grade, one of the girls wanted to know how the fish in the aquarium are able to breathe under water. The teacher presented the problem to the class, and eventually the class carried out several experiments to show there is air in water. In one of the experiments a glass of water was left standing by the window in the sun until small bubbles began to collect on the sides. The children noticed similar air bubbles on the sides of the aquarium and on the aquarium plants. After due consideration it was decided there is air in water and that cold water will hold more air than warm water will. Then one child suggested the aquarium be moved farther from the radiator; otherwise the water would get warm and there would be less air for the fish.

These teachers modified their teaching plans to take advantage of situations that could help to stimulate learning and make it meaningful. The modification in the second example was greater than in the first. If any great portion of the program is devoted to such unanticipated incidents or to plans developed concurrently with the teaching, some critics characterize the approach as incidental and likely to be accidental as far as learning is concerned. The critics maintain that a program should be planned in advance to achieve continuity.

Planning in advance is truly essential, but the plans should not be so rigid as to preclude taking advantage of unexpected opportunities. Each experience, whether planned or incidental, whether initiated by the teacher or by the children, should be seen as part of a coherent whole, one idea building upon another, the enthusiasm developed today leading to further progress tomorrow. When children are motivated by their own curiosity to seek explanations of the phenomena about them, the knowledge gained can be cumulative, with one idea leading to another in a logical manner, for the facts already understood serve as vantage points from which the unknown can be probed. Thoughtful plans and unexpected learning opportunities can all make contributions. Continual evaluation and further planning are essential, so that incidental experiences will fit with those planned into a logical sequence.

The investigations of children should contribute to gradually expanding concepts. The learning experiences of children should form a pattern of increasing understanding. The child's understanding of the world in which he lives should be developing gradually as new meanings and deeper insights are acquired a bit at a time. Each new experience or interpretation adds to the total concept, much as bricks and mortar add to a building, one brick at a time. The following example is but an incident, yet it can be seen also as a first step in understanding the weather:

The children in a kindergarten came running excitedly to the teacher, saying to come quickly, the playground was on fire! Hurrying across the grounds, the teacher found the sun shining on a moist surface, and with cold air above, the vapor from the paved surface was condensing as fog that looked much like smoke rising from the pavement. Inspection helped the children to understand they had seen water, like that from their own breath, rather than smoke, as they had supposed.

The children in this case were becoming aware of evaporation and condensation, learning the relationship of each to the other and to smoke. Related experiences should follow, whether in a day, in another month, or even a year or more later. The subsequent learnings need not be left entirely to chance but can be developed as circumstances and the logic of the subject make advisable. The child's own curiosity, if encouraged and guided, will press forward seeking further understanding. Each new meaning acquired by the child will add to the total concept. Having learned that water evaporates and condenses, he may wonder why. That heating causes evaporation and that cooling brings condensation could be listed in any text as the next steps in a logical development of subject matter.

To understand how a barometer measures air pressure, the child must know that there *are* barometers, that air *does* have pressure, and, first of all, that there *is* such a thing as air. Many of the early experiences of children are at this first stage, developing an awareness which will raise questions and lead to further learning. The child who never has seen a psychrometer will not be curious about it; but after he has seen it he may ask what it is for, and then how it works. In the process he may learn about humidity and its effect upon our bodies, and about evaporation and condensation. But first he must become aware there is something to question. The common practice of having children keep a daily record of the weather helps to make them aware that the weather does change, that we do have rainy days, windy days, and hot days; it consequently raises questions about the cause of rain or wind and the nature of clouds, and suggests that a thermometer and other instruments can be useful. With the children aware of the thermometer, still other questions arise: What do the numbers mean? What's inside the tube? What makes it go up? Why does it go down when placed under the window and up when closer to the ceiling? Becoming aware of the weather is the first step in learning about the weather.

Although one experience follows another and builds upon it, the second need not follow the first immediately in all cases. A lapse of time will give the child an opportunity to assimilate and apply what he has learned. Further understanding may have to wait for increased maturity or more advantageous circumstances. At other times, interest may lead from one experience to another so that a number of meanings may be developed in close sequence; this is particularly true in the work of older children. In either case the child's understanding is expanding, developing into a coherent whole. Each new meaning gained by a child should be seen by the teacher as part of an unfolding pattern, a gradually expanding conception of the world about us.

It should be noted also that progress in one area of science is closely related to progress in other areas of science and of the total curriculum. Lightning is electricity as well as weather. Progress in reading and progress in science, for instance, may be interdependent. Children who learn that fire must have air in order to burn can also understand how the fire department controls fires. The work of the fire department ordinarily is considered a part of the social studies. Well-rounded concepts in science do not develop in isolation but are closely related to all areas of human experience. Ventilation is more than a circulation of air: it is a matter of health. The weather forecasts may help to determine whether or not a class will go on a field trip or a picnic. An incidental or a planned experience may be part of the child's expanding concept of the weather, but the teacher may see it also in the broader context as part of the child's total development.

Fig. 8

Learning experiences in science should fit together in a coherent pattern.

Continuity from one year to the next should be sought. On some occasions high-school teachers have objected to the science training that their pupils have received in elementary school, saying that more damage than good was done. But some college instructors make similar remarks about high-school science, and similar views are expressed concerning achievement in other subjects. Behind such remarks there may be a real problem. The upper-grade teacher may be disturbed merely because his established routines are upset: his classes already know much of what he intended to teach them. In such a case a healthy solution is for the instructor to teach on a more advanced level, and with greater individualization. But there may be some merit in his criticisms of the preceding instruction. Ineffective textbook teaching can result in a distaste for science and very little understanding of it, with the result that a later teacher has to overcome both the undesirable attitudes and the confused impressions that the child has acquired. Likewise, an activity program that goes in for excitement with little real understanding robs later work of its high points and results in a superficial base upon which no structure can stand.

Although the maturity and background of a child puts some limitations on the work he can undertake, grade placement of subject matter is largely arbitrary. Many topics can be assigned as well to one level as to another, but there will be great variation in the treatment. The examples which follow illustrate both the similarities and the differences in the ways that three different ages have treated the same subject:

To learn how water disappears — evaporates — the children in a combined first and second grade put water into containers of various shapes. They used a syrup bottle as a measuring device to put equal amounts of water into an ice-cube tray, a glass bowl, and a mayonnaise jar, and then filled the syrup bottle itself. A metal cap was placed on the bottle, and all the containers were set on the window sill where they could be observed. One boy believed that the water in the syrup bottle would evaporate the most rapidly. On Monday morning, however, when the containers were examined, he concluded:

"It must be on account of the cover, and the water couldn't get out."

The class continued with their experiments, and in their discussions they talked about evaporation from ponds, puddles, the aquarium, and even from their own clothes.

A third grade had a similar experience: The children cut two pieces of cloth of equal size from the same material and then thoroughly wet each one. They placed one in the shade, the other in the sun. The one in the sun dried first, and the children understood that the heat had dried it, but where had the water gone?

"Back into the air," one girl said.

And another explained: "Something like vapor."

The teacher said yes, it was called evaporation. Many of them had heard the word before.

"That's what happened to the water in the dish we put on the radiator!"

"That's why our clothes dry!"

"That's why I have to keep putting more water in for my turtle — or does he drink it all?"

In a combined fifth and sixth grade, similar work was done by some of the children — more independently in this case — and demonstrated to the class as a part of their report. With a flashlight and chalk dust Susan demonstrated that a beam of light is visible because of dust in the air, and she explained how dust particles often serve as the nuclei for drops of water as they condense in clouds. She showed that moisture from the air will gather on the sides of a tin cup containing ice water, and explained that the same thing happens when moisture from the warm room gathers on a windowpane during a cold winter day. Working with Susan, Marilyn explained how water gets into the air by evaporation, and showed the experiment she had been conducting with jars of water, some covered and some uncovered, some above the radiator and some in a cooler spot.

Regardless of age or grade, each person should begin with whatever insight he may have and seek to develop his concepts from that point. The same topic can be taught at various grade levels, without needless repetition, wherever the understanding has not been achieved previously — provided that the instruction is modified according to the reactions of the people involved. From the nursery or kindergarten to the graduate school of a college the same topic frequently is studied, but with an approach and depth of insight that varies according to the maturity and background of the individuals concerned. Electricity, for example, can be studied by the Ph.D. as well as by the kindergartener. The teacher who knows the children in a certain class and is alert to their reactions will soon learn at what level those children can work. Children who have truly enjoyed their experiences and found them profitable will remember them with satisfaction and will be delighted to continue in that area at a later date.

Science can help to correct misconceptions and needless fears

Since misconceptions and needless fears are based upon a lack of understanding, the way to correct them is to build a true understanding. Judging by the prevalence of magazines devoted to astrology, for example, many people believe that their future can be foretold by the stars. Such fallacies cannot be removed by denial. People cling to their superstitions and other fallacious beliefs in spite of ridicule by the public, concealing their beliefs, perhaps, but clinging to them nevertheless. The new understanding must be developed as thoroughly as any concept, beginning with the essential basic experiences if those are lacking.

Confidence is derived from insight. One teacher tells of the time when the eight-year-olds in her class were frightened by a thunderstorm. The teacher began talking to them about the beauty of the lightning and how the friction of the air currents builds up the charge until finally a spark jumps from one cloud to another or to the ground, much as any static will. As the children began to relax and take an interest in what the teacher was saying, she went on to explain how the thunder is caused by the lightning, and how the number of seconds between the flash and the sound, divided by five, gives an estimate of the distance in miles; and on that basis she and the class speculated on the position and movement of the storm.

Then one child said, "It really is pretty good when you know how it works."

Whenever a storm came after that, the children were proud of their courage, born of understanding.

In an active program misconceptions become apparent and are easily corrected. Misconceptions may arise from erroneous interpretations of experiences in the classroom, in the home, or in the community. When frogs' eggs were brought to the third grade one day, the class had a vigorous discussion of the changes that take place as the eggs become tadpoles and eventually mature into frogs, and the children looked forward eagerly to having an aquarium full of frogs. Unfortunately, the eggs were too crowded in the small aquarium, and in a few days the embryonic frogs died. As decay began, a bad odor developed, so one day, before leaving for home, the teacher emptied the aquarium. Because the class had been studying how animals grow and develop and was planning to have rabbits for observation, the teacher took the opportunity to bring a pair to class. When the children arrived on the following morning, there was considerable excitement about the new rabbits; and one of the boys, noticing that the frogs' eggs were gone, exclaimed:

"Hey, look! We got rabbits from those eggs."

When children have freedom to express themselves, any misconceptions that occur will become apparent and can be corrected before they become firmly established.

In the following case a misconception developed from reading but was easily corrected. The third grade had been studying magnetism, and one day a group of boys came to the teacher in confusion, one of them insisting:

"The fish really aren't magnetized at all, are they?"

The teacher, now even more confused than they, asked what was meant, and it seemed that one boy had found in a book a picture which showed a child catching goldfish with a magnet, and after discussing it the boys had gone to the aquarium in another room and tried it themselves. It didn't work.

They showed the picture to the teacher, who then realized that the seemingly real goldfish in the picture were actually bits of metal.

"Now she tells us!" one of the boys exclaimed.

In this case the misconception was righted, because the boys were free to investigate. Even though it is well to avoid confusion as much as possible, a certain number of false impressions ordinarily can be expected and corrected in the normal development of any concept.

The activities chosen should suit the purpose

Some activities are misleading and may create a false impression. The commonly used tin-can telephone is an example. It is constructed by punching a small hole in the center of the bottom of a tin can and then slipping a cord through the hole and tying a knot at the end of the cord so that the cord will not pull back through the hole. With another tin can similarly attached at the other end of the cord, children can stand at opposite sides of the room, and the sound of a voice will carry nicely along the cord while one child holds a tin can to his mouth, the other child holds one to his ear, and the cord is held tight. It is obvious that the vibrations of the sound travel along the taut cord, for the movement can be seen or felt, and if the cord is slack or is obstructed in the middle the sound will be damped or obstructed. But the implication of the tin-can telephone is that a real telephone works in the same way; this tends to substantiate the common fallacy that sound travels along a telephone wire. Sound is vibration; what travels along a telephone wire is a variable electric current.

Another misleading device is the chemical garden, in which a number of chemicals are dissolved in water and as the water slowly evaporates, crystals are built in a manner that has the appearance of plant growth. Actually, the similarity to plant growth is completely superficial. Likewise, planting carrot tops is misleading, for planting the tops is not a normal or satisfactory way to raise carrots. If the activity is used, the false implication should be avoided and the true meaning stressed. An experiment or demonstration appropriate for one purpose may not be suitable for another. That carrot tops will develop new growth shows very well that food is stored in the carrot, and the evaporation of water from a solution shows how some crystals are formed. Any reference to the phenomenon as a garden is misleading and should be avoided.

Some of the supplementary books of suggested experiments for children include activities more suitable for entertainment than for instruction. Illustrative of such activities are fire-writing with chemicals, arranging a shaving mirror to produce phantom flowers, changing water to wine, preparing invisible ink, and making a magic flashlight that glows — apparently with no source of current. The books which include such recommended activities are designed more for the child's amusement at home than for use at school. Although some of the activities will have to be rejected for classroom use, others in such books can be adapted for use in developing the desired concepts.

Games and other embellishments can be confusing. To avoid confusion, experiments and other activities should be as straightforward as possible. Where children are learning the properties of magnets, for example, it is usually better to experiment directly with magnets to see what they will do than to confuse the situation by using the magnets in a fishing game, in a boat that can be towed with another magnet, or in other devices. After the principles are learned, applying them in such ways is of course another matter. Toys can serve many useful purposes when the emphasis is on investigation rather than on a game. If a child brings in toy dogs that attract or automobiles that push or pull each other without direct contact, many questions will be raised that can result in worthwhile investigations, provided that those investigations are designed to find the answers to the questions raised in as direct a manner as possible.

Some demonstrations may be overly complex. A demonstration that is too complex to convey the desired meaning may create a false impression or a tendency to accept the teacher's interpretation without analysis. Not only will the understanding be superficial, but the children will be encouraged to jump to conclusions and accept explanations without comprehending them. As one example, if a small amount of water is allowed to boil in a tin can for a few minutes and the can is then removed from the heat and stoppered tightly — air tight — when the can cools it will collapse. The demonstration shows the force of air pressure, but so many factors are involved that, for many of the younger children at least, the results are likely to be more spectacular than illuminating. The explanation is that the water vapor carried the normal air out of the can, and when the can was cooled the vapor condensed, reducing the pressure inside the can so that the normal pressure on the outside was enough to crush the can. If, to save time in the cooling, cold water is poured onto the outside of the can, still another confusing factor is added.

A good demonstration ordinarily should be simple enough to make the principle obvious. Where a siphon is used to demonstrate the pressure of air, as is commonly done, the explanation of a siphon is too complex to serve the purpose. On the other hand, when a person has already learned something of air pressure, the knowledge can well be applied to interpret the action of the siphon. Under the right circumstances, both these demonstrations of air pressure could be helpful, even though complex. Another example is the common one of the egg and the bottle. Being complex but sensational, it often is used with small children, in which case the excitement is transmitted, but not the understanding.

HOW CAN CHILDREN'S IDEAS BE UTILIZED IN A COHERENT PROGRAM OF SCIENCE?

A child will work harder for his own ideas than for those of someone else. The opportunity to participate in planning, to use and develop his own ideas, is a stimulus to active thinking and learning. To learn effectively the child must be seeking to achieve some purpose of his own, and this implies that his own ideas must have some expression. Children who are encouraged to investigate have many worthwhile ideas which in a democratic atmosphere can be utilized.

A seventh-grade boy found that when he placed two sheets of glass upright and close together in a shallow pan of water, the water would creep upward in an arc between the sheets. By devising his own means of demonstrating capillarity he developed more enthusiasm and much greater insight than he would have gained by merely following directions. He also was learning to think and act for himself. Initiative is a valuable trait that should be encouraged.

A child is impelled to explore his environment, and it is characteristic for him to act on his own initiative. Even when he is a willing participant in a group undertaking, his tendency to assert and defend his independence of action can be observed.

Democratic procedures are effective

In the classroom, as elsewhere, democratic procedures may seem slow and cumbersome at times, but such cooperative efforts do build soundly: the learnings undertaken are likely to be understood, not merely accepted. Children typically are eager to make suggestions, accept responsibilities, and share in activities. In science children can learn effective ways of working together, instead of learning to follow passively the dictates of one person. In a democratic atmosphere the ideas of each individual can be given consideration, perhaps modified, and wherever practicable utilized.

The opinions of other children often carry more weight with a child than do the words of an adult. The point was well illustrated one day as a man and wife, with their two small children, returned from a long walk. The father was carrying the youngest in his arms, so the other child insisted on riding in her empty cart. He blandly ignored the father's grumbling sarcasm about his looking like a baby riding in the baby's cart. But as they came near home, some of the neighborhood boys saw him and let out a derisive yell. Before the sound had died away the boy had jumped from the cart and was walking along beside it. A teacher ought to make use of the opinions of children; they get results.

A child's idea may lead to worthwhile learnings. Often there is real value in the opinions and suggestions of children. A child may think of something that simply did not occur to the teacher, even though the teacher has a much better over-all grasp of the subject. The idea may be a product of the child's background, all details of which are not known to the teacher. A child's suggestion may be better suited to his own circumstances or stage of development than anything the teacher has in mind.

In the following case the teacher welcomed the ideas of the children and found them useful. The fourth-grade class had been studying airplanes and had hung a number of models from a cord across one end of the room. When some of the children noticed that the background for the airplanes was not appropriate, it was decided that blue paper should be placed on the wall behind the airplanes. Clouds on the blue sky were suggested, but finally stars were decided upon, and the question arose of how to place the stars. Subsequently the class began to talk about constellations and what stars are and why they twinkle. A study of the sky had begun, and thus the ideas of the children led to many worthwhile learnings.

Another case also shows the value of a child's suggestions. One of the third-grade girls noticed that all the plants in the terrarium were growing in one direction. When this was pointed out and discussed, it was soon noted that all the other plants in the room were likewise inclined. Most of the children realized that the plants were bent toward the window, but they were not sure of the reason. The wind, the sun, rain, and air were all suggested as reasons. A little reflection helped to rule out some of the suggestions, especially with regard to the aquarium plants, since they were enclosed. Finally it was agreed that the light was the most probable explanation. To see how the plants would respond, the terrarium was turned so that the opposite side faced the window. Other experiments also were conducted to see how plants react to light. Without the suggestions of the children the teacher might never have noticed that such an excellent learning situation was readily at hand.

Using children's ideas helps to give training in democratic procedures. We clarify and develop our ideas by using them. The school should provide opportunity for children to learn to think and to act upon their thoughts. Thinking and planning should lead to action. Teachers sometimes object to long hours spent on curriculum-revision studies, and other meetings, when they believe that nothing will come of them. Likewise, children work with greater enthusiasm and more intense effort if they expect their ideas to be used. The ultimate reason for giving consideration to the concerns of children is that such a policy can get better results — better in terms of subject matter, as well as of attitudes and habits developed.

Planning should be thorough yet flexible. Plans made in advance should be modified in response to the reactions of the children. Outside the classrooms few people would expect to ignore the reactions of other individuals. For example, if a teacher were applying for a new position, the chance of success would be greater if adequate plans were made before the interview; yet if that planning were so rigid that the reactions of the superintendent, his questions, and his comments were ignored while the applicant proceeded with his own prearranged statements, the interview would be a failure. Likewise, in the classroom, planning should be thorough, yet flexible enough to permit adjustments to the other people involved.

No one should feel obligated to follow all the ideas children may have. That would be not only foolish but virtually impossible. "Cooperation" should not imply that just any impulse or whim of the moment will be accepted. Many of the children's ideas, however, are really worthwhile, appropriate for the circumstances. Where necessary the teacher can always say *no*, and thus need have no fear that the situation will get out of hand. It will seldom be necessary. Children are willing to evaluate their own suggestions, and they can learn in the process if the teacher will help them.

The classroom atmosphere should be conducive to serious investigation, with the freedom of action essential for such work. A child's idea may involve an extensive plan which will influence the work of his entire class, but as a rule the feeling of freedom to participate actively will be expressed in less pretentious terms as the individual works out the details of his own problems. For example, one sixth-grade girl, tired of holding a flask over an alcohol burner, devised a stand for holding the flask above the flame. She cut both ends from a can, punched holes in the sides to provide a draft and then, with the burner inside, placed chicken wire on top of the improvised stand and set the flask upon it. Such ingenuity is valuable to the individual and to society as a whole, and the classroom should provide an atmosphere that encourages its development.

Small children too will make use of their own ideas if given the opportunity. In the two- and three-year nursery a child was experimenting with tin cans and water. First she filled the larger can with water; then she attempted to put the smaller one inside. Of course the water was pushed out. She tried over and over again. Finally she emptied some of the water out of the larger can and then was able to put the small can into the big one without any of the water spilling. She smiled with satisfaction and went on to something else. She was learning about the displacement of water, a topic that would have meant nothing to her had the teacher simply told her about it. She was making use of her own ideas, learning to think for herself.

The teacher can encourage children to work out their own ideas by responding favorably and making use of their suggestions, by giving personal recognition when contributions are made, and by providing an audience and letting the child show or tell what has been discovered. The teacher can help also by offering suggestions, by giving enough assistance to overcome difficulties, and by providing the necessary time and materials to develop situations that encourage thinking. Sometimes the child's own initiative and the enthusiasm that goes with it will achieve what the teacher's directions alone would never be likely to accomplish.

The utilization of children's ideas assumes that the teacher will be open-minded and considerate of the child's view, and presupposes a personally secure teacher, one who can enjoy new situations rather than fear them. The same familiar routines that may give the teacher a feeling of security — because nothing startling is likely to happen — are just as uneventful for the children, and hence dull rather than stimulating. The teacher must not be afraid to try some of the child's ideas and depart a bit from the beaten path. It can be fun and can bring a spirit of camaraderie to the class.

Children can help to plan their own investigations

If children are given the opportunity to plan with the teacher, they can learn many relationships that must be considered in formulating the plans but otherwise would be overlooked or taken for granted. For example, a child who suggested that insects be collected and observed learned a basic fact about the life cycle of such animals, for he made the suggestion during the winter, when most

Fig. 9

The child's own questions and suggestions can be used in cooperative planning.

insects are in a dormant form, unavailable for observation. Planning helps the child to gain a depth of insight and also assists him to formulate and clarify his own purposes.

Where children help to decide what work is to be done and how it will be accomplished, they can develop constructive attitudes in the process. They can learn to appreciate careful planning and thorough workmanship. They can begin to comprehend and esteem the values which make essential the learnings undertaken.

The children and the teacher, planning together, should develop the most coherent plan possible. If there is a course of study it can help to supply some of the needed ideas and facts, and can help the children to decide what work should be undertaken. Through cooperative planning the work outlined in a course of study can be adapted to the child's own ideas and circumstances.

Utilizing the ideas of children in planning and conducting investigations is well exemplified in the following case. A fifth-grade class met with a special science teacher, and since there was no course of study to follow, the class itself chose the area for work. The suggested topics were listed upon the board:

> Different kinds of animals
> How does electricity work?
> What makes sound?
> What are chemical changes?
> What are the stars and planets like?

After the various possibilities were listed, the class considered what suitable experiments and other activities could be carried on, what could be learned in each case, and whether or not the necessary references, equipment, and supplies were available. Those who favored the study of animals, for example, gave reasons why such a study would be interesting and worthwhile. The instructor, of course, helped by suggesting possibilities in each area. The suggestion to study electricity was rejected by the class, because they had studied it previously and had no further questions in mind. The study of chemical changes proved to be the most challenging and won general approval. It was a timely topic, for terms such as *atom* and *molecule* were much in the news, and the class had done no previous work in that area. The next step was to list what might be learned about chemical changes. The children and the instructor agreed upon the following questions:

> What is a chemical change?
> What causes chemical changes?
> Of what importance are such changes?
> What are elements, compounds, atoms, molecules, acids?
> What do the symbols mean?

With the questions listed, it was decided that the next step would be to read whatever references could be found on the subject and then to experiment. Suggested experiments were found in the textbooks and in other books for children, including the handbooks of experiments that accompanied the children's chemistry sets. No great variety of chemicals was needed, and most were on hand in the science room; others were brought from home by the children, obtained from chemistry sets, drugstores, and grocery stores. It was obvious that some records must be kept if the experiments were to be reported accurately. A form for the reports was agreed upon. One of the better records has been included here to serve as an example:

Record of Experiment

Purpose: To see how saliva changes starch to sugar.

Procedure: We dissolved some cornstarch in half a glass of water. Then we poured some into test tubes and put some Benedict's Solution in each one. In three we put saliva, but not in the other two. We heated each one about 2 or 3 minutes.

Results: The ones with saliva turned a light brown color. The others stayed blue.

Conclusions: The brown color showed that there was sugar. Saliva helps change starch to sugar so we can use it. That is why we are supposed to chew our food well. Heating and cooking help too. It is a chemical change.

Interest in the experiments was intense, and in a few cases the instructor had to insist that the plans for an experiment — that is, the first two items of the record — be completed before the individual concerned could begin actual experimentation, in order to ensure careful planning. The results were recorded promptly in each case as the experiment was being done. On the other hand, the conclusions and applications were often clarified, with the instructor's help, when the oral reports were made. While experimenting, the children worked as individuals or as informal groups, and in all cases each individual kept his own record. Most of the children had completed several experiments before they were called together for the reports.

All who had conducted similar experiments reported together. For example, those who had done experiments showing that moisture is necessary for some chemical changes were in one group, even though they had not made their preparation together. Consequently an atmosphere of spontaneity was maintained. Notes were permitted, to help with the chemical terms and symbols, but no written reports were read. Because differences of opinion were revealed in the reports and numerous questions were asked by those watching, the reports were exceptionally vigorous and stimulating. Each group usually reported and demonstrated a number of more or less related experiments, and since many individuals had conducted several different kinds of experiments they often reported in more than one group.

In the general discussion that followed each report, the instructor emphasized questions that stressed the conclusions to be derived from the experiment and applications to everyday experience, in addition to the importance of accuracy, of an objective viewpoint, of not claiming more than the evidence justified, and of other scientific attitudes. The learnings were summarized to conclude the study.

Throughout the entire experience with chemicals and chemical changes the children largely made their own decisions and arrived at their own conclusions. Undertakings that utilize children's ideas usually follow no set pattern, yet the method used in this example was scientific. Freedom of action was not achieved at the expense of subject matter; the knowledge of chemical changes acquired by these children far exceeded what otherwise could have been expected.

HOW SHOULD WORK IN SCIENCE BE ORGANIZED?

The way the science program is organized has considerable influence on the way the science is taught. Without placing limitations on resourcefulness in the classroom, a curriculum guide can help the teacher to formulate tentative plans before initiating the work with children. Such organized assistance can help the teacher decide what learnings are likely to be most worthwhile, what experiences may help to achieve the worthwhile goals, what resources should be used, and how the desired coherence can be achieved. The school administration can help to formulate policies and develop the general plan of organization. But if too great uniformity of classroom experiences for a whole school system is sought, this can result in a loss of vitality and lower the quality of learning. Where no other assistance is provided, there is a tendency for instruction to be geared to a textbook or to the teacher's own outline, and then in spite of a conscientious teacher the work is apt to fall into a routine pattern that is familiar to almost everyone who has ever attended school. Without supplying actual teaching plans or a rigid outline of subject matter, an organized program can provide suggestions and assistance that will be helpful to active investigations in the classroom.

Finding a place for science in an already crowded daily schedule is a problem for many busy teachers. The problem is one of organization, for there is general agreement that science should be taught. If a school system is promoting science and has organized a program, that program can help to justify the amount of time that conscientious teachers devote to this area. How much time should be provided for science, and whether it should be taught in separate periods or fused with other subjects, are questions that must be resolved — by the teacher alone, if there is no school policy on the matter.

An effective organization will stimulate learning

A science program should be organized to have coherence. The organization should seek to provide situations that will stimulate learning. Desired learnings can be stated as problems, but the child's curiosity, his desire to find out, ordinarily provides the real problems that lead to active investigation. Such problems can be grouped as an area or topic to be investigated, and at least the immediate tasks to be undertaken should be planned with the children themselves.

The organization should be in terms of meanings. Common expressions, such as "The class will cover *leaves* this week," or "We plan to take up *turtles* tomorrow," indicate a tendency to stress encyclopedic facts rather than meaningful relationships. Ordinarily it is more advantageous to organize a study in terms of ideas rather than in terms of some object. Studying how animals grow is likely to be of more value than studying all about rabbits, and learning how animals survive the winter is of more value than "covering" the Baltimore Oriole and the English sparrow. A study of *Leaves* could be meaningful in spite of the title, but ordinarily the work tends to become involved with insignificant details, such as naming leaves when very little meaning is attached to the name, or recognizing certain leaves by their color or the serrated margin, or learning to distinguish an ovate from a lanceolate leaf. Collecting, identifying, pressing and mounting, making displays, leaf prints, and the like, though not without some value, tend to become activities with no clear purpose. If the real value of the work is in learning the function of leaves and their relationship to the rest of the plant, the work could be organized and directed toward that end, with activities selected to serve the stated purpose. An even broader topic, such as "How plants live and grow," might develop a still greater number of meaningful relationships.

Organizing work in terms of meanings need not imply that the work deals in vague generalities, but that experiences fit together in meaningful relationships — expanding concepts. In the following example the work was definite and of limited scope; the experiences were concrete, yet organized to stress the desired meanings:

One of the second-grade children came to school much excited because his rabbits had had babies. In the discussion that followed, rabbits and their young were compared with other pets, including cats, dogs, and chickens. The baby rabbits had a mother and a father, were born alive in a nest, and got milk from their mother. One child said he thought bunnies ate carrots, but the owner of the rabbits responded:

"Could you eat carrots without teeth?"

When the rabbits were two and a half weeks old they were brought to school for a visit. One child commented that he had a new baby brother who was six weeks old, and his mother had to feed, clothe, and wash him. His brother was a *real* baby!

Another child volunteered to bring his pet hen to school. The children asked if the mother hen had any baby chicks, and the first child answered with a definite "Oh, no. We don't have a rooster." Because hens lay the eggs, and baby chicks come out of eggs, the children were confused, but finally decided that since rabbits have a mother and a father the chicks must have both too.

In the meantime the class had read a number of books for information on how animals care for their young, and had learned a number of new words, including *rooster, chicken, rabbit, born,* and *lay.* They wrote stories about baby animals and how they grow and change, and a thank-you letter to the owner of a farm after they had visited the baby animals there. The children drew pictures of the farm animals that showed how each baby is much like the mother, and they even sang songs about chickens and rabbits. Two one-week-old lambs also were brought to school for a short visit. Almost daily the children brought reports of some animal's having had babies, and they told how the mother fed and cared for them, how the newborn were like other baby animals, and how they would change as they grew. Interest in baby animals was high. The work was organized to stress the way animals grow and develop instead of dealing with the specific animals as isolated cases. Long after some of the facts are forgotten, these children will continue with a general understanding of growth and development.

In addition to the desirability of stressing relationships, one reason for having a coherent organization is that in such an organization individuals of diverse abilities can work together, yet all can grasp at least the main idea, the idea stressed by the organization.

Another advantage of organizing in terms of an idea, such as how animals grow and develop, is that ordinarily a great variety of resources will be available. If one kind of animal is not on hand, another kind will do as well. In addition to pets and farm animals, there are animals in a zoo, in our houses, and everywhere out of doors. The children themselves exemplify the principles being learned. If the large, familiar mammals are not available, there are still moths, butterflies, caterpillars, maggots, birds, salamanders, turtles, fish, pond snails, frogs and tadpoles, spiders, dragonflies, the praying mantis, and grasshoppers. If, on the other hand, a class is studying "all about rabbits," nothing will do but rabbits or books on that specific subject.

The work may be organized in terms of problems or questions to be solved: What makes rain or snow, fog or clouds, dew or frost? Why does the wind blow? How can the weather be forecast? A study designed to help children appreciate the work of the Weather Bureau and the importance of the daily weather forecasts exemplifies an organization in which social values are stressed. The investigations may be directed toward essential principles of science, as when studying the movement of high- and low-pressure areas, cold air masses, warm air masses, fronts, and changes in the weather. The understanding may be spoken of as a unit on weather, a study of the topic, or investigations in that area. Whatever the designation, it is important that the organization be clearly oriented toward worthwhile meanings and broad and flexible enough to permit individual initiative and true investigation. Incidents may arise and problems may be solved that do not fit the over-all plan, but emphasis will be given to learnings that do, so that the program of instruction will be flexible yet coherent.

A coherent organization helps to reveal the relationship of one fact to another. In any organization the important point is that relationships — meanings — be stressed.

Adequate time for science should be provided. If finding a place for science in a busy schedule is a problem, there are several possible solutions. Rather than breaking the day into small segments, many prefer large blocks of time in which units of science alternate with experiences in the social studies, the arts, or other areas. Some prefer to integrate science with other subjects in a unified program. One sixth-grade teacher integrated science with health studies and alternated the two with arithmetic. In his opinion the arrangement worked well for each of the areas involved. Daily schedules often are inherited from the past and contain no provision for science, but if the importance of science is appreciated it will be worked into the program somewhere.

Should science be a separate subject or be fused with other areas of the curriculum? Whatever the answer, subject-matter lines must not be drawn too sharply if meaningful relationships are to be developed. The pattern followed in teaching science ordinarily will depend to a large extent upon the way the other subjects are organized. If other subjects are integrated, science will be also. Integration should not imply neglect of this vital area, as unfortunately it sometimes does. Nor should a separate period become a mere routine. Interest is lost from one period to the next if the periods are scattered, as, for example, if a half hour is devoted to science once or twice a week. It would be better to have the time that can be allotted to science organized in larger blocks and more frequent sessions, even if this means that no time at all can be given at a later date.

The organization should encourage scientific procedures. While plans are being made it may be helpful to think of the active investigations in science as commonly comprising several phases: (1) planning and initiating the work, (2) reading for information, (3) observing and experimenting, with continued reference work as needed, and (4) reports by the children and a discussion of what has been learned, whether from reading or from direct investigation. Such a procedure is an adaptation of the scientific method and is one good way of working, especially in science. However, many modifications can and should be made according to the circumstances. For the younger children who are unable to read functionally, the teacher may read aloud, or the reading may be omitted. In actual practice the work may not divide itself into well-defined steps. Reporting may be followed by further investigation and additional reports. The possible variations are infinite, yet it may be helpful to think of planning, reference work, direct investigation, and reporting as essential in an active program of science for children.

Investigations can be conducted within the limitations of a prescribed course. Many courses of study and curriculum guides in use today state at the beginning that the procedure outlined is suggestive only and that the teacher is free to vary the work according to the circumstances. On such a basis the manual can be a real help as a guide, as a source of ideas, or as reference material. The course of study should be considered an aid to teaching, not a restriction on the work of the class. But if in an actual case the outline is restrictive, although actual day-by-day requirements are not specified, much can still be done to give children opportunity to think for themselves and to provide for the use of individual initiative within the limits imposed. Where the sequence of problems or topics for study is already determined, the children can plan for themselves the specific activities that will be carried on, the sequence within the area that will be followed, and the adaptations that will be made, adjusting the work to their own purposes and desires. In many situations even the sequence of topics may be altered to give the children a choice, or the conditions of the moment may determine which problems are relevant and should be considered first. The sequence developed may parallel that already suggested in the course outline, but the children will have learned something in the planning and will have profited by being able to look ahead. By the end of the year it may be necessary to cover at that time any topics which remain. Experience indicates that the children themselves will see the necessity for completing the work and will accept the task willingly. School systems often expect the more capable teachers to make just such adjustments in the courses outlined, whereas those not quite sure of themselves can lean more heavily on the course of study.

Leadership can help to develop a science program

Although the individual teacher carries the basic responsibility in any teaching program, administrators and other leaders can stimulate and assist where assistance is needed. Cooperative effort can achieve much that may lie beyond the capacity of individuals, and cooperative effort needs leadership.

Possibly the first and most basic step for any school official who appreciates the significance of science in our society and seeks the development of an adequate program in the education of children should be to acquaint himself with some of the potentialities in this area. Reading will help, and if some of the teachers are already working with elementary science it will pay him to visit them, not only for what can be learned by actually seeing the work in progress but also for the stimulus that recognition of the teacher's efforts will bring.

Work already begun should be nurtured. An administrator who wishes to stimulate the elementary science program can begin with an over-all planning group, with a single school, or even with an individual teacher who is receptive to new ideas and ways of working. If possible, when new teachers are added to

Fig. 10

New teachers may be selected for their special competence in science.

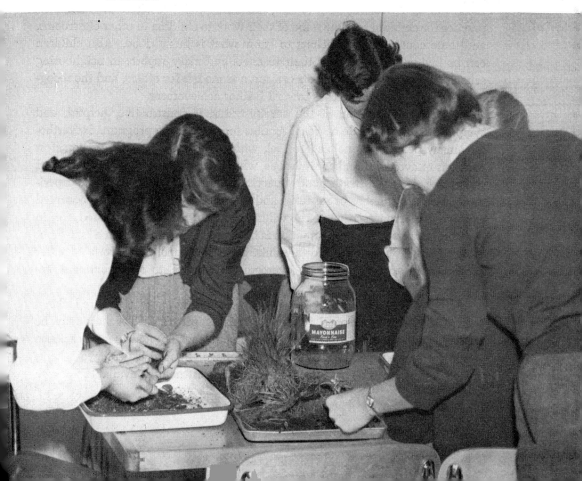

the staff they should be selected for their potential leadership in this area. Teachers can learn readily from other teachers wherever an example is set. The administrator or supervisor can encourage such learning by bringing good work to the attention of others, showing them what can be done. An account of the work accomplished by various teachers may be included from time to time in bulletins to the faculty or may be described at meetings.

The services of an outside consultant may be obtained, or successful teachers may be used as consultants. Successful teachers not only can set an example but may advise and assist fellow teachers, especially in their own buildings. But a teacher from one building also may be invited to another school to report and demonstrate some of the work accomplished, including charts, displays, and written reports of the children, any materials constructed or used, and experiments conducted. At such a meeting the teacher reporting can answer any questions the others may care to ask. Invitations may be given for teachers to visit classrooms where work in science has been in progress. Visits can be made after school hours if not feasible while the children are there. Some of the children may be able to remain to show teachers about and give explanations — an effective way of revealing the child's point of view. It is common practice for children to show some of their work to children in other classrooms, and these contacts help teachers to know what is being done. Also children can be invited to accompany their teachers and make reports in neighboring schools. Successful achievements can serve as models for others, and the recognition given will be a stimulus toward further achievement.

The personal attention of the administrator, if constructive, helpful, and sympathetic, can provide a great stimulus for the science program. Nevertheless, many people are inclined to feel, with some justification, that the safest course is to avoid unfamiliar situations, whether in science or in other areas of experience. If administrators and supervisors induce faculty members to experiment, a certain number of mistakes and adverse reactions should be accepted as inevitable. Appreciation of the willingness to try should be stressed, for, in spite of mistakes, a dynamic situation is better for the learners than a "safe" but static routine. Teachers and administrative personnel can work together cooperatively and effectively to overcome difficulties, to seek continual improvement.

In-service courses can be organized. Where outstanding teachers are lacking, a nucleus can be developed through a training program. Teachers may be notified of and encouraged to take courses in the teaching of elementary science — courses offered, perhaps, by a nearby college. Special classes, workshops, and conferences can be organized, if a qualified instructor is available for such

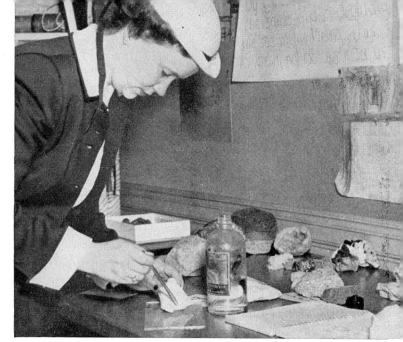

Fig. 11

In-service courses and conferences dedicated to science can help stimulate the science program.

a program, either from within the school system or from the outside. The nature of the program can be determined partly by the capabilities of the instructor but also by the needs and wishes of the faculty members themselves. In some cases it may be more advantageous to organize a workshop, with no one person instructing but all the teachers experimenting in their classrooms, getting suggestions from professional books, perhaps, and reporting back to the group about the reactions and achievements of the children. Wherever possible, the work of the children should be shown, and the members of the workshop should be given many opportunities to try experimenting and to try constructing, improvising, and using suitable teaching materials. The actual teaching experiences and the laboratory work of the workshop can be discussed with respect to effective ways of working, what accomplishment can be expected, the scientific principles involved, and similar problems that may arise. If it be so desired, the problems the teachers face can be listed and then used to organize some of the discussion time. Or it may be more convenient to follow the organization of some professional book — to the extent that the book meets the requirements of the immediate situation. The teachers who volunteer for such a training program are likely to be the more competent ones, the ones most likely to experiment and develop new ways of working — in short, the people most capable of becoming leaders. In any case, with a nucleus to set the example, progress in developing an elementary science program can be infectious.

Obstacles can be overcome. There are countless ways in which the leadership in elementary schools can help teachers overcome the obstacles involved

55

in developing this relatively new but vital area of instruction. If parent groups are acquainted with the work being undertaken, their sympathetic understanding will help to stimulate achievement and overcome difficulties. Most thoughtful parents are quick to realize the significance of science in the world today and readily give their support to the inclusion of science in the education of their children. Frequently the support of parents can be one of the largest factors in promoting such improvement in the curriculum.

Developing a course of study is a way of stimulating work in a new area, a way that should not be overlooked. A course of study can be helpful, if the organization is not too rigid. The syllabus may well include suggested procedures, note local resources that may have instructional value, and give sources of supplies, accounts of actual teaching experiences, and whatever else the teachers concerned think would be helpful. It may be advisable to stress the local situation in specific terms that are not possible for a professional book designed for more general use.

Responsibility for obtaining adequate books and concrete teaching materials to a large extent must be the province of administrative leadership. No great expense is involved, since a large portion of the essential supplies are not commercial items. Leadership is needed in obtaining and organizing the essential materials and in helping teachers to use them. These problems are discussed in another section; but it can be said here that in many cases the administration or other leaders could do more to stimulate their elementary-school science program by solving the difficulties involving supplies and other teaching resources than by any other one thing. Although the teaching resources are commonly a serious obstacle for teachers, the problem is relatively easy for the school administration to solve, and one with great influence not only upon what is taught but also upon the way it is taught — the effectiveness of the instruction.

STUDY GUIDE

1. From your own background find an illustration which shows that understanding is based upon experience. What is vicarious experience?
2. If possible, determine the extent of a small child's experience by questioning him regarding the kinds of rock he has examined, the reptiles he has seen, or the construction equipment, such as power shovels and derricks, that he has observed.
3. What sequence should be followed in science learnings? Explain and illustrate what is meant by an expanding concept in science.
4. To what extent should incidents be utilized in teaching science? Contrast a factual approach with work organized in terms of meanings. How can science

for children avoid haphazard activities on the one hand and vague generalizations on the other?

5. Cite a child's misconception that you have noted and explain how it might be corrected.

6. To what extent should plans be developed with children, and how? How should a course of study be used?

7. In the elementary-school classes you yourself have known, what has distinguished good science teaching from poor? How could the poor teaching have been improved?

HOW SHOULD WORK BE ORGANIZED

3

Guiding Children's Experiences

Interest in science leads down a road with many branches. To guide the child toward worthwhile experiences and understandings, a teacher should know some of the values in science toward which his efforts may be pointed. The technical achievements of science are not hard to recognize, but what can be accomplished in work with children? The teacher's view of what lies ahead influences the choice of undertakings when plans are developed, is expressed in the encouragement given to a child seeking information, shapes the advice given while an experiment is under way, helps to determine the meanings stressed when learnings are summarized. Guidance is exercised in many subtle ways, in the ready smile on one occasion, in the hesitation on another, through the helpful suggestion that occurs to the teacher, in the experiment that is considered suitable, or merely in the way a comment is worded. The opportunities a teacher can see in science have great influence on the work undertaken and on the results likely to be attained.

HOW CAN THE INTERESTS OF CHILDREN BE DIRECTED TOWARD WORTHWHILE ACHIEVEMENT?

Returning from a faculty meeting at which the issue was discussed, a teacher inquired of his own child:

"Is it better to teach children or a subject?"

"That's silly," the seven-year-old responded. "How can a subject learn anything?"

In education we should be concerned with the child and also with what a subject can offer the child. Students of the newer viewpoint in education, in their reaction to authoritarian teaching methods which have emphasized content to be mastered regardless of the learner, sometimes go to the opposite extreme, at which the child's interest of the moment is considered paramount. As with the driver of an automobile on a country road, it is possible to become so concerned with avoiding the ditch on one side of the road that we may plunge into the ditch on the opposite side. Our concern for the child should not blind us to the worth of potential learnings found in subject matter, nor should we become so preoccupied with a subject that the reactions of the child are overlooked — his concerns, the values that are important to him.

To what extent should interest be considered?

Interest is a quality in the behavior of children not easy to define but often plainly evident to teachers. Carol was a very shy girl, participating but little in the affairs of her third-grade class. But three days after she had planted beans the sprouts began to show, and Carol became excited. When the opportunity came to show the seedlings to the other children in her class, Carol completely forgot her shyness in her eagerness to explain what had happened.

There seems to be little room for doubt that a vital, active interest is essential in any effective learning situation, but frequently there are many practical questions about how to harness the driving force which is manifested as interest. A person learns best when absorbed in his work, and he is more apt to be absorbed in the work when he likes it, finds it pleasant, and believes it is worthwhile, important to him. The work should be challenging, but not overwhelming in difficulty.

Learning is effective when interest is intense, and thus getting the children interested in their work is of the utmost importance. Yet interest at any cost is too high a price. To be effective it must be the right kind of interest — interest that is inherent in the work itself. Tricks, sugar-coating, and irrelevant devices may gain a temporary excitement of a sort, but actually impede progress and serve as a distracting influence leading away from the desired goals. Hilarious disorder that neglects achievement can be no satisfactory substitute for a sober yet enthusiastic concern for the work at hand. The desirable kind of interest stems from the child's natural curiosity and is inherent in his active investigations.

There may be times when a teacher must insist that a certain task be undertaken or that once begun it be completed, but continued compulsion will result in dislike of the work. If it becomes apparent that the work does not appeal to the children, some adjustment should be made. The tasks undertaken may not be suitable, may be overwhelming in difficulty, or may be dull because the work has not progressed beyond what the child already knows. More active investigation involving real materials and experiments may give the desired impetus. The undertaking may lack meaning to the child and serve no worthwhile purpose that he can see. Other interests may be competing for attention; habits or physical or emotional difficulties may be interfering. To proceed in disregard of interest leads to all sorts of complications, both emotional and intellectual.

Interest in science is a goal of instruction as well as a means to an end. If interest is developed and continues, it can lead to far more knowledge than can be gained during the limited time available for instruction. The attitude developed may be of more significance, may have more influence on behavior than the facts acquired. Ordinarily, though, the problem is one of finding means to develop both interest and knowledge, not of choosing which to sacrifice, for the two are complementary. Interest facilitates the acquisition of knowledge, and knowledge gained under favorable circumstances develops interest and appreciation.

How can interest in science be recognized?

Throughout a day at school an alert teacher should be able to detect many clues to the interests of the children. Evidence of interest is not limited to the questions children ask and the objects they bring to class. The comments they make, the discussions they engage in voluntarily, the activities they pursue of their own accord, may be equally good indications of interest. The first-grader who, when he saw that ice had broken the bottle outside his classroom window, exclaimed, "Boy, that ice is sure powerful!" was evincing as much interest as though he had asked a question. And a second-grade girl was obviously enraptured as she bent over a hamster's cage, absorbed in watching the hamster eat.

"Look, they have teeth just like a rabbit's," she said. "They sure are sharp! They cut through carrots so easy."

The question a child asks may not be conclusive evidence of his interest. A sixth-grade girl asked, "Is it true, when the leaves turn over it is going to rain?" Another child dismissed the question by stating that the leaves move like that because the wind is blowing, as it is likely to be just before a storm. The question may have been an indication of interest, but on the other hand many questions represent only a casual thought and may not indicate as deep or extensive a concern as the adult assumes. Or the question may have been primarily a social one. The person who in passing inquires about one's health, or how the weather is that day, may not want a case history or a treatise on weather conditions. Knowing the girl who asked about leaves as a forecast of rain, her characteristic behavior, her mood at the moment, and the situation that prompted the question, the teacher may have been able to judge how much interest the question revealed. Had the teacher been in doubt, ways of delving into the problem were available. The girl's response would then have helped to reveal the value of her question.

The concerns of children are manifested in many ways. The fourth-grade boy who found a squirrel almost dead, took it home and cared for it, and eventually brought it to school was obviously interested. The response of the other children when he showed the animal revealed that they too had become interested. They were eager to care for the squirrel and to watch it, spent much of their free time at the table by the cage, and engaged in arguments about similar animals. Several of the children found animal stories to read. Interest, or the lack of it, is plainly revealed in the behavior of children.

Children have a great variety of interests in science. A great number of studies have been conducted to determine children's interests in science.[1] Some reveal interest in one phase of science, some in another, thus indicating that children may have a great variety of interests, involving all areas of the environment. The results also suggest that the interests are not static but vary with the circumstances. A child with electrical equipment on the table before him is likely to be interested in electricity, but a short while later, when a colorful blue jay is perched on a limb outside the classroom window, the child's interest will be biological. The teacher's own interests seem to have a marked influence also, and if the teacher's interests are broad and varied the influence is good. The studies suggest that children may be unable to predict what will interest them, and that perhaps the manner of studying has a more direct bearing on interest than the subject matter involved. There is some evidence that boys and girls may differ slightly in their science interests. If differences do exist, they need not be accentuated. Electricity, for example, is important to every child, and experience in that area should not be reserved for only half the class. The broad general training of an elementary school is essential for everyone. Girls and boys both need to understand all aspects of their environment.

Potential interests may be more significant than those of the moment. It would seem fruitful for teachers to be more concerned with children's potential

[1] Frederick L. Fitzpatrick, *Science Interests*, New York, Bureau of Publications, Teachers College, Columbia University, 1936.

interests than with those of the moment. Sometimes the initial interests may serve as a point of departure, but as the work proceeds the teacher will be concerned with how the children respond, what initiative they show in learning situations, as in the following cases:

One of the girls in the second grade brought a turtle to school. The turtle was placed in a bowl where it could be watched, and the class read about how to care for it. One day Rickey said his father had told him that turtles hibernate. He wanted to know why theirs had not done so. Consequently soil was brought in from outside, placed in the bowl, and the bowl put in a cool part of the room. By the next day the turtle was out of sight in the soil. Within a week the children began to worry, wondering if the turtle was alive or perhaps lost. So they took it out and washed the bowl. When the turtle was supplied with new quarters, he promptly returned to hibernation, but by then the children understood. From their concern for the turtle, the class went on to consider how other animals spend the winter.

A third grade had a similar experience. Their turtle hibernated, out of sight in the earth and moss of the terrarium. Then one day it appeared again, although the weather was very cold. Its eyes were closed, and it moved very little. The sun was getting stronger, and the children noticed that water had condensed inside the glass. The evaporation and condensation of water were discussed. Eventually the turtle began to move about freely, and when the top of the terrarium was removed, it was discovered that with the sun shining on the terrarium the air inside had become very warm, almost tropical. The terrarium was moved to a cooler part of the room away from direct sunlight, and the turtle returned to peaceful hibernation.

The teacher who has seen how children respond in a case or two, such as the ones just recounted, would not hesitate to introduce the concept of hibernation. Even without any indication of previous interest the teacher would have reason for thinking that a genuine interest could be stimulated by setting the situation — that is, by obtaining a turtle and a terrarium and providing opportunity for observation. The teacher need not wait for children to stumble onto a new idea but can, so to speak, put the idea out where the children will run into it. Interest is vital, but work need not be limited to the interests children already have.

How should children's questions be answered?

Children ask many questions, and those questions often provide evidence of interest which the teacher may direct toward worthwhile learnings. Since interest is developed from experience, the child's question also implies that he

Fig. 12

Ordinarily the best way to answer a child's question is to let the child investigate for himself.

has acquired some knowledge and has the capacity for a degree of understanding. But a child's question commonly is a groping for something of further interest, rather than a well-defined problem, and need not always require an answer in exactly the terms in which it was asked. The child may say, "What kind of rock is that?" or "What is the name of that bird?" for want of a better question, when actually he would like to know something about the rock or the bird, anything the teacher may be able to tell him. No teacher can hope to know the names of all things the children may ask about. There are 625,000 species of insects alone, each with a name of its own, in addition to countless other animals, wild flowers, trees, and other plants, rocks and minerals, and the stars of the sky. Furthermore, the name may be of less value than some other answer. Even if the teacher is uncertain about the name of the rock, he can point out that the pebble has become rounded, probably in some stream. In the case of the bird, the teacher may call attention to its short, stout bill for cracking seed, indicating that the bird apparently lives on seed. In each instance the answer, or some similar one which the teacher may be able to give, very likely will please the child, and the teacher has directed the child's concern toward an important concept.

Worthwhile questions can be emphasized by helping the child to find an answer. With a broad view of the total understanding sought, the teacher will know which questions are likely to be significant and can pass lightly over those that have less value. If the child's question seems trivial, or for some other

63

reason the teacher thinks it would be unwise to give emphasis to it at that time, a direct answer will usually end the matter. If not, and the child persists, the teacher should reconsider; perhaps there was more to the question than was at first apparent. When a child asks for the name of something or for an explanation, and the teacher gives the name or an explanation without enlarging upon it, the child ordinarily will be satisfied without pursuing the matter further. On the other hand, the teacher may believe that the interest should be encouraged. If so, it may be better not to give a direct answer but to help the child find out for himself. Some child may ask why a compass points north, and the teacher can give his question emphasis by helping him to find books and to locate or devise experiments with magnets. The question can be taken up with other members of the class also, and the discussion may provide further stimulation. Any answers obtained from the books or from experimentation can be reported to all concerned. Each problem solved ordinarily will raise still other fertile questions. By stressing the questions that seem most promising, a teacher can lead a class toward worthwhile learnings.

A tangible answer is more likely to be meaningful than a verbal one. The answer to a child's question should be in concrete terms. For instance, a second-grade class, while studying weather, placed a thermometer in hot water and then in cold to show the rise and fall of the mercury. One child then wanted to know what would happen if the thermometer were placed in snow. As the snow that prompted the question was readily available, the class acted on the idea, rather than being satisfied with an easier but less meaningful verbal answer.

The child's own answer to a question is likely to be limited and functional, rather than comprehensive and abstract in the adult sense. When asked what friction is, a first-grade child said, "Well, friction's where two things are rubbed together."

A visitor to a sixth-grade class asked a group of boys at the science table how their electric motor worked, and Ronnie gave an answer characteristic of a child. He said, "You hook wires on here and here, and run them over to the battery, and with magnets here, it works." Then Dorman, who had built the motor, continued the explanation, showing how the magnets would pull the other magnets around and how the magnets changed poles when the current came in the other way.

After a study of children's explanations, in which children gave their interpretations of experiments and answered direct questions, Oakes concluded that children are inclined to think and speak in concrete terms.[2] An adult is apt to

---

[2] Mervin E. Oakes, *Children's Explanations of Natural Phenomena*, Bureau of Publications, Teachers College, Columbia University, New York, 1947, p. 93.

give an abstract, wordy explanation, whereas a child would prefer to be shown.

A fifth-grade teacher reported that one of her boys came to her desk before school, his eyes sparkling, holding something in his hand. He said, "Do you want to see something?" And he placed on her desk a small magnifying glass, saying, "See what happens when I move it back and forth in front of words."

She said, "Do you know why this happens?"

"No," he replied, "but I know it does."

Scientists likewise stress limited, functional descriptions rather than ultimate answers. Each fact obtained through direct investigation is considered established. Thus an "explanation" of a nuclear particle may be a description of its behavior in a cloud chamber.

Adults often give verbal explanations in terms of their own experiences rather than those of the child. Teachers would do well to limit their explanations to the facts already established in the child's mind, pointing out relationships to other experiences the child has had but avoiding meanings and implications that are beyond the child's understanding.

OF WHAT VALUE IS SCIENCE TO THE NONSCIENTIST?

Science and the applications of science are the most distinctive features of our culture and have much to offer education, whether education is viewed as preparation for life in the world today or is considered a means of developing "cultured" people. Surely a cultured person should have some acquaintance with the most distinctive features of his own culture. The insight and the attitudes we derive from science are of inestimable value to the individual and to society as a whole, in terms of both material rewards and the more subtle qualities that characterize a fine human being.

Although he performed very little effective research, Francis Bacon's influence on science was tremendous, for he brought to public attention the great role that science and the methods of science could play in society. Education today can and should make a similar contribution. The advancement of science and of society itself depends as much upon the assimilation of new discoveries as upon the research which produced those discoveries. Both are links in a chain and are equally necessary.

All should appreciate the achievements of natural science

History shows that our present way of life is largely the result of past scientific achievements. For example, Faraday discovered that by moving a magnet near a coil of wire an electric current could be induced in the wire. Today our electric generators are based upon the principle he discovered. How dependent we are upon such a source of electricity becomes evident during a storm when lightning strikes the power facilities. Factories are shut down, and much of our transportation is at a standstill. Our houses are in darkness; the refrigerator, vacuum cleaner, and countless other appliances will not operate. Even amusements are held up until facilities are restored. We are living in a world of science and its applications.

For every major discovery, such as that of Faraday, there are many hundreds which seldom come to public attention yet nevertheless add to the knowledge and skills which make our complex civilization possible.

How many of us owe even our lives to the achievements of medical science will never be known. The epidemic that might have eliminated us, or perhaps our parents, was halted at its inception. Our problems are not all solved, but the plagues of Biblical times and those of the Middle Ages, such as the Black Death, which decimated whole populations, are no longer the serious threat to our health or very existence that they were in former ages. Without the knowledge of infectious diseases that Pasteur, Koch, Lister, and a host of others have obtained, many of us would not be living today. Contrasting the birth rate in times of depression with the rate in times of prosperity shows that even our lives are dependent upon material prosperity, which in turn is largely dependent upon scientific achievements. The world today supports an ever-increasing population at a level of prosperity that Malthus thought impossible. There are over twice as many of us on this planet as there were a hundred years ago.

Our lives are directly dependent upon the supply of food. In the United States the average yield of corn per acre in about ten years increased approximately 50 per cent when hybrid corn was first used commercially. Increased production helped us to survive the war years and then to feed the hungry, war-torn countries abroad. The development of hybrid corn was a direct result of fundamental research in genetics, and is but one example of research that has aided the farmer.

Our material welfare, with respect to both necessities and luxuries, is a product of scientific research. Scientists are quick to point out, nevertheless, that research should not be limited to the development of practical applications. Speaking at Vassar College in 1922, Marie Curie said:

> But we must not forget that when radium was discovered no one knew that it would prove useful in hospitals. The work was one of pure science. And this is a proof that scientific work must be done for itself, for the beauty of science, and

then there is always the chance that a scientific discovery may become, like radium, a benefit for humanity.[3]

Science will provide the opportunities of the future. In the early history of this country, when times were hard and opportunity lacking, many people moved westward to seek their fortunes in the plains and rich valleys of the West. Europeans in search of opportunity came to the new world. Now the frontier is largely gone. The unexploited resources that give opportunity for success and hope for the future are provided today by research in science. The future is of great concern to young people.

Progress in science brings hope to those who otherwise would face misery and death. The discovery of dicumarol, a substance which reduces the tendency of blood to form clots in the body, provides a treatment for the most common, immediate cause of death in patients over fifty-five years of age. With the discovery of cortisone and ACTH, so great was the promise of relief for arthritis and other painful afflictions that one chemical firm began running a series of newspaper advertisements to explain why their limited production was at the time unable to meet even the urgent needs of those who sought relief. Truly, science holds out the only hope for many people. Eventually, no doubt, we shall simply take for granted the present achievements of research, much as we now take for granted the achievements of the past.

Science has great influence on human behavior

The material advantages of scientific achievement are easily seen, but no less important and far-reaching is the effect of science upon our thinking. Our ancestors, like primitive people even today, were superstitious, not because of limited mentality but owing to lack of information. Without the understanding which science has brought us, we would have similar beliefs today. Except for major decisions, consciously arrived at, we ordinarily are not aware of the extent to which our behavior, even highly emotional behavior, is conditioned by our understanding and our point of view. We no longer believe that spirits inhabit every bush, nor do we treat illness with magic and sorcery as our ancestors did. Yet some still govern their lives by the stars, for they lack a true understanding of the constellations.

The accounts of witchcraft in New England show plainly the effects of fear based on ignorance. Today we do not believe that any old woman, no matter

[3] Marie Curie, *The Discovery of Radium*, edited by Ellen S. Richards (Monograph No. 2, Bureau of Publications of Vassar College), as quoted in: Harlow Shapley and others, *Readings in the Physical Sciences*, Appleton-Century-Crofts, New York, 1948, p. 352.

how ugly and queer, can prod us with unseen weapons, inflict strange maladies, or bring about a storm at sea to endanger our lives. It seems evident that whatever people do is based upon their beliefs — their understanding. Research has provided us with knowledge and has become a vital force in shaping our beliefs and thus our actions.

While the discoveries of science have had great influence, many beliefs and ways of thinking not in accord with the findings of research continue to influence people who have not learned the facts. It has long been the practice of farmers to save the smaller, unmarketable potatoes for seed; to the extent that this practice is continued, inferior qualities are reproduced. A knowledge of biology would eliminate many popular misconceptions. Some speak of "bad blood," of hair turning gray overnight; others assume men have a monopoly on brains and that alcohol in the blood will prevent infection. A host of misconceptions are concerned with prenatal influences, as, for example, the fear that if a pregnant woman reaches upward the umbilical cord will be wrapped about the neck of the fetus and the infant will be choked to death at birth. Some assume that birds and other animals forecast the seasons rather than simply respond to them, and hence regard the southward flight of geese as an omen of approaching winter. A common belief is that squirrels and other furry animals grow heavier fur at the approach of a severe winter and also reveal their mysterious sense by storing more nuts or making other special preparations. In New England, and perhaps elsewhere, the Woolly Bear caterpillars are foresighted enough to develop a wide reddish-brown band around their middle in case a mild winter is expected and a narrow band for a cold winter; thus credulous people are provided with a handy forecast of the seasons. The weather, being of common interest, is the basis of many false beliefs. That lightning never strikes twice is merely an expression to some people, a belief to others. Some people teach their children that stepping on an ant will bring rain and that toads will cause warts. Many of us were early embued with a great dread of even the common garter snake.

The average person, or even the specialist, certainly will be unable to learn enough facts to correct all possible misconceptions, but he can readily develop an attitude that will make him less receptive to mystical interpretations and open-minded enough to suspend judgment and to consider new facts when he encounters them. In many ways more damaging than the holding of false beliefs is the fact that a person may lack any concept at all of the vistas science has revealed. Even many apparently well-educated people will avoid conversations in which any phase of science is involved — will dismiss the subject as beyond their understanding, often with a shudder of distaste. Their education has included not even a glimpse of the fascination and the significance of science as it affects the average person.

Science and our society are interdependent

Many thoughtful persons have stressed the need for a broad public understanding of science and its implications in our society. A few well-trained technical workers are not enough. The efforts of the scientists and technicians can be defeated by a lack of sympathy and understanding or by the inability of the public to cooperate intelligently. In the past a lack of public sympathy and understanding often has hindered the advance of science. In the seventeenth century Giordano Bruno was imprisoned, was held for seven years, and finally was burned at the stake for teaching that the universe is infinite, and not centered upon the earth as was commonly believed.

As spokesman for the Executive Committee of the American Association for the Advancement of Science, Warren Weaver has written:

> It is clearly recognized that the diffusion among the general public of knowledge about science and its methods is a difficult, slow, and never-ending job. . . . But in our modern society it is absolutely essential that science — the results of science, the nature and importance of basic research, the methods of science, the spirit of science — be better understood by government officials, by businessmen, and indeed by all the people.[4]

Public policies involve science in many and varied ways. Perhaps the most direct way is through government support of research. Should funds for public health services, for military and for agricultural research, be curtailed or perhaps increased? Should the National Science Foundation be given more ample financial support, as requested, or is the money already allocated being wasted? How may we best conserve our national resources, or control atomic energy? Are reclamation, electric-power, and flood-control projects worthwhile, or simply "pork-barrel" politics? Should the Weather Bureau, the Bureau of Standards, the Bureau of Mines, the Department of Commerce, and various other government departments or agencies be permitted to conduct research at public expense? The ordinary citizen cannot hope to answer such questions satisfactorily by himself, but he can have the basic understanding needed to judge various points of view when the issues are presented to him, so that some distinction can be made between selfish interests and the public good. Elected officials look to the public for support of undertakings they sponsor and decisions they make. The officials themselves are a part of the public too, and their

[4] Warren Weaver, "AAAS Policy," *Science*, 114:472, November 2, 1951.

knowledge of science, or lack of it, can be attributed in most cases to their formal education. As science becomes increasingly involved in our way of life, we need some basic understandings for our welfare as individuals and also as citizens with responsibility to society as a whole.

Not only is our society dependent upon science, but science in turn is dependent upon the public for continued achievement. Research must be financed through the government, industries, and private endowments. That much is obvious, but there are more subtle ways in which the public influences the work of science for good or bad. Scientists themselves are influenced by the concerns and beliefs of people about them. The problems chosen for investigation reflect those concerns. The work of Pasteur, for example, plainly reflects conditions at the time in France. Where science and the scientists are held in esteem, the respect not only serves as an incentive for achievement, with attendant public recognition, but will help to induce young people of ability to become workers in science and related fields. On the other hand, a lack of respect can discourage those who are inclined to investigate. In fact, children are often discouraged by such attitudes today, when adults frown upon their questions and repulse their efforts to explore. In this regard, Detlev W. Bronk of Johns Hopkins University has written:

> There is opposition to curiosity first in childhood. Only the most patient parent encourages its free development at the expense of his personal peace. Only the wisest teachers discard the easy methods of didactic instruction to follow as counselors at the heels of students who freely satisfy their curiosity. Even in the scientific laboratory the student's curiosity is suppressed and the laboratory becomes a training ground for technical manipulation rather than a place for intellectual exploration. The present tendency to create an educational system which thus suppresses curiosity for the sake of "efficient" education robs modern civilization of the true scientists it needs.[5]

Well known is the case of Galileo, whose work was condemned by a commission of men who knew nothing of science yet forced Galileo to renounce the truths he had discovered and make a public apology for his work. The potential influence on scientists and their research of attitudes based on ignorance is indicated by the remark Galileo is reported to have made after his trial:

> The pleasure which I have taken hitherto in making observations on new phenomena is almost entirely gone.[6]

At a later date William Harvey wrote regarding his discovery of how blood circulates in the body:

---

[5] Detlev W. Bronk, "Science and Humanity," *Science*, 109:477, May 13, 1949.
[6] Quoted in J. G. Crowther, *The Social Relations of Science,* Macmillan, New York, 1941, p. 327.

But what remains to be said upon the quantity and source of the blood which thus passes is of so novel and unheard-of character that I not only fear injury to myself from the envy of a few, but I tremble lest I have mankind at large for my enemies, so much does wont and custom . . . and doctrine once sown and that has struck deep root, and respect for antiquity influence all men. Still the die is cast, and my trust is in my love of truth and the candor that inheres in cultivated minds.[7]

The public can do much to encourage science, or can be unsympathetic, even antagonistic. A lack of sympathy is commonly based on lack of understanding. The elementary school can help with constructive experiences in science, developing both appreciation and a degree of understanding that will make cooperation possible.

In time of crisis it is realized that the nation's strength is largely in the knowledge and skill of its people. Discussing the mobilization of scientific, engineering, and medical manpower, Charles V. Kidd has reported:

As the pace of the nation's defense effort accelerates, demands for scientific, engineering, medical, and other technical manpower are pressing more closely upon severely limited resources. The shortages that have already developed, and those that are clearly ahead, have both alarmed those who feel their effects most sharply and brought a measure of public action.[8]

To be fully effective, the achievements of science must be known. Many agencies are at work helping the public to assimilate the progress of science. Writers, librarians, museum staffs, and the scientists themselves all help; but if the public is to be educated effectively, the job must be initiated by the schools, especially the elementary schools where basic adult attitudes are developed, and where virtually the whole public can be reached. The responsibility for an informed public rests upon the public schools.

WHAT LEARNINGS SHOULD CHILDREN ACQUIRE FROM SCIENCE?

Science itself is an interpretation of the environment, and the basic objective of instruction in this area likewise should be to help the child make an adequate *interpretation* of his own environment as he encounters it. Ability to interpret — to understand — implies that the person concerned will be better able to

---

[7] William Harvey, "Anatomical Essay on the Motion of the Heart and Blood in Animals," reprinted in *The Autobiography of Science,* edited by Forest Ray Moulton and Justus J. Schifferes, Doubleday, Garden City, 1946, p. 109.

[8] Charles V. Kidd, "Mobilization of Scientific, Engineering, and Medical Manpower: An Interim Report," *Science,* 113:737, June 29, 1951.

adjust himself or to modify the physical world about him in accord with his own needs and the needs of society. Fundamental also are the *skills, interests, appreciations,* and constructive *attitudes* that go with sympathetic understanding.

It is generally recognized today that we live in a world of science, that science is deeply involved in our way of life. The insight that science can bring and the constructive attitudes that go with it can be of inestimable value to each individual and to the society of which he is a part.

Worthwhile understandings should be stressed

Instruction in science should be directed toward important principles, principles that have reality and value for children, rather than stress isolated experiences or detailed bits of information. Just as the reader of a newspaper ordinarily must select which items he will read, since there is not time to read everything, so in the schools a selection must be made; there obviously is not time to learn all the facts known to science. The reader of a newspaper will select articles that have significance and interest for him; the schools likewise should select content and activities that are in accord with the purposes of instruction.

Textbooks, courses of study, and the professional literature suggest many worthwhile learnings; other possibilities may develop out of the circumstances at the time. In as vast a field as all of science, the potentialities are almost unlimited. Any knowledge may have value, but in everyday circumstances time and other limitations make a selection necessary. The mere fact that a particular activity has been undertaken signifies that others have not. Whether deliberately or not, selections must always be made. The issue can be evaded simply by following a textbook or syllabus in which someone else has made the selection of content, but circumstances vary, and no one can foresee what will be most pertinent in a particular classroom at a particular time. Also, unless some modification of prearranged subject matter is permitted, the initiative is taken from the children, and investigation in the true spirit of science is not possible.

Unless the teacher has clearly in mind what he hopes to accomplish, a class is apt to drift aimlessly among details, or, in actual practice, instruction on the spur of the moment may be guided by motives that the teacher would never consciously accept as worthwhile. The objectives or purposes of instruction are important in determining not only what shall be taught but also the way it is taught and the emphasis that is given. A teacher's own objectives in many subtle ways influence everything that is done in the classroom, and thus it is important to examine those purposes.

The teacher's goals may reach far beyond the child's motives of the moment. Ordinarily the teacher will see values of which the children are unaware and so may guide the children toward profitable learnings. The experiences of a combined fourth- and fifth-grade class will serve as an example. On the day before spring vacation the children were clearing their room, gathering up work that had been on display, when one child remarked, "The room doesn't look so pretty now."

Having in mind the plant study she intended to carry on, the teacher suggested they get some plants for the room after vacation. Several children offered to bring geraniums and other potted plants.

"Perhaps we might even raise some," the teacher said, pressing her own plans.

The idea was greeted with enthusiasm, and several children immediately offered to bring soil, flower pots, and seed.

One girl said, "It's funny how a plant comes from a seed."

"To see how plants grow, we could do some experiments," the teacher suggested.

"Experiments!" The word was magic. "Oh! Like in the science books?"

It was their first venture in science. The boys and girls begged permission to take books home to read during the vacation and find some experiments to do.

True to their promises, on the morning after vacation the children came in with seed, boxes, and flower pots full of soil. Plans were made that morning, and questions were listed for investigation:

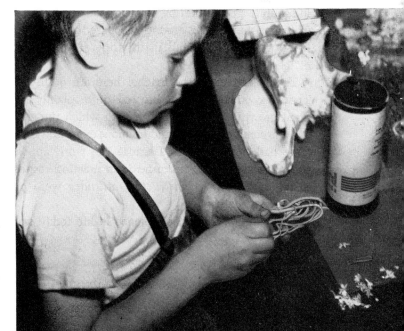

Fig. 13

Children will investigate of their own accord, but they need the guidance and assistance of a teacher to make the work most profitable.

How do plants grow from seed?
What do plants need to make them grow?
How do plants get food and water?

Many of the children were prepared with ideas and experiments. In each case the experiments were directed mainly by the children who had brought the materials and knew what to do. To answer the first question, bean seed were soaked, periodically examined, and a record was kept of the changes that took place in growth. Pictures were drawn of the seed each time they were examined, and the pictures were made a part of the record.

To answer the second question, beans were planted in soil and in pebbles; all were kept in the light at the same room temperature and were watered regularly at the same time of day. In a few days the beans sprouted — those in the pebbles a little faster, it seemed — but in three weeks the ones in soil were larger, had more leaves, and began to develop pods, whereas those in the pebbles never did mature. The class concluded that plants must have soil. Similar experiments were conducted to show the need of water, sunshine, and warmth. A geranium not watered for a week turned brown, whereas another was still green. Bean seedlings kept in the closet for a week became a pale green, yet those in the light remained well colored. Seedlings placed outside the classroom window grew but slowly in the cool weather of early spring.

To learn how plants get water, the class placed a bean seedling, roots first, in a jar containing red ink. In a few hours the vessels through which water rises had become visible, for the roots and stem were red, and a short while later the veins of the leaves. Also to show that water is taken in by the roots, not by leaves as some of the children had surmised, the class used two petunia plants in separate pots, watering the roots of one in the customary manner. With a water-resistant collar around the base, the second plant was watered on the leaves only. The second plant withered in a few days, whereas the first remained normal.

The objectives of the teacher here are quite obvious and easy to analyze. These experiences were directed quite plainly toward an *understanding* of plant growth. The enthusiasm with which the children undertook their work and the comments made and opinions expressed revealed that more than knowledge had been gained. Because the work appealed to them, the children became cooperative, enthusiastic in meeting responsibilities, and constructive in point of view. *Constructive attitudes* were among the foremost of the teacher's objectives.

That an *appreciation* of science in life today was acquired became evident somewhat later when a news report of scientific achievement was discussed in class. The children had gained respect for science and the work of scientists. Furthermore, it was evident that the children had developed new *interest* in their environment and had gained certain practical *skills* in the care of plants.

In another classroom situation the initial impetus came from the children themselves, yet it is evident that the teacher directed the experiences toward worthwhile learnings. While playing with a plastic cosmetic bottle, children in the kindergarten discovered that by compressing the sides they could force air out of the bottle. The teacher explained what was happening and helped them to see that they could get the same feeling by blowing onto their hands. They decided that they were blowing air out of their mouths, just as they had forced air out of the bottle. The children seemed interested; so the teacher helped them to do other experiments with air, such as blowing out the flame of a candle with air from a paper bag. The purpose was to show the children that air is something real, although we cannot see it.

As in the preceding example, a teacher can guide the undertakings of children, but upon what basis should the teacher decide that certain learnings are worth pursuing whereas others are not?

Some learnings are more essential than others. In general, learnings that are important to people and affect their welfare should be stressed. A matter of health or safety, for example, is of utmost importance:

After an epidemic of colds and absences during the winter months, the teacher and children of a fourth grade became concerned with the ways in which colds are spread and how they can be avoided. Therefore the teacher asked the science consultant to meet with the class. At this session one of the girls wanted to know how it is that if germs are the cause of colds, wet feet can bring on one? For a while the class considered that point — how a chill can lower resistance to germs — and there were many questions regarding germs and what they are like. So plans were made to prepare cultures of bacteria, and at the appointed time a committee met with the consultant, sterilized petri dishes, and prepared a culture medium.[9]

At the next opportunity the consultant met with the class again, and the committee explained to their classmates what had been done. Then the cultures were inoculated, the class deciding for themselves just what inoculations would be made. One petri dish was opened, and a child volunteered to cough into it; someone blew his breath into another, and then each dish was immediately closed, labeled, and placed on a table for observation. In like manner a third dish was touched by someone's finger tips, and a dead fly was placed on an-

[9] See also p. 305.

other. The remaining dishes were left unopened for comparison. As a source of protozoa, an infusion was prepared by merely placing a number of lettuce leaves in a bowl of water. In a few days decay was apparent in the infusion, and by that time considerable growth of bacteria could be seen in the petri dishes that were inoculated. Accordingly, two microscopes were brought to the room, and bacteria were mounted on a slide for one microscope and a few drops of the infusion mounted for the other. The microscopes were left throughout the day for the children to observe individually whenever they had free time. The consultant dropped in occasionally to see that the microscopes were still in focus.

Near the end of that day the consultant returned, and the class gathered in a semicircle for a discussion of their observations. Because the infusion containing the protozoa had been placed in the cavity of a depression slide, there was plenty of room for movement, and the animals that were visible at one time would differ from those moving into focus a moment later. Thus no two people had quite the same view, and there were marked differences in the observations reported. Even the bacteria, though inactive, inspired many excited comments. The children made rough sketches on the blackboard to indicate what they had seen, and modifications were sometimes added by another observer as the children pooled their knowledge. Everyone was vividly impressed by the reality of microorganisms. The role of microscopic plants and animals in beneficial processes, as in cheese-making or the digestion of food, was considered in addition to the harmful effects. The classroom teacher stressed the reasons for keeping fingers and pencils out of mouths and for turning the head when coughing, and it seemed at the moment that no child in the group ever again would be inclined to disobey these admonitions.

That a knowledge of microbes can prove to be vital is evident, but other understandings can be essential too. The newspapers frequently report deaths, injuries, and loss of property from fire, high-voltage electricity, floods, and similar hazards. Unfortunately, it is apparent in many cases that with greater insight and understanding the tragedies could have been avoided.

Although considerations of health and safety are important, they are not the only essential learnings. Some understandings have considerable influence on the material status of the people involved. Some insights help individuals to make wholesome social adjustments, to understand themselves, and to enjoy their surroundings. Some insights may bear on important decisions the individual must make, decisions that may affect not only the individual but a whole community. Because of his knowledge an individual may support a worthwhile cause, may avoid building his house on the flood plain of a river, may know how to care for a garden successfully. Understandings that are likely to have the greatest influence are the understandings that should be sought.

Understandings that have common applications are of great value. Understandings that apply in many situations are more worthwhile than those that are unique. It may be interesting to know that each flower of the Wild Yellow Lily has six stamens, or that Touracos are tropical birds which lay three white eggs in a nest built of sticks; yet such information ordinarily will have less value than an understanding of electricity, for electricity and electrical appliances are common in our way of life. Likewise, knowing how to identify a pin oak has less value than knowing the function of the oak leaf, because that function is typical of leaves of all plants. Although a single, unrelated fact may seldom find application in normal experience, many of the principles and generalizations of science repeatedly bear on everyday thought and action.

That which is common need not be considered trivial. A housefly is less spectacular than a tarantula but, being more common, is of greater relevance to our health. A classroom aquarium stocked with life from a nearby pond can be more meaningful than one filled with tropical fish. The unique or unusual is often intriguing but of less functional value. With rabbits, English sparrows, and the tent caterpillar, understandings can be developed that apply to animals everywhere. The unusual and the spectacular need not be ignored, for they may contribute to the interpretation of more common experiences. Although other values must be considered, the very frequency with which some learnings find application makes those learnings worthwhile as goals of instruction.

Circumstances help to determine what learnings are suitable

Plans that are highly desirable in one situation may be less satisfactory in some other. A particularly advantageous situation may not only give the child a zest for learning but provide the basis for understanding as well. Circumstances modify both the goals and the means of achieving those goals.

A meaningful situation provides opportunity for learning. Occurrences in the home, school, or community develop natural problems that call for solutions. One of the second-grade girls, during the morning period for sharing experiences, related how a milk bottle left on her porch the night before had broken; and the class was curious to know why it had broken. Someone suggested that freezing was responsible, and so it was decided to try an experiment. Two bottles were filled with water. Although one failed to break when left outside in the cold weather, the ice that formed did push up out of the bottle to form what the children called a "funny top piece." Another bottle, one with a screw-

Fig. 14

Here it is easy to under-
stand that as a tree grows
the expansion causes the
bark either to crack or to
peel.

type cap, was broken by the ice. Both cases aroused many thoughtful comments, and the children concluded that water, as they put it, "must get bigger
when it freezes."

"Ice takes up more space than water" was another explanation.

Evidence of further thought came out later in the week when one of the
children said to the teacher, "You know, that water freezing is why we can't live
in our summer home in the winter." As the child continued it became apparent
that she was relating the simple experiment with the bottles to the freezing and
cracking of water pipes in the winter.

Circumstances helped to make the experiences with the freezing water suitable. The real situation gave added significance, a deeper meaning to the concept developed.

In another case, when Edward was stung by a hornet in the school yard and
Peggy by a bee on her way to school, the children concluded it is good to have
birds about that can eat insects, for too many insects would be most unpleasant.
Circumstances helped to develop meanings in this case that otherwise might
have been unattainable. A good program in science will neither ignore such
opportunities nor will it be limited to incidents that occur by chance.

The maturity of the child helps to determine what learnings are possible.

The learnings selected as immediate goals and the experiences through which the goals are pursued should be appropriate to the maturity of the children. The interests of a child and his capacity for achievement change with age, and accordingly the activities and learnings he undertakes should change also. The sudden enthusiasm for cleanliness and neatness that may be acquired by an adolescent boy would have been unattainable at an earlier age. Other changes that occur with growth may not be as amusing, but may be just as fundamental to learning. General behavior, skills, ways of talking, and apparent interests are discernible differences. Though not always sharply defined, such differences are characteristic of the various ages and must be considered in developing an effective educational program.

The activities of children in their free time provide clues to the spontaneous impulses and abilities that are characteristic of the various ages. Small children have not learned to discipline themselves or to follow long-range goals; the work undertaken must appeal to them at the moment. The interest must be intrinsic. Immediate action is characteristic of small children, whereas the older child can make plans and can see farther ahead to appreciate more remote values, and the anticipation can be a stimulus toward careful preparation. But even the older children fall short of adult standards for perseverance and are likely to shift from one interest to another, though possibly returning at a later time. With increasing maturity comes an increasing spirit of independence, and children should find increasing opportunity for making some of their own decisions. The capacity for cooperation also is closely related to age. Small children like to be together, but typically each will pursue his independent way in carrying on his own activity. The behavior of one is apt to be rough or inconsiderate toward another; an adverse reaction from the second child is shocking to the first. Small children are in the process of learning how other individuals feel and respond, and cooperation is still difficult.

Children become more skillful as they increase in age and experience. Accordingly, the work that will appeal to a child of six and will be meaningful for him may differ considerably from that which is suitable for a child of nine. In three years the older child may have acquired enough skill that tasks which were frustrating at six may be challenging at nine. On the other hand, those activities which are exciting to the six-year-old may be tedious and boring three years later. To construct a telegraph set from a tin can and scrap lumber, for example, a child will need strength enough to cut the metal. He will need skill in the use of his hands to assemble the set. If instructions for the work are to be obtained from books, the child will need skill in reading. A child's physical development, his size, strength, and manual dexterity, help to determine what he can do. The activities undertaken must be modified accordingly.

The long-range goals for education, in the elementary school at least, are the same for children of any age; but the immediate objectives and the activities undertaken to achieve them vary with the maturity of the children. Like anyone else, the child is more apt to learn what appeals to him, serves his own purpose, and is within the range of his ability. To be highly effective an educational program must be in accord with the characteristics of the children concerned. A program that in effect opposes the natural impulses of the children will be confronted with unnecessary difficulties.

Individuals differ in their rate and pattern of development, and although helpful generalizations can be made about the typical interests, behavior, and abilities of children at a given age, each individual should be taken as he is, not as someone has characterized children of his age. A teacher who is aware of the reactions of the children, who is considerate and has respect for each personality, should find little difficulty in adapting the work to individuals at their present stage of development.

In short, then, to select the learnings and learning experiences, consideration should be given both to the inherent value of the desired learnings and to what is most appropriate for the child at his present stage of mental, physical, and emotional development. Regardless of the value inherent in the objectives, they can be achieved only by the child himself, and his capacities must be given consideration.

The personal problems of the children help to determine what learnings are needed. The emotional circumstances are among the factors to be considered in determining the child's readiness or need for certain experiences. In one case, because some of the nursery children were afraid of animals, the teacher tried to foster an increasing interest in the hamsters that were in the room. Stories were read about animals, and the children were encouraged to tell about their own experiences. A great deal of attention was given to feeding and caring for the hamsters, but the timid children were not forced to help or even asked to watch. One morning the teacher saw a child who was fond of the hamsters explaining to one of the timid children how the hamsters built their nest. Later during the same morning, the timid child approached the teacher and asked if he might feed the hamsters! He had overcome his fear; his attitude was changing.

Emotional disturbances may be more obvious in the nursery than in the upper elementary grades, but at any level adjustment is essential for the welfare of the individual. The sixth-grade child who through cooperative effort in a science activity becomes accepted in his group has made a vital emotional adjustment. An activity which encourages such adjustment is likely to be worthwhile.

A balanced curriculum should be maintained. Emphasis on individual differences sometimes conveys the impression that a completely different program must be planned for each individual. But human beings are much alike wherever they may be. Many impulses are common to all ages and abilities, though possibly not expressed in the same form or to the same degree. All are motivated by curiosity, for example, just as healthy people of any age are moved by hunger. The needs that people have in common are fully as important as the differences that distinguish one individual from another. Both should be considered in planning the work in science.

Local situations that affect the child's point of view and background of understanding will influence the curriculum and will help to determine what undertakings are feasible and desirable. In one group the children for as long as they can remember have been surrounded by the mechanical equipment of a farm, by the planting, cultivating, and harvesting of crops; in their daily chores they have helped to gather eggs and feed the cattle; they have observed new-born rabbits and are familiar with the internal organs of animals slaughtered for meat. Another group of children in another community have lived within the limitations of an apartment house and the restrictions of sidewalk and playground, but with the advantages of museums, zoos, and well-stocked libraries. The two groups are headed toward the common objectives of education, although their points of departure are not the same.

The opportunities and responsibilities which come to a child outside school help to determine his attitudes, his background of understanding, and his need of instruction. The typical six-year-old lives in an environment that is more restricted than that of an older child. The child whose parents take him on trips will have a broader horizon than the child who is limited to his own neighborhood. The child's present way of life and his expectations for the future help to determine his aspirations, his capacity for new learnings, and what instruction will be of the greatest value for him.

As children mature and gain experience, however, they also gain increasing ability to generalize and to interpret that which is more remote. Even though a child lives high in the Rocky Mountains he will need many of the same understandings that are necessary for a child who lives in a fishing community along the coast. One child's way of life may not be as different from the other's as it first seems.

Science does not function alone in the curriculum, and accordingly other endeavors must be considered. The science activities contemplated may enhance and supplement the other studies already under way in the classroom or they may compete with them for time and attention. A common policy of elementary schools is to maintain a balanced curriculum in which all areas of living are represented, and likewise it is considered advisable within the field of science to encourage a child's potential interest in all aspects of his environment. Thus children who have had many experiences with plant and animal life, for example, will be encouraged to delve into new fields. The child who has developed a great interest in chemical changes, perhaps as a result of his experiences with a chemistry set, will be helped to see that other areas too can be fascinating. The individual who eventually may specialize will need breadth of view; all individuals live in a world in which problems and opportunities encompass many fields.

The future is uncertain, and predicting what learnings will be of the greatest value to a particular individual is indeed hazardous if such evaluations are made in terms of some narrow utility. But regardless of what the future may hold, understandings that help a person adjust to his environment will prove to be of value.

Emotional qualities and skills are significant learnings

The objectives of experience in science include development of constructive attitudes, continuing interests, appreciations, and skills. Attitudes, appreciations, and interests are emotional qualities not easily distinguished from each other, but all are of great importance if the knowledge gained is to function well in actual life situations.

Science experiences can help to develop appreciation of the world in which we live. A fourth-grade teacher, after working with her class for the first time on a problem involving rocks and the changing surface of the earth, related that her own appreciation had increased as a result of the work. On her way home for the Christmas vacation she crossed the mountains from New York to her family home in Ohio. She had made the trip regularly for years, but this time the trip was no longer dull routine, for she could see the folded strata of rocks, evidence of mountain building, and streams that had cut down through the rocks as the mountains were lifted up many, many years ago. She was surprised by her own ability to make interpretations and delighted that a limited experience in science could make her trip exciting.

In another case, while a sixth-grade class was studying the physical features of their region, one of the girls went with her family on a week-end trip through the nearby lava fields in the states of Washington and Idaho. Upon their return the parents said that a friend who accompanied them, an engineer, had been amazed at the girl's ability to interpret her surroundings on the trip. Needless to say, the family was immensely pleased and impressed by the fact that elementary work could add so much to the pleasure of a trip.

The world in which we live is more than rocks and soil, mountains and valleys; it has become an industrial society with technical apparatus in its homes, a new vocabulary, new insights. Basic attitudes are developed early, and the elementary-school experiences of children help to determine the attitudes they will have throughout life. The world needs people who can appreciate the accomplishments of science, can sense the possibilities and the hope of the future, and are able to lend at least moral support to the solution of problems through research.

A continuing interest in science can be developed. Instruction in science should develop interests that persist. In many respects an interest that continues may prove to have a greater, more lasting effect upon the life of an individual than almost any given bit of knowledge could have. A concern for science can lead to the acquisition of knowledge and to its use. The effect of the interest is apt to be cumulative over a period of years. Interest and appreciation come with understanding, and the individual who has many interests, who appreciates his surroundings, gains a full life. For many people science will have recreational value, and it can enrich daily experiences for all.

Among the hobbies based on science are photography, amateur astronomy, bird watching, and gardening. Some people maintain aquaria; others build model airplanes, and many collect rocks, shells, butterflies, wild flowers, or other articles of scientific interest. Although the elementary schools are in no way vocational, interest in science can form a basis for a life's work and may lead to an eventual choice from the increasingly extensive fields of the basic and applied sciences. In addition to research, the occupations based on science include the numerous branches of engineering, modern agriculture, medicine, aviation, meteorology, and a great variety of positions in chemical, electrical, and other industries. Furthermore, science is the basis of the work of the electrician, the radio and television repair man, the nurseryman, and the salesman who should thoroughly understand his product. Even such a varied activity as housekeeping involves many potential applications of scientific principles in the care of children, the preparation of food, and the operation of electrical and mechanical equipment. Interest in science, once developed, can become a major influence throughout the life of the individual.

Constructive scientific attitudes can be developed. One fundamental purpose of science experiences in elementary schools is to develop a scientific attitude. Such an attitude is essentially dynamic; it leads to effective action. The individual who has a scientific attitude will base both thought and action on the best knowledge available, and he will suspend judgment where reliable information is lacking. There are many desirable human qualities which can be derived from a scientific attitude. Children can learn to be cooperative, to work together as scientists do for the solution of common problems. They can learn to be open-minded, willing to alter an opinion in the light of new evidence, rather than biased or dogmatic. They can learn to be constructive in point of view, seeking and expecting to find logical explanations and solutions of problems; and they can learn how to obtain information that is reliable. Whether or not such goals are achieved will depend upon the manner in which the work of the classroom is conducted. If the spirit of the class is one of active investigation, if the problems are real and scientific attitudes are applied in practice, these attitudes will be learned.

Good attitudes and subject matter are correlative. Today as educators we are concerned not only with the facts children learn but also with the attitudes they form toward those facts. The mood of the individual provides the spark that will determine how and to what extent facts are used, rather than ignored. Thus in a sense the facts of science provide the vehicle, but the attitudes, appreciations, and interests supply the power to make them function.

In practice, emphasis on the attitudes and interests that make a well-adjusted human being may be accompanied by an unfortunate depreciation of subject matter. In reacting against an older tendency to emphasize knowledge in isolation from other values, it is possible to swing to the opposite extreme where the qualities of a good citizen are stressed in isolation from content. In this case one extreme may be as bad as the other. Knowledge has little value without an attitude that will lead to constructive application of what is known. Knowing better but not doing better has been a common result of emphasis on subject matter alone. On the other hand, desirable emotional qualities are not developed in isolation. An interest must be directed *toward* something; similarly, an attitude cannot exist by itself. If anything said or done leads the child to think that the work he is doing is not very important, his constructive attitude will suffer.

A good citizen must believe that his goals are worth striving for and not dependent simply upon his interest, his mood of the moment. The truth is, such values actually *are* inherent. A knowledge of high-voltage electricity, for example, can be a life or death matter regardless of the individual's interest or mood. Teaching procedures may be varied in accord with the child's feelings, but the value of the knowledge persists nevertheless. We all like to feel and should feel that what we are doing is important, worthwhile for its own sake. We resent being given "busy work," work that has little inherent value. How would teachers feel if the superintendent gave them busy work, producing a course of study, perhaps, and inferred that it mattered little what kind of course they developed, because the real purpose was to develop the teachers' own attitudes? Very likely the attitudes developed would not be the ones the superintendent had in mind. In building attitudes, care must be taken not to disparage the value of the content and experiences upon which good attitudes are based.

An active program can develop practical skills. In an active program of investigation, many worthwhile skills can be developed. As children work with electrical equipment, tools, simple apparatus, as they care for pets, for plants and other experimental materials, they not only learn ways of working, of solving problems: they develop numerous manipulative skills involving both large and small muscles. Constructing a telegraph set, an electric buzzer, or a cage for animals can be a creative experience in which manual dexterity is developed, just as in any other construction work. Ability to read a thermometer, to interpret a weather map, to read a news report involving scientific terms may be considered skills, as are habits of accuracy in measurement or observation, and ability to devise experiments, to demonstrate and report before a group. If reports are written, additional skills are involved. Where children work together, cooperating on their investigations, skills are developed in human relations, in dealing with people. Knowledge without the skill to use it has but limited value.

Effort should be directed consistently toward the accepted goals

By keeping in mind the goals of instruction, a teacher can guide children into worthwhile experiences. A marksman is more likely to hit the target when he can see it clearly; a tourist is more likely to arrive if he knows where he is going; and education is more likely to achieve its objectives when efforts are directed consistently to that end. Use should be made of local resources, for instance, yet a trip to a local rock quarry can be worthwhile only if the quarry exemplifies and clarifies the ideas being studied and perhaps stimulates questions for further investigation. Traditional procedures, like novel experiences reputed to be good, may be either worthwhile or a waste of time depending upon the purpose or lack of purpose that prompted them.

An example which contrasts immediate purposes with long-range objectives. A fifth-grade class studied the rocks, soil, and topography of their locality in the Connecticut Valley. They observed the nearby hills that were formed long ago by glaciation. They talked about the ice that once covered the land and saw boulders that were left behind as the ice melted. Striations, where the great mass of ice made deep scratches in solid rock, were observed near the school and their significance considered. The children inspected ledges of rock which formed from lava flows in bygone ages. They saw the channel of an old river, long since dry, that once flowed where some of their homes now stand. Sandstone and shale were found freshly exposed in the channel of a small stream where the stream had cut away the overlying soil and rock and helped to shape the surface of the earth. A nearby bank of shale, long exposed to the weather, was crumbling to form clay. All the observations were made within walking distance of the school.

In their room the children built collections and displays, performed a number of experiments, and found what they could in books about rocks and changes in the earth. They carried on numerous discussions of their findings as they sought to interpret their observations. Because the work proved interesting and the opportunity developed, a short sketch of the local geological history was presented by the class on a Hartford radio station.

Upon analysis it is easy to see that the children were developing concepts of time and of changes in the earth, and that such concepts were among the long-range objectives of the teacher. These and similar objectives serve to guide learning in profitable directions, even though the child's immediate purpose is likely to be more limited in scope.

Evaluation should be made in terms of the goals. As has been suggested, the real purpose of instruction is not simply to build a fine collection of rocks or a display of bird nests, nor is the purpose to cover all the material in the area being studied or in a particular textbook. Building a collection or reading a book may help to achieve the desired goals; but when covering the book becomes an obligation which restricts the work of the class, it has become the real goal, whether recognized as such or not.

The generally accepted objectives of science teaching, as previously indicated, are to gain a *functional understanding* of the environment and to develop *constructive scientific attitudes*, with attendant *skills, appreciations,* and *interests.* Progress is made a little at a time toward such remote goals. Actual perfection is seldom achieved or even expected. Understanding of the environment can be sought but never completely achieved. Interest is a matter of degree, and increased skill is always possible, even for the most skillful. Success is measured in terms of progress — by the increase of insight, the change in attitude, the depth of appreciation that has become apparent.

Evaluations should be made as the work progresses. The effectiveness of instruction can be judged by the actions of the children and by their conversations. A general enthusiasm for the work will usually indicate that the work is effective in achieving the desired emotional qualities and very likely also the understanding. In a previous illustration where the girl used her experience with the milk bottle to explain the freezing of water pipes in the winter, evidence was provided that the knowledge gained was functioning in her thinking. The children who gathered rocks during play periods and after school hours, and those who voluntarily took home books in which to find experiments on plant growth, were giving evidence that real interest was being developed. The timid child, by asking to feed the hamsters, revealed that to some extent at least he had overcome his fear of animals.

For a class studying the earth's changing surface, perhaps, questions such as the following must be answered as the work progresses: Is collecting rocks still an effective activity, or has it become an end in itself? Are the children reading about erosion without really understanding what it is? Are they becoming concerned, or are they complacent about an actual gully which is developing at the corner of the school grounds? Written examinations can give a part of the picture, but judgment is admittedly difficult, for evaluation is more than tests and grades.

To assume without consideration that following a given routine will automatically attain the desired goals may perpetuate ineffective work. It may be that one set of objectives is listed in the course of study and used for discussion purposes, whereas other, less desirable objectives are functioning to determine the actual instruction. In many respects evaluation must be a matter of considered judgment based on observation as well as on whatever data are available from tests or other work completed. The usual tests do not reveal, for instance, to what extent knowledge gained is applied in day-to-day activities, the ultimate purpose of the instruction. Superficial judgments, however, provide no satisfactory answer to the obvious limitations of tests. All the information possible should be obtained and used in making thoughtful evaluations.

A constructively critical appraisal of the teaching and learning situation will help to make the work effective. Constant checking and improving should become habitual. Classes should gather together occasionally to consider whether or not their efforts are effective and what can be done to improve. One logical time for appraisal is at the end of a topic or problem. These group evaluations should not become personalized or critical in a negative sense; on the contrary, credit should be given to those who are able to analyze their own work objectively. Such analysis is a first step toward improvement. Every navigator must take his bearings frequently if he is not to wander aimlessly from his avowed course.

The methods used should be those that get results. Are newer methods of teaching better than the old? Should an experienced teacher abandon all the old familiar ways of working and use new methods reputed to be good?

The only reasonable justification for any teaching method, old or new, is that it gets results, the kind of results considered acceptable in terms of the objectives. Teachers should be cautious about undertaking recommended procedures that "don't make sense." For if the advice seems unreasonable, very likely the implications are not what was intended by the one giving the advice. Words have different meanings for different people. For a person who has seen children working in a business-like manner with real interest and definite purpose in an effective classroom situation designated as "progressive," the term will have quite a different meaning from what it has for another person who has seen children running up and down the halls and classrooms in a confusion of pointless activities labeled "progressive." To the second person, progressive teaching could not be considered good; whoever claims that it is must be talking utter nonsense. Likewise some teachers schooled in the newer methods regard with horror anyone who advocates using textbooks, because of the unhappy experiences the term brings to mind. Neither of these views is entirely right or entirely wrong. Most conservatives, for example, agree that slavish adherence to a text is uninspired. Most progressives would seek to avoid disorder and confusion. Both may have their positions misinterpreted. The really good teacher is one who is constantly improving, and improvement comes to those who are open-minded enough to try new ways that seem promising and objective enough to determine which ways are actually effective when used. A good teacher who prefers a comparatively formal program will not overlook the attitudes being developed, for example, while concentrating on subject matter. The good teacher who favors newer methods will have no need to concede that achievement in terms of worthwhile subject matter has been sacrificed in an effort to develop good attitudes. Effective teaching methods will succeed in teaching more of the right kind of subject matter, largely because of the favorable attitudes and good habits being developed at the same time. Whether or not a certain method works often depends upon how it is used, and hence what is best for one instructor may not be best for another. A teacher should consider suggestions of ways that have worked for others, but accept only those that seem reasonable and succeed in actual use. A newspaper cartoon made the point very well. It showed a girl swinging at a golf ball, with an instructor standing behind her giving advice. The caption read: "There's not one flaw in your style or approach — now try to hit the ball!"

STUDY GUIDE

1. What are the science interests of children? What evidence of interest have you noticed that could lead to valuable learnings in science?
2. What can the teacher do to stimulate interest and to recognize and guide interests already developed? To what extent should interest be considered in developing plans?
3. If a child should ask what makes an electric bell ring, or how a pulley can lift things, what would be a good answer, and why?
4. In the elementary school, to what extent can a program of active investigation help to meet the need for scientists and engineers without neglecting those children who will become housewives, farmers, or mechanics?
5. When a child brings a rock to class or asks how rocks can have veins, should a study of rocks be undertaken immediately? Upon what does the answer depend?
6. Compare the objectives recommended in this chapter with those proposed by some other reference and with your own opinion of what should be accomplished.
7. In terms of the emotional qualities and skills developed in science, compare a good classroom situation you have known with a poor one that is likewise familiar.
8. Give an example to show how work that would be stimulating and meaningful in one situation might be less successful in another.

4

The Scientific Way of Working

Children's investigations are much like those of the research worker. Both are motivated by curiosity, and both depend primarily upon direct examination of the objects and phenomena in question. The work of an adult, of course, is more advanced and more detailed, but it commonly depends upon the same sort of observation and may be reported orally or in writing. The research worker and the child are headed in the same direction, traveling in the same manner. One is merely farther down the road than the other.

One of the greatest of modern physicists, Max Planck, has written:

If we see, hear, or touch something, it is clearly a given fact which no skeptic can endanger. . . . If you give the child a toy, let us say a rattle, he will find that the tactile sensation is always accompanied by a corresponding visual sensation . . . he also perceives a certain regular auditory sensation. . . . What then does the child think as he makes these discoveries? First of all, he wonders. This feeling of wonderment is the source and inexhaustible fountainhead of his desire for knowledge. It drives the child irresistibly on to solve the mystery . . . he will not tire of repeating the same experiment ten times, a hundred times, in order to taste the thrill of discovery over and over again. . . .

To the research scientist, no less than to the child, it is always a gratifying experience and an added stimulus to encounter a new wonder, and he will labor

industriously to solve the riddle by repeating the same experiment with his re-
fined instruments just as the child does with his primitive rattle.[1]

DEVELOPING SCIENTIFIC ATTITUDES

Much of the success of science is ordinarily credited to the manner in which
scientists work, the way they conduct their investigations. Because scientists
tend to have similar points of view, they approach their problems in a similar
way. There are many common elements in the procedures that scientists use to
carry on their investigations. The approach that a scientist uses is determined
by the circumstances, the nature of the problem, and the resources available,
but also by the investigator's own point of view, his attitude and the habits he
has learned. The basic attitudes and habits which guide scientific work can be
developed in the elementary school and are of great value in all walks of life.

What are some scientific attitudes children can learn?

Like the scientist, a child is concerned with endless questions about what,
how, and why. The school should preserve and develop the child's natural
curiosity, his eagerness to investigate, to learn. Direct investigation, the basis
of all science, is highly effective in the classroom; and the attitudes that are
essential to effective research are also valuable in other undertakings.

Logical, objective interpretations. For his explanations, the answers to his
questions, the scientist turns to observations and experiments rather than to
unsubstantiated authority alone. In the classroom as in science, authority
should be considered valuable only in the sense that an opinion based on
research is not to be ignored or taken lightly — nor is it to be accepted merely
out of respect for the individual. Like the scientist, a child should expect to
find logical explanations, should not accept superstitious or mystical interpretations. On the other hand, this view need not imply that phenomena and spir-
itual values which have not been fully explained do not exist. The energy of
an atom existed even before it was discovered by man.

The scientific attitude of objectivity can be valuable in a cosmopolitan population. Like the scientists, children should base their opinions on the evidence,
rather than react to the personalities involved. It matters less who presented the evidence than what the evidence is. A scientist may be of royal
blood, like Robert Boyle, or he may be a person of very humble origin, like

[1] Max Planck, "The Meaning and Limits of Exact Science," *Science*, 110:320–322, Sept.
30, 1949.

Isaac Newton or Michael Faraday; he may be rich or he may be poor, but all that matters is his work in science. His results are judged on their merits; opinions are valuable to the extent they are substantiated by reliable evidence. The worker is judged by the results he achieves, by his insight into problems, by the accuracy and skill of his investigations. When a group of scientists work together, they work essentially as equals. In the schools too, when problems are being considered and results evaluated, the discussion should be impersonal, democratic.

Accuracy and suspended judgment. Reasonable accuracy is a desirable quality in many undertakings. In the classroom as in research, thorough investigation requires that careful observations be made and accurate records kept of exactly what has been observed, not of what someone thought should have happened. Scientists cautiously refrain from claiming more for their experiments than is justified by the evidence, and children also should avoid jumping to conclusions. Children can learn to distinguish between their observations and their interpretations, for additional evidence may alter the interpretations, but if the work is accurate the observations will stand. To be accurate, observations must be checked carefully. There is less danger of error in the observations when they are recorded promptly, recorded while the scientist or the child is still observing, while a second look is still possible. Where the report includes both the results and the processes by which the results were achieved, other individuals will be able to repeat and check the work.

Accuracy, however, is a relative matter. An accurate measurement with a yardstick may appear hopelessly crude if checked with a micrometer. Work that is accurate for a small child may be inadequate for an older child, and the scientist will require still greater refinement in his research. Children should develop increasing accuracy in their investigations, but should not be pressed beyond their ability or beyond the degree of accuracy needed for the problem at hand. To insist on a micrometer's accuracy where the yardstick's will do quite as well is to cultivate false values.

A thorough investigation requires careful planning in advance, yet equally essential is the capacity to adjust plans when unexpected situations arise. The investigator must be open-minded rather than dogmatic. In the laboratory, in the classroom, or in daily affairs, a person should consider all the reliable evidence available and base his opinion on that evidence; at the same time he should recognize the possibility that new evidence may change the picture somewhat. Being willing to revise his views because of new evidence does not imply that the scientist vacillates or is lacking in convictions. Unless the evidence indicates that he should alter his views, the scientist will cling tenaciously to his opinion, for to him an opinion which disregards the evidence is untenable.

Upon matters about which the evidence is inconclusive he will suspend judgment. Even though circumstances may require the child to act upon partial
information, he can become aware of the uncertainties involved and regard
them as factors in the situation.

Although few of the children from the schools become research workers, our
schools today accept the development of good attitudes and habits among the
major objectives of education, and science has much to offer in this respect. The
influence of science and scientific attitudes on our ways of thinking and acting
is great, and is by no means limited to the laboratory.

How can scientific attitudes be exemplified?

The lives of great scientists reveal many of the scientific attitudes in a
manner that is vivid and appealing to children. The stories can be used to
dramatize the attitudes we seek to develop. Emulation of heroes is a force
largely neglected in present-day education, but one that could well be used to
develop constructive ideals. The qualities of patience, persistence, and thoroughness are well illustrated in the biographies of famous scientists.

The biographies of scientists. Marie Sklodovska was a Polish girl of good
family but limited means who went to Paris to study, met Pierre Curie, and
married him. Fascinating accounts have been written of how Marie and Pierre,
a professor of physics, worked together, overcoming many difficulties, in their
study of radioactivity. Admirable human qualities are revealed in the stories,
and basic scientific attitudes are clearly illustrated. In writing about her
mother's life and work, Eve Curie has commented on the qualities of a true
scientist:

> Radioactivity so fascinated the young scientist that she never tired of examining
> the most diverse forms of matter, always by the same method. Curiosity, a
> marvelous feminine curiosity, the first virtue of a scientist, was developed in
> Marie to the highest degree. . . .

> The radioactivity was a great deal stronger than could have been normally fore-
> seen by the quantity of uranium or thorium contained in the products examined!
> scientist's first response to an unexpected phenomenon. She started her measure-
> It must be an error in experiment, the young woman thought; for doubt is the
> ments over again, unmoved, using the same products. She started over again ten
> times, twenty times. And she was forced to yield to the evidence. . . . The lay-
> man forms a theatrical — and wholly false — idea of the research worker and
> of his discoveries. "The moment of discovery" does not always exist: the scien-
> tist's work is too tenuous . . . spread over several days of decisive labor.[2]

[2] Eve Curie, *Madame Curie*, translated by Vincent Sheean, Garden City Publishing Co.,
Garden City, New York, 1940, pp. 156–58.

Although scientists are objective in their work, the term implies no lack of enthusiasm, as the biographies well show. More than the usual quota of enthusiasm obviously is required to carry through a long and involved series of investigations. Biographies can help children see what is meant by a scientific attitude.

Scientific attitudes and ways of working are also revealed in the life of Pasteur. Among his many experiments were some in which he sought to learn what was causing the French wines to spoil. He found that tiny organisms cause not only fermentation but decay and disease as well. Until his research the cause of sickness was unknown, although people had many mistaken ideas about it. Pasteur found that heating would destroy germs, and today we call the process *pasteurization*. Two of Pasteur's most famous experiments illustrate the use of controls. In one experiment fifty sheep were divided into two groups; one group was immunized and then both groups were exposed to anthrax. The immunization proved effective, for all in that group survived, whereas all the unprotected died of anthrax.

In an earlier experiment Pasteur proved that organisms develop from other organisms, rather than being generated spontaneously. This experiment not only illustrates the use of controls but has the advantage of being simple enough for children to repeat. Pasteur used goose-necked flasks, but a number of test tubes or bottles will do as well. The containers should be filled with beef broth or bouillon, plugged with cotton, and sterilized for an hour or more in the top of a double boiler. The cotton then may be removed from half the containers and the contents exposed for a while to the air. Only the exposed contents spoil. When Pasteur conducted the experiment it was already known that microbes bring about spoilage; here he showed that the microbes came from outside and were not generated spontaneously in the flask.

How scientists devise experiments to test their ideas and the careful planning that is done in preparation may be illustrated by the account of how Benjamin Franklin performed the kite experiment in which he sought to find out whether lightning and static electricity are the same. His own account gives specific directions for constructing the kite, and he pointed out that precautions were taken against the dangers involved, for he stood under a shelter, holding only a silk ribbon, which will not conduct electricity when dry. Rather than jump to conclusions merely because he could produce a spark with the current that came down the kite string, Franklin gathered additional evidence before concluding that lightning is electricity. He found that the current would attract particles, just as static electricity will pick up bits of paper, and just as hair will be attracted to a charged comb. Fires could be started, he wrote:

... and all the other electrical experiments be performed, which are usually done by the help of a rubbed glass globe or tube, and thereby the sameness of the electrical matter with that of lightning completely demonstrated.[3]

Edison is often considered more inventor than scientist, yet numerous descriptions of his life and work are available and can be used to exemplify scientific attitudes, such as curiosity, thoroughness, and enthusiasm for work. The childhood experiences which led to his adult research can be an inspiration to children and can give the teacher a clue to the kind of experience that may develop a continuing interest and functional understanding of science, in contrast to Edison's own unhappy, unsuccessful schooling.

Science in the news. Current developments in science, as reported in newspapers and magazines, likewise may supply illustrations of how scientists work and of their attitude toward their investigations. Such reports have the added advantage of being more immediate and real, being within the child's limited span of experience, although some may be too complex. Newspaper clippings which report progress in science may be posted on the bulletin board, and statements which stress desirable attitudes may be underlined. The articles commonly emphasize the difficulties overcome, the years of prolonged research, the necessity for careful and accurate observations. They may reveal how the research was planned, whether or not control groups were used, and how the scientists interpreted their evidence. If some indication of an unscientific attitude is apparent, it may be the fault of the reporter rather than the scientist; but in any case the class can learn by evaluating the work and discussing the attitudes involved.

In studying the work of scientists it is often advisable to study some of the phenomena with which the scientists were concerned. If the discovery of a new vaccine or antibiotic has been reported, for example, the children could study bacteria and might even prepare a few cultures in petri dishes and test tubes. A class studying the life of Edison or reporting the construction of a modern electric power plant might also learn about electric lights and how a generator produces an electric current, and may study other phases of electricity as well. Frequently the emphasis may be reversed: a class studying electricity may learn what attitudes motivated Edison, Franklin, Faraday, and also scientists of more recent days. For the child, with his child's point of view, it is well to stress in addition the youthful activities of great scientists and the personal qualities and experiences which helped them as children to get their start in life.

[3] Benjamin Franklin, a private letter, in *The Autobiography of Science*, edited by Forest Ray Moulton and Justus J. Schifferes, Doubleday, Garden City, 1946, p. 236.

How can the teacher help children learn scientific attitudes?

It is generally recognized today that character is not built or attitudes successfully taught through exhortation and admonition alone. Even though a person supposedly knows what is right, he may not act upon that knowledge. On the other hand, it also is well known that little progress toward the development of good attitudes is likely to be made unless some definite plans are formulated. With other demands more immediate and pressing, remote goals are likely to be overlooked. One definite step toward the development of scientific attitudes can be taken by reading aloud to a class the biography of some outstanding scientist and considering his point of view and his way of working. The children in the class can be encouraged to read additional biographies and to recount certain portions that illustrate some of the character traits of the scientist. Through the use of biographies and current reports of achievement in science the teacher can help children learn what scientific attitudes are, and to learn them in an atmosphere of sympathy and approbation, an atmosphere that cannot be achieved by urging.

But if scientific attitudes are to influence the child's behavior, something more than knowledge and sympathy is required. The attitudes must begin to function in practical situations, in issues that arise, in problems that are considered, in opinions that are expressed. Scientific attitudes can begin to function even before they are analyzed. First of all, the teacher must seek to exemplify a scientific attitude. Such attitudes should become habitual in all situations and not be restricted to science lessons. Rather than posing as an authority and thereby negating the attitudes sought, the teacher should find satisfaction with the children in learning something new whenever possible. The teacher should be interested in the child's questions and help him in his efforts to investigate. No teacher should be disturbed if found in error, for correcting errors is a part of increasing understanding. The class should be concerned with what is right, not who is right, for all should be working together to gain understanding, not competing to show who knows most. If the teacher is open-minded, does not jump to conclusions but is willing to hear and consider the opinions and evidence of others, regardless of who is believed right, then children can be asked to hear all sides, and with an example set, will likewise become broad-minded.

As part of his investigation, a scientist reads the literature pertaining to his problem, to see what already is known before he begins his own experiments. Children likewise should read some of the literature that is available and suitable to their purpose, suitable to their age and skill — but the work must not end without opportunity for actual experimentation. It will do little good to extol the merits of scientific attitudes if the child's own investigations are confined to books. For the sake of accuracy, scientists record the evidence while it is before them, not after the experiment has been dismantled and the opportunity for accurate observation gone. Likewise children can be taught to make accurate reports, provided that the teacher considers that reasonable accuracy is important and reacts accordingly, with help and with sympathy for the difficulties that must be overcome. Children can be taught to avoid exaggerated statements based on vague generalities. What actually happens, not what is assumed or described in a book, should be reported. If scientists reported what was expected rather than what was observed, much that is new would never be learned.

Children to a large extent adopt their attitudes from the people with whom they come in contact, but children are not alone in this respect. The scientists themselves are influenced in their method of work, and in the attitudes they express, by the responses of other scientists. The research worker is accurate, not only because the research demands it but because the individual worker gains respect through the accuracy of the work he reports. The scientist is cautious in the claims he makes for his investigations, because overstatement would cause him to lose the respect of fellow-scientists. The more careful, thorough, and objective the worker may be, the higher the esteem in which he is held. Approval comes not from bold, exaggerated claims but from practicing the attitudes we call scientific. Social pressure is a strong force.

A similar atmosphere can be developed in the classroom, an atmosphere in which scientific attitudes and the appropriate behavior meet with the approval and esteem of teacher and classmates. Children learn their attitudes in real-life situations, responding to other people and the circumstances at hand. The analysis of scientific attitudes will help most when considered in terms of immediate problems: how to report the observations made that day or how to solve the question at hand, or the necessity for keeping an accurate record of the experiment the class has undertaken.

Children like to investigate, and they can easily learn to refine their approach to problems. But if the emphasis placed on attitudes distorts those attitudes, makes them appear unreasonable, the approach should be modified. Scientific attitudes definitely are not unreasonable — quite the contrary. Insistence upon standards too high for the children can become unpleasant. If the attitudes taught are to be genuine, it is important to preserve the natural excitement of investigation, the thrill of discovery, and the feeling of doing something really worthwhile.

Although the scientific approach to learning is particularly well adapted to science, it by no means need be limited to that one area of the curriculum. In fact, the modern or progressive trend in education today is an effort to apply the scientific approach to all of education, and it was recognized as such by John Dewey when he said that we should make "the method of intelligence, exemplified in science, supreme in education," and when he urged that we accept "systematic utilization of scientific method as the pattern and ideal of intelligent exploration and exploitation of the potentialities inherent in experience." [4] In short, the methods that have been successful in science are also considered the methods most profitable in the schools, although in one case the facts discovered are new to our culture and in the other case are new only to the individual. The scientific way of working is an effective way to learn.

Does fantasy encourage children's interest in science?

In choosing books for science it is advisable to avoid those which mingle fact and fantasy, as in the following:

"Wake," says the sunshine, "it is time to get up!"
"Come, come, come," says the warm spring rain. "You have work to do, little seed."
"Thank you, rain and sunshine, off goes my snow blanket. Thank you, Mr. Wind, off goes my blanket of leaves. Here I come," says the seed. "I had such a good sleep. I shall eat the lunch in my basket. Then I shall feel strong." [5]

A romantic treatment of natural phenomena is unnecessary and misleading. The realities of our world are much more attractive to children when not beclouded with extraneous sentimentality. Rapturous exaltation of the beauties of nature, by author or teacher, may actually lead to an aversion for whatever is being described. The child should develop his own enthusiasm, and it will be genuine. The teacher or the text can be enthusiastic without becoming maudlin. The following is not very revealing as a description of evaporation and condensation:

As soon as it dons its magic cap, it flies off in the atmosphere invisible to our eyes; and the next time any of its parts are evident to our senses, they may occur as a portion of the white masses of cloud sailing across the blue sky, the cloud which Shelley impersonates:

[4] John Dewey, *Experience and Education,* Macmillan, New York, 1938, pp. 100–112.
[5] Vesta Withrow, *The Story of Seeds,* Little Wonder Book 104, Charles E. Merrill Co., Columbus, 1935, revised 1947, p. 31.

"I am the daughter of Earth and Water,
And the nursling of the Sky;
I pass through the pores of the ocean and shores;
I change, but I cannot die."

We have, however, learned the mysterious key-word which brings back the vapor spirit to our sight and touch. This word is "cold." For if our drop of water, in its cap of darkness, meets in its travels an object which is cold, straightway the cap falls off and it becomes visible. If it be a stratum of cold air that meets the invisible wanderer, it becomes visible as a cloud, or as mist, or as rain. If the cold object be an ice pitcher, then it appears as drops on its surface, captured from the air and chained as "flowing tears." [6]

The lines about a cloud may be excellent poetry, but they are not good science. Inclusion of poetical expressions with the work in science will result in confusion, unless particular pains are taken to point out the limitations. The implication of such "sugar-coating" is that children have no real interest in science and need some device to make the work palatable. Any teacher who has seen children react to a program of active investigation, or has noted the curiosity that children show in their ordinary behavior outside school, will know that the science itself can be inherently attractive. Rather than a palliative being needed, experience and educational research both indicate that children are irritated when the factual information they are seeking is obscured by a fanciful story.[7] Poetry and fanciful stories have their place in our culture, but fantasy is not good science any more than a scientific report is good fiction.

Children often react adversely to emotionalism which they themselves do not feel. Snow crystals viewed through a hand lens can be truly fascinating, but in the following statement about snow crystals the meaning is obscure, and the artificial enthusiasm is apt to leave the reader cold, or even derisive:

With a hand lens we enter a wonderland of miracles and stand in awe before the majestic beauty of geometric forms, the most divine in the universe, a revelation of the marvels of nature.

The distinctive traits of human beings should not be ascribed to animals, as when Black Cat speaks to Gray Mouse:

Come out, my friend; all is forgiven. I have been thinking the matter over and have decided to be more tolerant.

[6] Anna Botsford Comstock, *Handbook of Nature-Study*, Comstock Publishing Company, Ithaca, N.Y., 1911, twenty-first edition, 1929, pp. 850–51.

[7] Alice Williams, *Children's Choices in Science Books*, "A Study to Discover Some Elements of a Book in the Field of Science That Appeal to Children," Bureau of Publications, Teachers College, Columbia University, 1939, pp. 152–53.

It is false to have animals acting or speaking as people do. It also is confusing to consider nature a person:

Because the snail moves slowly, Mother Nature has given him a house into which he can escape.

The statement which follows implies premeditation on the part of the bear, which is untrue and can easily confuse children:

So that he might live in the cold, cold North, the polar bear grew fat with a heavy wool coat.

Children can be confused easily about what is true and what is not. When stories are read in which animals wear clothing, walk upright, and behave like people, or the trees and the wind have spirits, children should know that the story is imaginative and should not confuse the fantasy with reality. As adults who already know the truth, we may assume that no one will take the fantasy seriously, yet in terms of history the more objective viewpoint we take for granted is quite new. The Germanic tribes of Europe, like our American Indians, actually believed that each bush and stone had a spirit which could wield great influence. Our delightful story of Snow White and the Seven Dwarfs and our Christmas-time heritage of Santa Claus have come to us from the day when adults actually believed that the woods were peopled with powerful spirits. A few were kindly elves or dwarfs, but most were malevolent and threatening. In the child's own imaginative play, he knows when he is just pretending. But if the teacher or the books mingle fact with fantasy, the child may be unable to tell which is truth and which is make-believe. It is true that an active imagination is characteristic of genius, but the genius knows what is real and what is hypothetical. Facts and fantasy both have value, but they should not be confused as when combined in a science lesson.

USING A SCIENTIFIC APPROACH TO PROBLEMS

To explain what science is, an eight-year-old said, "It means to find answers to questions." It is axiomatic in science that answers should come from direct investigations, involving observations and experiments.

A first grade, for example, was primed with several questions to ask when they visited a chicken hatchery. The man at the hatchery opened three eggs, which had been in the incubator different lengths of time, and the children could see for themselves how a chicken forms in an egg. Later, when someone wanted to know if the chickens have teeth, the bill of a rooster was opened, and the children could see the tongue but no teeth. The next question was, "How does the rooster hear?" To answer the question the rooster's head was examined, and a small opening was found on each side covered with little feathers that looked like fuzz. Direct investigation is an effective way to answer a question.

A sixth grade cut open a number of flowers to see how the seed form at the base, and what they saw helped to answer the questions they had raised.

When a rabbit arrived in a second grade, the children asked many questions. The teacher suggested that they watch the animal for a while to see how many of the questions could be answered through direct observation, and when the class gathered for a discussion later, everyone had something to report. Wherever possible, questions should be answered through vivid, meaningful observation and experimentation.

Fig. 15

Planning, experimenting, and reporting are fundamental steps in a scientific procedure.

How should experiments be conducted?

Experiments can be used to solve problems that arise, to determine the facts where some uncertainty exists. The following example will help show how experiments can be devised to solve real problems:

"What makes so many worms come out when it rains?" someone asked as the first grade gathered on a dark morning following a storm.

A number of hypotheses were proposed by the class:

"The worms come up to get a drink."

"They come up to take a bath."

"Worms like mud; so they come up and swim around in it."

"They don't like too much water in the ground; so they come up to dry in the wind."

After a discussion of these and a few similar suggestions, the class decided that the best way to learn about worms would be to bring some into the room, where they could be observed. With the worms on the surface it was easy for the children to collect as many as needed. The worms were put into two boxes of soil; one box was left dry, and the other was soaked with water. In a short time the worms in the watered soil returned to the surface. The class was uncertain why, but after some dry sand was placed nearby, the worms moved onto the dry spot.

"Guess the worms come out because they don't like too much water," was the comment heard, and all agreed.

"I'd like to know where all the rain comes from," someone said, and with one problem solved, the interest carried on, as so often happens, to a related problem, and the class was launched on a study of the weather.

Even small children can plan their own experiments. In the following case, the teacher had no hand at all. Dorothy and Thelma, two first graders, on a winter day were looking out the window where an icicle hung within reach.

Dorothy said, "There's an icicle, and I'm going to eat it."

"They're dirty," Thelma responded.

"Who says?"

"Ever'body."

"Well, O.K., but let's see if it really is. Let's put it in a dish on the radiator, and then when it melts, we'll see if it really is dirty."

Working as individuals and as groups. Actual experimentation is commonly preceded by a discussion in which questions are raised and plans for the work are developed. A background of reference work may be needed. If the chil-

Fig. 16

Opportunity to experiment is essential to the scientific
way of working.

dren are unable to read appropriate material, the teacher may read to them
instead. In some cases, individuals or small groups then may work on various
phases of the same broad topic or problem, observing individually or doing a
variety of experiments. The reports and the discussion which follow will serve
to tie the work together and help the children to arrive at some general conclusions. On other occasions, however, instead of working individually on a variety
of related experiments the entire class may collaborate on one large undertaking, as the first grade did in experimenting with the worms. Circumstances will
help to determine which procedure is preferable. Where many simple, appropriate experiments are possible, the individual work can be very effective, for
it is active, makes provision for individual differences in the choice of undertakings, and helps to develop initiative. In other cases, where close supervision,
guidance, and assistance by the teacher is needed, a group undertaking with
the teacher leading may be preferred.

Adapting the "experiments" from books. Simply following the directions for
an experiment in a book is not in accord with the true spirit of investigation.
Although the original suggestion may come from a book, the experiment should

Fig. 17

Experiments described in books can be used to solve real problems.

serve some purpose, as in the solution of a problem. Children should be encouraged to use their own initiative in modifying the procedure according to their own ideas and the situation at hand. On some occasions the problem may not be sharply defined. The purpose may be simply to find out, to see what will happen, how something works. The procedure outlined in a book should serve more as a suggestion of what can be done than as directions which must be followed.

In one case the teacher suggested doing certain experiments to answer a question that came up in class. While studying the weather, the fourth grade had become puzzled about what causes the liquid to rise or fall in a thermometer tube. The question was raised one day, and the next day the teacher had the necessary equipment ready and suggested doing some experiments — common ones found in many books, including those the children were using.

In one of the experiments the children applied heat to a long horizontal wire from which a weight was suspended, and the sag was measured in terms of the height of the weight above the table. In another experiment the children heated a flask, the neck of which was under water, and noted the escaping bubbles of air. When the flask was allowed to cool they saw that water entered the flask. In still another experiment a flask with a narrow neck was filled with water to a mark near the top and then was heated until the water overflowed. In these experiments and all the others selected for the class, the children could see what happens when solids, liquids, and gases are heated.

After their period of experimentation the class came together again to report their results, and they had no difficulty in reaching a solution to their problem. In each of the experiments the material had expanded when heated and contracted when cooled. Obviously heat had caused the liquid in a thermometer to expand; when cooled, the liquid contracted. The children came to their own conclusion on the basis of the evidence. A number of experiments from books had been used in the solution of their problem.

Control experiments. Wherever possible, scientists use control experiments. The need for controls was understood by the children in a third grade when they planned a nutrition experiment with laboratory mice:

Teddy said, "Let's feed the mice bad food like candy, cokes, and coffee."

The children thought that was a wonderful idea, until Grant spoke up: "After a while they will probably get thin and die; so let's not feed them food that is too bad."

A bit of discussion followed, and it was generally agreed that no one wanted Mopsy and Frisky to die; so it was decided to feed them bad foods for a while and then change to good foods. However, one of the girls, appearing dissatisfied, asked:

"How can we tell if the mice are getting thinner when we don't have a fat mouse to go by? Why don't we feed Frisky good food to see if she will get fat and feed Mopsy bad food?"

And so they did. For the sake of accuracy it would have been well, if practicable, to have used a larger number of mice. The ones on the normal diet would then have been called the control group and the ones on the deficient diet the experimental group. So that there will be no doubt regarding what causes the poor health and loss of weight that results in such an experiment, the two groups should be as nearly alike as possible and be treated exactly the same way in all respects, except for the diet which is being tested. If the sex, the initial size, or initial state of health had been different, perhaps the one group would have shown less growth in spite of the diet. If one group had been in the light and the other in the dark, or one in a large cage and the other in a small one, or one group cleaned regularly, perhaps petted, while the other was not, there may have been uncertainty regarding whether or not such additional factors influenced the results. Except for the factor being tested, the two groups should be as nearly identical as possible.

If there is any reason for doubt, children ought not to rely too strongly upon the results of their own experimentation. The reliability of the work, it should be understood, may not be great, even though the investigations are essential for the child's own understanding. Nevertheless, the accuracy of the work, for either the scientist or the child, is increased if controls are used and if the experiment is repeated many times. The probability that unknown factors will influence the results is less the more times an experiment is repeated, and of course children seem to sense this, for in their undirected attempts to see how something works they commonly repeat the manipulations many times before being satisfied. Where many or all of the children in a class wish to try an experiment for themselves, a tally can be made of the results obtained by the various individuals, and thus a satisfactory degree of accuracy can be attained without laborious repetition by one individual. Using a large number of specimens in an experiment likewise helps to give reliable results. In plant growth experiments, for example, the more plants are used the more conclusive are the results. If the amount of equipment is limited, some experiments may be repeated a number of times with the same materials; for example, in determining the reaction of a plant to light, using but one plant, the plant could be shifted to a number of positions in the room and the response in each case noted.

Observations. Observation, like experimentation, is a fundamental part of scientific investigation. The investigations of children ordinarily include much observation; children learn by watching the behavior of a salamander, for instance, or by noticing changes in the weather, inspecting the crystals in a stone, or observing the operation of a crane or other machinery. Observations and experiments can be made more explicit by including measurements, such as thermometer readings, the height of a seedling in a plant growth experiment, or the depth of water in a tin can or other improvised rain gauge.

How should demonstrations be conducted?

The word *experiment* is often used broadly to include *demonstrations*, but the connotations of the two words are quite different. Experimentation is a method of investigation, but a demonstration serves another purpose. The demonstration is a graphic way of explaining what is already known. It offers no proof. A child is demonstrating when he shows his class that the air in a balloon will expand when the balloon is held over a radiator, and he may explain that substances expand when heated. His demonstration will help to make the idea understandable. However, to prove such a broad generalization much more evidence would have to be gathered, and the work would have to be conducted with greater accuracy than would be practicable when a child is merely reporting to a class what is already known. A scientist may spend months or even years gathering evidence in an extensive series of experiments, but he may report them in a matter of minutes. If in his report he shows what was done, his report includes a demonstration.

In a demonstration the results are known in advance and are simply being shown to someone else. The fifth-grade children who worked with chemicals were experimenting when they made their investigations individually or in small groups, even though the books they were using may have given some hint of what results to expect. The children were doing the work to find out for themselves. But in their reports the spirit was quite different: the children making the reports already knew what would happen and were simply showing the others, demonstrating. A demonstration indicates, suggests, or shows what the facts may be, but it does not prove them. The purpose of a demonstration is simply to explain. In some situations a demonstration in the classroom will serve the desired purpose, but it should not be confused with experimentation.

Demonstrations by the children or the teacher. A question that often arises is whether the teacher should perform a demonstration or have the children do it. The more active children are, the better they learn, but the teacher's greater skill in demonstrating and explaining may compensate for the relatively passive role of the children. In general it would seem that children should report whatever experiments they themselves have prepared. In such cases each child will be familiar with the work he is reporting, and if all needed materials are ready, the child's demonstration of his own work should be effective. Making the report and doing the demonstrating that is a part of it is a learning experience in itself. The chance of success will be greater if the teacher stands by ready to help, not only with planning the report but in presenting it as well. Some instructors sit at the table with each group, participate in the discussions, and assist with the demonstrations whenever necessary.

On some occasions it is wise for the teacher to perform the demonstrations. It may be that the teacher is introducing some new concept or stressing a point that needs attention. In addition, if no child is prepared, or the demonstration is difficult to perform, or some other circumstance makes it advisable, the teacher may decide to do the demonstrating. Such occasions can be stimulating and can set an example for the children — and hence may be a rather common occurrence — but they should not dominate the program to the point where the children become a passive audience.

Ordinarily, the more active children are, the better a teacher can judge from their behavior how the work is progressing. In a teacher demonstration, on the other hand, care must be taken not to exceed the child's capacity to understand. The child's interpretation may not be the one intended by the teacher.

In the case which follows, the teacher recognized the difficulty, and no harm was done. The first grade had been discussing clouds, their relationship to rain, and the fact that clouds are not solid, since airplanes can fly through them. So the teacher told the children that on the following day she would show them how clouds are made.

On that next day, as the teacher gathered her materials for a demonstration, someone said, "Look everybody, Miss Langley is going to make a cloud!"

Miss Langley was somewhat puzzled by the comment and wondered what the child expected, but she continued with the demonstration. She had a tin cup with ice water, and as moisture from the air condensed upon the cold surface of the cup, increasingly large drops of water were formed. The children offered the usual explanation that the cup might have leaked, yet no holes could be found, and after the outside surface was wiped dry the dew would reappear. The top of the cup was covered, too, at a child's suggestion, and yet the moisture continued to gather. Eventually the children began to understand what was happening: the moisture was condensing from the air. The demonstration seemed to be a success.

But then someone asked, "Now, Miss Langley, are you going to make a cloud?" And the other children waited expectantly.

The children had understood condensation insofar as they had experienced it, but they could see no relationship to the formation of a cloud. The broader concept remained to be developed.

Teacher demonstrations require a minimum of time and can be presented just as the teacher sees fit; however, the insight gained may not be as great as is often supposed. Children learn best through their own efforts, so ordinarily the teacher's demonstrations should lead to investigations by the children themselves or should help to interpret what has already been done.

Frequently, after children have seen a demonstration, they want to try it themselves. Because such direct experience is fundamental to really functional understanding, it may be wise to give the children the opportunity they seek — immediately, if possible. The equipment can be left on a table to be used during a suitable work period; a few people can experiment at a time while the others work at other tasks.

Unexpected results in demonstrations and experiments. Teachers sometimes fear that a demonstration will fail before the class, with resulting embarrassment to the teacher. However, in a truly experimental situation the one conducting the experiment does not know in advance what will happen, although he may have some expectation, some hypothesis. Consequently there is no loss of prestige, whatever the results may be.

The outcome of an experiment may be unexpected, but sometimes unexpected results may even heighten the interest. Many of the greatest discoveries in the history of science were unexpected, "accidental." Recognition should be given to the child or adult who is alert enough to detect the unexpected and resourceful enough to act accordingly. A teacher can avoid loss of prestige by never taking the false position that an experiment must turn out in a certain way. Greater emphasis on the child's own investigations will help to preserve the experimental view, the idea of letting the children find out for themselves rather than having the teacher show or tell what will happen.

Even in a demonstration, should something unexpected happen, the attitude can shift and become experimental, whether it be the children demonstrating or the teacher. We are told that Oersted was demonstrating before a class when he discovered that an electric current will deflect the needle of a compass. That principle is now the basis of many electrical measuring devices. In the elementary school, too, unexpected results can be an opportunity for learning.

When a demonstration fails to turn out as expected, a teacher may be tempted to "help it along" a bit in a subtle way to get the desired results. With the air removed from a tin can, for example, the books say that a tin can will collapse — but suppose in an actual case the can does not collapse. What should the teacher do? Should he step on the can while the children are not watching, or should he set it aside and change the subject, hoping no one will notice? Obscuring the actual results of a demonstration to avoid "failure" reveals a mistaken attitude. The purpose of a demonstration is to show what happens, not to obscure it. There are many reasons why a demonstration may not turn out as predicted. If the reason is not known, judgment should be suspended. Often the unexpected results will provide the stimulus for an ideal learning situation. Many demonstrations are simple and invariably turn out as expected; others are more complex. To convey the impression that a complex situation is simple is to teach a misconception.

For effective teaching, unfamiliar demonstrations ordinarily should be tried in advance to avoid confusion. But if something unexpected does happen, an experimental attitude will avoid the embarrassment which otherwise comes to one who assumes the role of infallible authority.

How can we arrange for excursions in science?

Field trips have a prominent place in a program designed to explain the environment. First-hand contacts through excursions and other means are essential in making interpretations. The environment must be perceived to be interpreted. A child who has never seen a pond, or has seen ponds only superficially in passing, is unable to interpret effectively the interdependence of pond life. Some materials can be brought into the classroom for convenient, detailed examination. Other materials and situations must be observed in the field, or some of the meaning, some of the relationships, will be lost. A cocoon can be seen in a classroom with little realization of its true place in the reality of the outdoors. The formation of bedrock exposed in a nearby hillside cannot be brought to school; a pebble from the bed of a stream can be, but in the classroom it will be only a rounded pebble, not a part of a stream bed involved in erosion.

Teachers give many reasons for not taking the excursions that they think they should. Uncertainty in one form or another is the usual reason: uncertainty regarding transportation, accidents and liability laws, discipline, uncertainty regarding administrative opinion and regulations. Because local situations do vary, no answer or solution can be given, but almost invariably the obstacles fade when examined closely. The facts are not as bad as the fears. On the other hand, field trips should not be taken simply because trips are reputed to be good. There always should be an essential purpose, a purpose the children themselves can see.

The purpose of a trip. There are many circumstances in which a field trip will serve a worthwhile purpose. A class may need information regarding some problem that has arisen, some study being undertaken. Studying how plants grow, for instance, the children may need to see for themselves where the new growth occurs on the trees and bushes of the school grounds, the park or wood-land nearby. In discussing the sky, someone may question the statement that Mars is red. Is Mars red like a ripe tomato? The planet will have to be located and observed for the question to be answered satisfactorily. A field trip may be used to verify and apply information already gained. After studying the weather, a class may well visit the airport, where observations are made. Study-ing erosion, a class may visit a nearby farm to see what is being done to prevent destruction of the fields. Excursions at various intervals of time may be used to observe changes, such as the apparent movement of the stars, the growth of plants, or the passing of the seasons. Another purpose of a field trip may be to raise questions and acquire initial impressions that will make a study meaning-ful. A visit to the zoo or a farm may raise many questions regarding how animals get their food, protect themselves, and rear their young. The visit will provide the stimulus for study and the observations to make it understandable. Thus field trips may be used to introduce a new topic or problem, or to verify and apply knowledge as the culmination, the conclusion, of a study. An excur-sion may be used to conclude one portion of a study and to raise questions for the next phase of the undertaking. Or the trip may be used at any point to gather needed information, to answer significant questions.

Any trip that a class takes should be an essential phase of the study being made. The children should know why they are going and be anxious to accom-plish that purpose. Giving the children a part in developing the plans should help to give them a clear purpose.

The preparation for a trip. To be effective the excursion must be well planned. The plans will vary with the nature and purpose of the trip. In making preparations for the trip, the school principal should be consulted regarding school policy, and then plans can be made accordingly. The office must know when the class will be away. Does the school provide a form for obtaining the parents' permission? Does the school provide a school bus in case transportation is needed? Should the class use the public transportation system, or must the children arrange to share the cost of chartering a bus? If a bus must be chartered, a telephone call to the bus company will bring an estimate of the cost, and the charge to each individual can be computed to see if the money can be raised. The principal will know whether there is a fund to help any child unable to pay, and care must be taken that none be embarrassed. Ques-tions of liability and insurance enter in if private cars are used. Such matters are controlled by state laws and local regulations and hence vary somewhat from one locality to another. Questions of safety and school responsibility must be considered. Arrangements will have to be made in advance for permission from the owner or manager if private property is to be visited. The necessary letter can well be a class undertaking. If possible, the teacher should visit the scene in advance to anticipate and prepare for the learning situations and any possible difficulties that may be avoided.

It is a good idea to invite parents for the trip. To invite them is a friendly gesture. With large classes, a few extra adults can be very helpful to the teacher in conducting the trip; and the parents may like to keep in touch with the work of the class, especially when something of more than usual interest is being done.

If notes are to be taken, if questions are to be answered, they should be planned in advance. Any equipment that will be used must be available. Before the trip begins, the toilet facilities should be used, for none may be available along the way. Before the group leaves, a notice may be posted on the blackboard, stating where and when the class is going and when they will return. Consideration should be given to the discussion that will follow the trip and the activities that may grow out of the experience. Children should know what to anticipate, but on the other hand, it is possible to overdo requirements and preparations, for the children cannot anticipate completely what they have not seen.

Conducting a trip. Even when transportation is provided, much of a field trip ordinarily is made on foot. Because of the excess energy which children may have at the beginning, especially in the excitement of a first trip, it is wise to start out at a brisk pace until the excess energy has been used, and then the pace may be slowed without the children's darting here or there in impromptu games of their own design. Lines are not necessary, and may even interfere when the class halts to observe and discuss some point of interest. A compact group should be maintained, nevertheless, so that discussions can take place along the way and so that the class will not become separated. It is convenient for the teacher to move at the head of the group; one of the children, or an adult, if available, may be delegated to bring up the rear and see that stragglers do not drift far behind. In the city the instructions may be to stay on the sidewalk but in as compact a group as possible, and to allow room for other pedestrians to pass. For safety, the teacher should pause at each intersection until the group is compact before crossing the street or road. Where there is no sidewalk, laws commonly specify that the left side of the road, facing traffic, should be used. When extra adults go along, many teachers prefer to divide a class into small groups, each with an adult; this practice is helpful in a city, where, with other people about, a group may become separated. It does make it rather difficult to have discussions along the way.

Fig. 18

In studying science children can learn to work together.

No trip at all is better than allowing the excursion to become a lark; a strictly businesslike attitude must be maintained if the trip is to be worthwhile. If a trip must be cancelled, or it becomes necessary to turn back even after a trip has begun, the children will see the justice of the action if it is taken calmly and as a matter of necessity, for no work can be accomplished if disorder and excessive excitement prevail. The teacher will, of course, be as sorry as the children to have the plans fail, but with disorder someone might be hurt, or at least the school might be given a bad name. The teacher should not attempt to blame anyone, but under the circumstances an effective trip would be impossible. Since children invariably are anxious to make excursions, there will seldom be serious difficulty on the next occasion a trip is planned, and a lesson in self-discipline will have been taught.

After a trip, if a letter of appreciation is needed, it can be written by the class. There may be a need to discuss questions raised by the trip, and whatever continuing activities were planned may now begin.

WORKING TOGETHER COOPERATIVELY

Cooperation is a prominent feature of the scientific way of working. Cooperation is expressed through the exchange of ideas and information in reports of discoveries and processes. It is expressed through the numerous other ways in which constructive persons with common interests help one another. In science, people of diverse backgrounds and abilities contribute to the common effort so that progress can be made. Children in the schools can learn to work together cooperatively, sharing ideas and giving assistance much as scientists do, each contributing what he is able toward progress in learning.

Of what value is cooperation?

Our way of life is as dependent upon cooperation as upon competition — perhaps more so. A ball team cooperates as well as competes to defeat the opponent. A player, to make the team, must be able to cooperate better than any competitor for the position. A business establishment can meet the competition by developing cooperation within the organization and through better service to the public. Thus cooperation and competition are interrelated, fundamental factors in living. People cooperate to build dams for electricity and flood control, projects that will bring benefits which no one person could obtain by working alone. In our way of life we are all dependent upon the cooperation of our fellow-men.

Competition is obvious in many respects; the necessity for cooperation is frequently more obscure but is none the less vital. Where competition becomes excessive, it may destroy cooperation. The ball player who is too intent upon making a good showing personally will be less capable of teamwork. Much of our emphasis upon competition today seems to have come from a misinterpretation of Darwin's "survival of the fittest." Darwin himself stressed the survival value of cooperation in social animals: people, or any animals that are able to cooperate, may survive in times of stress where individuals competing against each other would perish.

> I use this term (struggle for existence) in a large and metaphorical sense including dependence of one being on another.[8]

Cooperation in research. Cooperation is a prominent feature in the work of scientists. Scientists nowadays tend to work in teams, as members of a large staff, upon problems too extensive for an individual working alone with limited facilities. Even those who work alone are cooperating, for they keep in touch with what others are doing in their field and are well informed regarding past achievements. Their own work likewise is reported so that other investigators may profit by any progress made. Although the laboratories may be widely scattered, the communication is such that in effect the scientists are working

---

[8] Charles Darwin, *The Origin of Species by Means of Natural Selection* (1859), Random House, Modern Library ed., New York, p. 52.

together on common problems. In many cases, not waiting for reports at the completion of their work, scientists correspond through private letters or publish progress reports and hypotheses, opinions not yet substantiated. In any case, anticipation of the report, which will be published and perhaps delivered orally at some gathering of scientists, is a large factor in directing the nature and quality of the work throughout the entire investigation. Even though the scientist may not be aware of the cooperation involved, his work is stimulated by conditions at the time and is made possible by the facilities for research that our culture provides, and when his report is published it will contribute to the general fund of knowledge that makes progress possible. Cooperation is a large factor in the success of scientific research. When military necessity requires secrecy, cooperation is inhibited and progress slowed. Scientists object to secrecy and wish to hold it to a minimum.

Cooperation in the classroom. Children too can work together profitably, cooperating for their own and the common good. The social situation, properly directed, can be a stimulus to good work, in addition to helping the children learn how to cooperate with their fellows. Like a team of research workers, children can plan together, give mutual assistance in the work wherever needed, and then report back to the group, each person making his own contribution toward solution of the problem at hand. The teacher, of course, should be a part of the cooperating group, guiding the efforts in worthwhile directions, making suggestions, stimulating interest, helping to provide materials and overcome difficulties, helping with interpretations and giving recognition for achievement — much as a research director guides and assists the scientists with whom he works.

Anticipation of the oral reports. Whether the child be reading, observing, experimenting, constructing, or undertaking a combination of activities, throughout his work anticipation of the report to be made will be an incentive to thorough preparation, just as it is with the adult scientist. For that reason the reports should not be neglected, nor should they become a dull routine. If a thorough report is needed, it should be written, with only the more vital, interesting parts of the work reported orally. For the same reason, experience indicates that oral reports should be informal, with questions asked and comments made whenever needed, and the reading of prepared papers avoided. Any portions of a report not vivid enough in the mind of the reporter to be made without a paper will be dull listening for the remainder of the class. In an informal situation, any essential points overlooked in the original report can be brought out as the discussion continues. Where needed, brief notes can be used. Reports should be stimulating enough to convey the desired meanings.

Children as well as scientists look forward to the reports they will make, and ordinarily with considerable pleasure. A second-grade girl, for example, brought in a pair of guinea pigs, told her class about them, and let other members of the class feed them the food she had brought. At recess she took the animals with her onto the playground, and children from all over the school had them out of the cage playing with them. After recess two of the girls and the guinea pigs were missing. The teacher found the girls in the first-grade room showing the guinea pigs, explaining to the children about these animals. Whenever we have something of interest, showing it to other people and telling them about it is normal behavior, Outside the classroom children seldom miss an opportunity to do so.

Written records and reports. Reporting may be done in numerous ways. Where investigations have been conducted largely by individuals, the oral reports may be essentially individual. In such a case, any records prepared may be but a series of individual written reports and sketches bound together, in addition to any general conclusions reached as a result of the discussions following the oral reports. The written reports for a group undertaking, and possibly for the individual investigations also, may be the product of group discussion and analysis, and may represent the conclusions of the class as a whole. Charts, booklets, displays, and culminating activities may be considered forms of reporting.

Written plans and reports help to make thinking definite and exact, and give practice in using writing skills in meaningful situations, situations that provide a stimulus and a purpose for the writing. Written records encourage careful observation: to write the record a child must observe closely. The records are useful for reference as the work progresses and comparisons must be made. Records provide useful information for oral reports and help in keeping parents and the school principal informed regarding the accomplishments of the children. As time goes on the records provide evidence of the child's progress, which brings justifiable satisfaction to the child, as well as to others, and thus is a stimulus to further achievement. Where records are kept and used the typical curve of forgetting is broken, and a lasting impression remains.

There are many advantages to written plans and records, but on the other hand, the mechanics involved in writing can become such an obstacle and so impede the investigation that the satisfaction derived from experimentation is lost. Keeping individual plans and records is especially difficult. Knowing the children and observing their reactions, the teacher can decide whether or not preparing written records and reports will press the children beyond their ability. In any case, the thoroughness and accuracy of the work will vary with the

Fig. 19

When a child learns something new he should be allowed to
tell the other members of his class about it.

age and skill of the children. Planning together as a group, where the teacher
can help the class through the difficulties of paper work, will ease the pressure
in many cases without losing the values inherent in careful planning, recording,
and reporting.

Discussion and evaluation of the work reported. Whether or not written
records are prepared, the discussion which results from the oral reports should
help the children to interpret the work they have done and aid them in reaching
general conclusions. In addition, if the children help to evaluate their own oral
reports, the evaluation can be an effective means of stressing the desired values.

Having concluded their reports of chemical experiments, a fifth grade took
time to evaluate the work completed. The instructor asked what features of the
work and the manner of reporting that day were especially worthwhile and
interesting. Was the attitude scientific throughout, the point of each experiment made clear? How could improvements have been made? What overall

conclusions could be made, what common applications? What questions were raised for further investigation? In such a way, commendation was given for achievement, and effective methods of working and reporting were stressed. The attitude throughout was constructive and helpful; censure was avoided. The method used gave the children opportunity to evaluate and think for themselves in terms of immediate situations, and the opinions expressed by the children themselves gave praise for work well done and provided a stimulus toward further improvement.

How can provision be made for individual differences in science?

Where children work together on different phases of a common problem or on a number of related problems within a given area, the advantages of cooperation and of individualized effort are both attained. Variety is provided within a cooperating whole, and groups are formed, not arbitrarily or rigidly but informally, as common interest draws certain individuals together. Where children all read the same books, observe the same experiments, and follow the same directions throughout the day, there is little for the individual to contribute, for each already knows all that the others might show or tell. On the other hand, if the individuals work in quite unrelated areas, no one is likely to be much concerned with what the other person has accomplished, and again the advantages of cooperation are lost. Cooperation and individualization are both desirable values, and neither should be attained at the expense of the other.

Because individual concerns sometimes do extend to worthwhile problems or topics not of interest or value to all members of a class, provision can be made for work periods in which individuals may pursue their separate interests. On the other hand, no one should feel obligated to have a separate interest; the work period may be used by some for continued study in an area of general interest. To a large extent the school program can provide for individualization within the cooperating group experiences. Consideration for individual differences need not be stressed in a manner that eliminates cooperation with other members of the class. Private tutoring would not be desirable, even if the teacher had time to work on that basis. Individual attention within the cooperating group experience ordinarily is more effective. Even people who can afford private tutors prefer sending their children to schools, because children need to learn cooperation through working together.

Special interests and well-rounded individuals. When individuals pursue their own separate interests to an extreme, instead of cooperating in common undertakings, the broad experience essential to well-rounded persons may not be obtained. A child who has developed great interest in chemistry, for example, is to be commended for that interest; yet if he is reluctant to work with anything but his chemistry set, he will become narrow, and progress even in his chosen field may be blocked. In one actual case a scientist failed because he was unable to prepare intelligible written reports of his work. Some breadth of experience is essential even for a specialist.

Differences of opinion are commonly due to a difference in experience. Each individual interprets the present in terms of the meanings previous experience has given him. A familiar story from India is told of blind men describing an elephant: The blind men who felt the tail said, "An elephant is like a rope," but those who touched an ear contended, "An elephant is like a fan." Other blind men felt the legs, and said, "An elephant is like pillars." Those who felt the head insisted, "An elephant is like a water-pot." Those who felt the tusks argued, "An elephant is like a plow-pole." And the men fell to quarrelling violently as a result of their limited views.[9] To avoid a comparable situation, schools hope to develop well-rounded individuals with a broad view.

While preserving a balanced program, however, it is good policy to encourage special interests and abilities within that program. Throughout history many of the outstanding performances in science, the arts, and other fields were achieved by people who were not in all respects well-rounded individuals. Instead they specialized, followed a marked interest, developed unusual talents. A person can be broadminded and yet enjoy a special interest in which he develops considerable proficiency. Special interests often have their roots in the early experiences of children.

The sixth-grade boy who shows marked ability to work with machinery, for example, should be encouraged to follow his interest — not discouraged. Each individual should have the satisfaction of doing well in at least one small area. With the talents he has cultivated, the child can make valuable contributions to group undertakings and thereby can establish himself as a constructive member of the class. Without abandoning his interest in machinery, the sixth-grade boy should learn that a good mechanic, engineer, or inventor must have some understanding of mathematics. He will need ability to express himself orally and in writing. In history he can learn of the Industrial Revolution and the influence of machinery on our way of life. The arts are involved in the design of attractive equipment. Gradually the child can be induced to build on a broad base, and he will come to see that even for the mechanic or engineer life is more than machinery alone.

[9] "Blind Men and Elephant," a parable attributed to Buddha, in *The Grateful Elephant and Other Stories,* edited and translated by Eugene Watson Bulingame, Yale University Press, New Haven, 1923, pp. xxi and 79–82.

The schools can preserve and even stimulate the special interests of children, yet encourage a well-rounded development.

Variations in background, interest, and ability. Complete uniformity of accomplishment among the various members of a class is unattainable. Individual differences do exist, and the aim should be to help each person develop his own talents regardless of averages or other comparisons. Fortunately, an active program of science appeals to a wide range of abilities. Some people note that science is complex enough to challenge the inquiring minds of gifted children; others remark that science, with its experiments and observations, is concrete and active and thus appeals to children of low aptitude who like to work with their hands. When two children connect a dry cell to a miniature lamp and socket, causing the lamp to light successfully, one may learn that the heating is due to resistance of the filament to an electric current, and before he is through he may gain some understanding of the chemistry that produces the current in the dry cell, whereas the other child will be satisfied to know simply that connecting the wires will cause a lamp to light. Although the amount of insight differs, each child has had a satisfactory experience. Where tangible materials are used, each individual can comprehend as much as his ability permits.

Further provision for the individualization of instruction can be provided through cooperative planning and discussions that will reveal the varying backgrounds and interests in the class. Opportunity for individual initiative and a flexible program with a variety of books and other resources will provide a situation in which all the children need not be expected to read the same assignments or do identical experiments. Above all, the teacher should get acquainted with the children and react to them as individuals.

The problem of providing for a great range of individual abilities was faced by the husband of one teacher when he was asked to show, in the school assembly, some slides he had made of his trip to Alaska. As grades one through twelve were included in the same assembly, he was concerned about what to say in explanation that would be suitable for such divergent ages. But he did a very good job of handling a difficult assignment. When he had finished, after all his efforts to keep his comments simple enough for the small children and yet interesting to the older ones, the initial question asked in the discussion period was by a first-grader, who said:

"Mr. Smith, when you were up in Alaska, did you get any slides of the Aurora Borealis?"

Which suggests that individual differences are more than a matter of grade level.

STUDY GUIDE

1. What justification is there for considering a scientific way of working appropriate and effective in the classroom? Of what value is the development of scientific attitudes?

2. How can scientific attitudes and ways of working be taught? Describe a good teaching situation in science and explain how it would develop desirable attitudes and ways of working.

3. Find the biography of a scientist or a news report of research to see what scientific attitudes are exemplified.

4. Locate an experiment in a science book for children, at the grade level you prefer, and indicate how the experiment could be used in the solution of a real problem.

5. Explain and illustrate how the "failure" of an experiment may provide a learning opportunity.

6. What is the purpose of a demonstration, and how should it be conducted?

7. How can films be used to advantage in science?

8. How can field trips help to achieve the objectives of education in science? If a class were studying machinery, what kind of trip might be useful? What arrangements should be made for such a trip?

9. How can children work together yet each individual be free to exercise his own initiative? Should the work in science be individual, in groups, or for the whole class?

10. Science is sometimes referred to as a democratic process. What are the qualities that make it democratic?

5

Science and Related Learnings

Some educators advocate the integration or fusion of science with other subject-matter areas to emphasize meaningful relationships within broad fields. In the elementary school a significant number of leaders favor a complete reorganization of content in terms of problems in realistic situations. Whatever curricular organization may be preferred, most educators agree that relationships are meaningful and should be stressed.

If the central purpose of education is to develop cultured individuals well adjusted to life in a democratic society, then science has much to contribute to the total program of the schools. Science has become a part of our economic life, our entertainment, our general philosophy and outlook on life, our physical and emotional well-being. It helps to determine what skills we need, the interests we have, the appreciations we develop. The example set in science can make a large contribution to the development of responsible attitudes, personal integrity, cooperation, and the ability to solve problems. Just as science has become an integral part of life today, the implications of science can be found throughout many areas of the school curriculum.

Science can provide the stimulating experiences that give meaning and purpose to reading and other communication skills. In fact, an active program of investigation can become a stimulus to the entire school program.

STIMULATING THE READING PROGRAM

One way in which science can stimulate a child to read is illustrated by the following case. Billy was in the fourth grade. While lingering about the science room one day, Billy expressed an interest in chemistry; he said he had a chemistry set at home but the directions were hard to understand, and he hadn't yet learned how to use it. The science teacher offered his help if Billy would bring the set to school. Billy did, and in every spare moment for a few days afterwards he was there in the science room getting help, frequently asking the meaning of technical words. Anyone who has used the manual for a chemistry set will realize that the instructions are not easy for a person unfamiliar with chemical terminology. But Billy persisted. He followed the directions and performed a number of the experiments listed in the book, now and then getting assistance, although the science teacher gave help only when asked.

After several days of help at random moments, Billy took the chemistry set over to his classroom and was there given an opportunity to show some of the experiments to his classmates. It was his own idea to put the harder, more technical words on the blackboard behind him; then he read them off the board to the class as he performed the experiments and explained them. The other children were fascinated and impressed. Billy had achieved success through his own persistent efforts. But he was hardly more thrilled than the teacher who had considered Billy a serious reading problem and was amazed at what he had accomplished.

Developing an understanding of words

Reading as a means of acquiring information in science is limited during the early years by the child's lack of skill in reading. If the science program be limited to reading, obviously very little science is possible for small children. Particularly in the early grades, science can and should stress first-hand experiences as a means of learning. A profitable relationship is achieved where science provides the basic experiences to make reading meaningful.

The primary child's language is concrete. The words children learn first are nouns, the names of familiar objects, and then verbs describing familiar actions. His words are concerned with the immediate situation. Ability to speak in terms of the remote or the abstract is acquired gradually as the child's background of experience becomes more extensive. Children are bothered less by the length of words than by lack of understanding of what words mean, either because the words refer to an abstraction or because the experience to make them understandable is lacking.

Numerous studies show that environmental factors have considerable influence upon the growth of vocabulary. Rapid vocabulary development following a trip to the seashore, or a similar experience, has been reported. Words are used to express feelings as well as meanings. Both the meanings and the feelings expressed are the product of direct experience. Children from restricted, monotonous, or otherwise uninspiring environments commonly have small vocabularies.[1]

Science is concrete, rather than abstract, if properly taught. The boy who has just seen ink form when two chemicals are poured together can understand what is meant by a chemical change. The child who has seen his plants wilt can understand what a book means when it says plants must have water. Words that seem easy to an adult may be hard for the child; and, conversely, what seems hard to the adult may be easy for the child. The child's experience is more limited than that of the teacher. His background of experience also is likely to be quite different from that of the teacher. The difference in background may permit the child to use with understanding a word that seems difficult to the teacher. The child who has a chemistry set at home may delight in using such words as *ferric ammonium sulfate.* He may surprise the teacher with the strange and technical words, but he himself has seen the crystals in a bottle and may have used them in an experiment. Likewise, he can understand what a chemical precipitate is; the words have meaning, because he has seen precipitates form when he pours two chemicals together. Other implications of the words may escape him, but at least one meaning is definite and vivid, not at all hard to remember or to use.

While a fifth-grade class was studying science, there was a marked emphasis upon direct experiences. Yet when the children summarized what had been learned, the first thing they said was:

"We've learned a whole lot of new words."

And it may be added that all the words were common ones concerned with the immediate surroundings. A word is not hard to remember if it has meaning and was learned in a stimulating situation. Reading practice involving words alone can be ineffective, mere verbalism. Science can help to make everyday experience understandable and reading effective. Certain dictionaries have recently been criticized for defining one word in terms of others and those

---

[1] Dorothea McCarthy, "Language Development in Children," *Manual of Child Psychology,* edited by Leonard Carmichael, John Wiley & Sons, New York, 1954, pp. 527–28; 557; 584–97.

others in terms of still others until a cycle is complete. But the same criticism can be applied as well to other verbal explanations, for unless some of the words are based upon experience, the explanation establishes nothing.

Developing a need for books

In the early years of school, one of the greatest values of science is in what it can contribute to the reading program, not only through making words mean-

Fig. 20

Word meanings are learned through direct experience.

ingful but through increasing the child's zest for reading. If the child has a purpose of his own, it is surprising what he can accomplish — but if he doesn't care, how little he can do is well known to any teacher.

In a second-grade class in which almost all the children followed a television program of the Buck Rogers-fantasy type, the children were talking about a new "square planet" that supposedly had been discovered in the story. The teacher shifted the discussion from square planets to real planets. Is there really a square planet? What are planets? What planets are known for sure? What are they like? The discussion was a rousing one and brought out a real need for information. The next morning almost half the class came to school with books on the subject. Several children brought as many as the community library would permit. Another child came with his father's geography book. One person brought two volumes of the Book of Knowledge, and several people had other reference books from their homes. The reference work which followed involved surprisingly advanced material. Ability to find printed materials and apply them where needed is one of the goals of a reading program. Science experiences can help to achieve that goal.

Children of all ages can learn to use books as a source of information. One day, on a table in the kindergarten, Herbert found a book which pictured magnets. Excitedly he rushed to the teacher with the book, exclaiming:

"Here's some magnets like ours. What's it say?"

His interest did not wane as the teacher read what was written. Undoubtedly he was gaining an appreciation of the ability to read, and beginning to think of books as a valuable source of information. Seeking information in science, older children learn to use indexes and tables of contents, and to do reference work with encyclopedias and card catalogues.

Science and reading can be mutually helpful. One day a first-grade child brought to school a story book concerned with the life of an ant. After the story was read, the children raised many questions about what ants are like, where they live, what they eat. The interest was so intense that it was decided to obtain some ants for the classroom; through care of the ants and observation of their behavior many of the questions would be answered. In this case reading led to experience in science. Of course the science experiences also led to further reading, making a cycle in which both the science and the reading program profited by a close relationship.

A science program that deals with real materials and experiences is vital to children and can serve as the stimulus for reading and for other areas of the curriculum as well. Reading authorities agree that reading is more effective in conjunction with other subjects, where the child will have a need, some purpose, for using the printed page.[2]

Developing reading readiness through science experiences

Science also can stimulate the reading readiness program. Two baby chicks brought to school by one of the children in a kindergarten excited a great amount of attention. On a trip the class made to the library, several of the children asked for stories about chickens and how they live. Upon returning to school, the children leafed through the books, looking at the pictures. The books were in frequent use. Although the children themselves could not read, they were eager to have the books read aloud. Interest in books was stimulated through observation of the baby chicks.

In another case, a hen was brought into the kindergarten and kept there in an improvised cage for several days. The interest of the children was spontaneous, and was especially intense when the hen laid an egg. Having the hen was the stimulus for reading stories about chickens and farms. The teacher read the stories aloud. The children were avid listeners, and much time was spent later looking at the pictures in the books. Several new stories were located and brought to the teacher to be read.

This kindergarten group used their first egg to make an eggnog out of their morning milk. The children remarked upon the fact that the egg was warm when laid. They compared the hen with a rabbit which they had kept for a while earlier. The hen was kept warm by feathers, whereas the rabbit had fur; the two animals made different noises and ate different kinds of food. A duck egg and a goose egg were brought to school and compared with the hen's egg. Eggs were saved until there were enough to make a cake. The ingredients for a cake were listed on the board. In the children's own words a letter was dictated to the teacher inviting the mothers to eat the cake with the children. A party was planned, and the plans also were written on the board. In these experiences the children were learning to express themselves in words, learning how to refer to books for information, and developing an interest in reading materials, as well as gaining knowledge in science. They had a basis for understanding the words that were used; interest was spontaneous and genuine; and they had a real purpose for using written materials.

[2] National Society for the Study of Education, the Forty-Eighth Yearbook, Part II, *Reading in the Elementary School,* University of Chicago Press, Chicago 37, Illinois, 1949, pp. 7–8, 11.

Beginning to read, stimulated by science experiences

A first-grade class gathered together each day in the early part of the year and dictated to the teacher whatever they considered had been of especial interest that day. In the children's own words these statements were written on the board. The reports were duplicated by the teacher each week in the form of a newspaper on sheets of typewriting paper, folded once in the middle. Each day's report was under a separate date line and included a report of the weather for that day. Since each child had a copy, the teacher would read the newspaper with them before it was taken home to the parents. The true flavor can best be gained from a direct quotation; the excerpts given here are predominately scientific, although in the newspaper no such distinction was made:

Tuesday, September 24
Today is the second day of school.
The children wrote two stories.
The stories are called *The Fire* and *Fishing in the Summer.*

Wednesday, September 25
This morning we talked about making our room look nice.
We will bring flowers and plants.
We will paint pictures for our room.

Thursday, September 26
Betty brought a little plant.
She brought it to decorate our room.
It is called ivy.
We like the plant that she brought. . . .
Curtis wants to know what happens to smoke.
Jack surprised us.
He brought us two pots of ivy.
They make our room look pretty.

Friday, September 27
Now Curtis knows what smoke is.
Smoke is soot.
Smoke goes up in the air.

Thursday, October 3
Patti and Jenifer brought plants.
We think our room looks like a garden now.
We went to gather leaves today. . . .
Leaves are dead when they fall from trees.
They die because they do not have enough water.
When it gets cold the water does not reach the leaves.

Monday, October 14
Molly brought beautiful autumn leaves.
She got them in the country.
Fish breathe air in water.
Air gets in the water from the plants and from the air on top of the water.

Wednesday, October 16
A big boy named Michael brought us a hamster.
He is brown and white with a little black.
He looks like a rat, but he has a very short tail.

Friday, November 1
We went to Riverside Park . . . to get cocoons.

Tuesday, November 19
Dickie made a blue boat.
Alex made a yellow ship.
Julie brought a compass to school.
Jimmy brought a family of rats.
There is a mother rat and five baby rats.

Wednesday, November 20
Curtis brought a turtle.
We put the rats in a bigger cage.

Friday, November 22
We saw two movies.
One movie was about frogs.
There were frog eggs.
The tadpoles grow out of frog eggs.
Then the tadpole grows into a frog.
We saw frogs eat.
They have funny tongues.
The other picture was about boats.

Where reading is for a purpose, children gradually become acquainted with words, and using printed materials becomes spontaneous and desirable; until eventually the children are able to read whatever is of interest to them. Because progress is not uniform, books on different levels of ability and on a variety of topics should be made available. If books can be obtained from a library, the teacher may select some that are suitable and have them on hand, either in anticipation of a problem or topic that may be studied or after a question has risen and information is needed. Where a choice of books is available, the child ordinarily will select something that is significant to him and not too hard to read. The teacher's advice often will help the child to make a suitable choice. The teacher frequently may read with groups or with individuals to help them to further their purpose, whatever it may be; and in the process the children are learning to read.

Learning to read for information in science

At any age a close relationship can be maintained between reading and active investigation in science. In the primary grades, in which great emphasis is placed on learning to read, teachers commonly welcome science for the stimulus that meaningful experiences can give to the reading program. Gradually, however, as children gain skill in reading, the relationship of science to reading is reversed, and reading becomes a tool subject that is useful in the science program. A description of the science work in a particular third-grade class at the beginning of the school year may help to illustrate how the ability to read can develop from science experiences:

Robert found a turtle, brought it to school, and asked what kind it was. The teacher did not know but helped him to find a book that told about turtles. The book was too hard, but Robert was interested and insisted he could read it himself. The book was intended for the fourth grade; Robert was at the bottom of his third grade in reading ability, although his aptitude rating was close to normal. The teacher hesitated. She had no good alternative to propose and was reluctant to discourage him. The book was too difficult, but she thought that perhaps it would be better to let him find out for himself; so she let him proceed.

After a while Robert came to the teacher and announced that his turtle was a box turtle. The teacher was doubtful and asked how he knew. He told her that he could tell by the shape of the shell, the markings, and the way the turtle was able to pull in its neck and head. He demonstrated by poking his finger at the turtle, making it withdraw. Still doubtful, the teacher asked if the book said that. So Robert read what the book said, and with almost no difficulty.

Robert read more about turtles, especially about how to keep turtles and what to feed them. At intervals he came to the teacher to ask the meaning of a word. Often he had already determined the meaning from the context and would ask if that was what the word meant. After a while the teacher suggested that he tell the class what he had learned about turtles. Feeling new power, Robert preferred to read to the class from the book, and he did. The children were impressed, for they had known he was a poor reader. The boy reported to several other classes in the building, including the kindergarten. He insisted on reading from the fourth-grade book there, too. The kindergarteners played with the turtle and ignored Robert while he read aloud from the book, but everybody was happy.

Since Robert got so much attention, others began finding excuses for reading to the class. Max found a story about a painted turtle and took it home to read. His uncle found him a painted turtle in a store. Max felt such an urgent need for the turtle that his uncle had to bring the animal to school during the morning so that Max could have it when he read to the class.

Mae brought in a caterpillar, placed it in a jar with branches from the shrub it was found upon, and closed the jar with cheesecloth over the top. The caterpillar formed a cocoon in the jar, but many children doubted that it was a cocoon, because the cocoon pictured in the book was different. Later Mae found another cocoon. This one was exactly like the one pictured in the book. Somewhat later another person in the class found a book at the library which explained that there are different kinds of cocoons, and the difficulty was resolved.

When a salamander was brought in, a place to keep it was needed; so an empty paste jar large enough for a terrarium was located. Several children brought sod, and, with the jar horizontal, the sod was placed inside. A doll dish was used for water, and the sod was built up about it, as if the dish were a pond. The salamander lived on insects and other small life in the sod. A land snail was added, and more grasshoppers were brought in than could be used. Through their observations the children became familiar with some common animals and learned how they behave and how they get their food. Still other facts were obtained from books about these and similar animals. The information gathered was shared by all members of the class in an exchange of ideas and opinions. Some of the facts were printed on reading charts as a record of what the class had learned.

The same class had an aquarium tank. Wanting something to put into it, they planned a trip to the pond. The teacher's motive, of course, was somewhat deeper, for she knew that the aquarium could provide numerous learning experiences, much as the terrarium had done. On the way to the pond the class collected many different kinds of seed and observed birds, grasshoppers, spiders, and a variety of spider webs. Dragonflies were noted at the pond. With a dip net the class got more snails than they could use, a small crayfish, several nymphs, a frog, which was released after a few days, two polliwogs, and a number of small water animals which at the time they could not name. They also took quite a few water plants, and back at the school used the plants to stock their aquarium. The aquarium did well at first, but after a few days it was noticed that the plants had been eaten, and the nymphs soon died. After reference to all available books, the class decided that the aquarium was overcrowded with animals. Some of the snails and other animals were taken home by the children, and another trip to the pond was made to obtain more plants.

The aquarium did very well then, and in a few days many new snails were born.

In preparing for the aquarium and maintaining it, the children did much reading about how aquaria should be cared for — kept out of the sun, with the water aerated, and not overstocked with animals. They wrote stories and told each other what they had found about nymphs, dragonflies, tadpoles, about frogs and how they change, and about snails and how some are born alive whereas others come from eggs. Sketches, charts, and other written records were used when reports were made.

When someone came in with what was thought to be a cocoon, the children looked through books to see what kind it was. They located a picture which identified it, but the book said it was a spider's egg sack. No other stories about spiders could be found, except one that was highly romanticized and unsatisfactory to the children for their purpose. Fortunately, it happened that a man in town was an authority on spiders. The principal took the class one afternoon while the teacher and a small group visited this man for information. They reported back to the others, telling about much they had seen which had fascinated them. Later the class was shown a film on spiders, after which the group that had reported on spiders was seriously challenged, because they had said that the trap door of a trap-door spider is concealed and hard to see, and yet the one in the film was plainly visible. A letter was written to the authority. He replied by telephone — he needed no practice in writing letters — saying that it depends upon where the spiders are and what materials they use in making the trap door. The man sent a spider's trap door to the class so that all might see it, and the problem was resolved, but in the process much purposeful reading was done, as well as much science learned.

Reading authorities point out, "It is obvious that instruction in reading should be closely related to the teaching of other school subjects," and among the goals of reading instruction are increasing ability to locate, evaluate, and organize pertinent information.[3] Not only can science contribute to these and other goals of the reading program, but a close, mutually beneficial relationship can be developed with other areas of the curriculum as well.

SCIENCE AND THE LANGUAGE ARTS

The first requirement in any speaking or writing is that there be something to say. When a social undertaking is developed in the classroom, communication is a natural outgrowth, a product of the circumstances. We all like to tell other

[3] *Ibid.*, pp. 138–46.

people when we have something to reveal; in fact, the greatest difficulty often is to control the impulse to speak. When children talk because they have something to say, the speaking is more effective, more functional; hence there will be greater ability to meet similar functional circumstances in real life situations.

Vital experiences provide the thoughts essential for communication and also the impulse. When science is taught as active investigation of the environment it can help to provide those circumstances which furnish both the substance and the stimulation for social intercourse. Illustrations from the science work of an actual class, a kindergarten, may serve to indicate some of the possibilities:

Word got about in the building that baby hamsters had been born in the kindergarten room. Because the kindergarten children had brothers and sisters in the third grade who were interested, it was decided to invite them down to see the new hamsters and the polliwogs as well. Ordinarily the child who made the contribution or observed something of interest would be allowed to tell about it, but since all had participated in the work with these animals, the class had to choose those who would speak to the third grade. Two were chosen, a girl to tell about the polliwogs and a boy to explain about the new hamsters.

In the question-and-answer period, when the third grade came, all the kindergarten participated. The children in both groups were sincerely cooperative throughout. The kindergarteners were eager to be helpful in showing the animals and explaining to the older class. One of the third-graders said that he did not understand:

"You say they swim like fish, eat like fish, and breathe like fish — then aren't they fish?"

"No," Toby replied, "they're polliwogs!"

"But what's the difference?"

Toby said, "Polliwogs grow into frogs."

Another third-grader asked, "What happens to the tail?"

A kindergarten boy said, "The stomach grows around the tail."

The teacher later helped to clarify that point.

Steven, one of the kindergarteners, said, "That's what we call development."

The term had been used previously only in regard to the growth of the children themselves. This work had given the word a breadth of meaning.

The same class had a terrarium for a while. There was a slug in the terrarium. One child noticed how little the slug had moved during the morning. When he remarked about it, the teacher asked what *sluggish* meant: did it mean *fast* or *slow?* In the discussion which followed, the first child's observa-

Fig. 21

Science experiences provide situations in which the language arts can be cultivated.

tions were questioned, for another pupil said that sometimes the slug moved fast. As a result everyone watched for several days and finally concluded that sluggish meant slow-moving like a slug. For some time after that the children delighted in using the word on every possible occasion. It is out of such experiences that word meanings are built, and words are basic to most of our communication.

Among the language arts which the schools seek to develop is the ability to speak effectively to other people, whether in conversation, in general discussions, or while appearing before a group. The child who has become fascinated with turtles, perhaps, or who has discovered that ink can be made by means of a chemical change has something exciting to show his classmates, and words of explanation come readily. Even the more shy children are moved to express themselves under such circumstances. Frequently children who are unable to speak effectively in the classroom are quite voluble on the playgrounds or at home where they have something to say, and, absorbed in the issue at hand, forget their self-consciousness.

When a number of children have had similar, but not identical, experiences, and all are related to the problem at hand, the basis for a good classroom discussion is provided. When one child reports that adding water to some dry substance, such as baking powder, will bring about a chemical change, perhaps some other person has found that heating also will bring about chemical changes, or that the change may occur when two solutions are simply poured together. Other individuals may have discovered that some chemical changes can be detected by a change of color, some by the appearance of a precipitate, by a new odor, by a gas bubbling from the solution, or by other means. Each person contributes what he has learned about the subject under consideration. Some of the class may have found from their reading that cooking, burning, decay, digestion, and rusting are all familiar examples of chemical change. A worthwhile discussion can be based upon the pooling of such information and upon the reactions and differences of opinion that arise. Using a variety of books helps to make possible an exchange of ideas in discussions that are real and stimulating.

Science experiences can provide stimulating situations which elicit speech — conversations closely akin to those outside the classroom, and hence improvements in speech are likely to endure. When the snails in one classroom aquarium bore young, there were many excited comments. The children shared their

Fig. 22

The first requirement for effective speaking or writing is to have something worth saying.

observations and opinions. Plans had to be made for removing the fish lest the tiny snails be destroyed. Out of such experiences children develop a vocabulary and the ability to express thoughts clearly and forcefully. Without significant experiences there is little need for communication.

In an active science program there are numerous occasions for putting reports into writing, in which case spelling and penmanship as well as the ability to organize and present ideas on paper are given essential roles and can be developed in functional circumstances. Some classes make special reports, others prepare newspapers, magazines, booklets, charts or posters and displays, letters, or perhaps notebooks; these may be either individual or group undertakings. Note-taking and outlining can be taught when needed. The child who seeks information on crayfish may find it in books, through careful observation of the crayfish, and by listening carefully to what other people say about them. Listening attentively, as well as effective speaking and writing, is a goal of the language arts.

Science can provide situations in which the child has a real need for speaking and writing effectively, a strong desire to tell others what he has in mind.

SCIENCE AND THE FINE AND PRACTICAL ARTS

During an art lesson in a third grade the teacher held a paper against the blackboard, illustrating the point about which she was speaking. She moved the paper along the board, and it happened that the paper clung to the wall. The children were surprised at what had happened; the teacher recognized that static electricity was responsible. Since the interest had shifted, time was taken to investigate the static electricity. In this case work in art led to work in science; at other times science may lead to experience in art, for in real-life situations there are close relationships between the two fields.

Typical of activities which involve both art and science is the construction of murals to illustrate the water cycle or how animals survive the winter. A display of rocks, showing the effects of weathering, can also be a study in artistic arrangement. Placards will need to be printed to give the theme and explain the display; the printing and arrangement of such posters is, of course, a typical art activity, here in functional circumstances. A sand table may be arranged to depict a desert habitat, the dependence of animals upon plant life, how animals care for their young, or some other theme and at the same time deal with balance, proportion, color harmony in nature, and other artistic considerations. A great number of classes have made clay models of dinosaurs, and one class arranged them in a scene on a convenient table with a mural background showing how life must have been at the time dinosaurs were on the earth.

Other common art activities which may involve science are the preparation of booklets and reports with sketches and attractive covers, the preparation of leaf prints which show variety in structure and suggest the function of leaves, and the consideration of design and arrangement in cobwebs, snowflakes, flowers, and other natural objects. Sketching may be concerned with the forms of trees, streams, clouds, and animals. Stick figures, simple or more elaborate, are often effective for those children who need to express ideas but lack skill in drawing.

The science of light provides a helpful analysis of color, and music can be understood through the physics of sound. The practical or industrial arts are essentially applications of science in many cases. The making of soap involves a chemical change, and dipping candles suggests the chemistry of burning. In the industrial arts a child may construct a toaster or an electric motor and study the practical uses of such instruments. In science these instruments can be used while learning the principles of electricity. In elementary-school work there need be no clear distinction between the two fields, for indeed no clear line of distinction exists in the adult activities themselves.

SCIENCE AND THE HEALTH PROGRAM

Experience indicates that health work based on exhortation and rules is unpopular with children and ineffective as a means of influencing behavior. Rules for sleeping with the window open or for eating green vegetables each day are not likely to be as effective as understanding how air circulates and knowing the effects upon the body, or seeing the effects of improper diet upon laboratory rats in a nutrition experiment. Probably because they get so much of it, children learn to disregard admonition, but they are deeply influenced by what they see for themselves. Most children who have seen weird-looking protozoa moving about under a microscope, or have seen bacteria from their own fingers grow on a culture, can readily learn to keep their fingers out of their mouths.

Teaching safety is an important part of the health program. A child who in science has seen a wire become hot when shorted across the terminals of a dry cell will be able to understand how short circuits in a house may start a fire, and he will be able to see also why a coin should not be substituted for a burned-out fuse. Some cleaning solvents are inflammable or explosive. The directions on the container are hardly enough when the basic principles are not understood. Gas stoves, coal heaters, and the mechanical equipment in our homes involve certain hazards that can bring death or injury. Cases are frequently reported in the newspapers. Such hazards should be understood to be avoided. Strong acids have the reputation of being dangerous, but the lye used to open the drain of a kitchen sink is equally potent. With a little more insight many accidents and much ill health could be avoided. Science can help to provide that insight.

Just as science can aid the health program, so can human applications make science instruction more vital to children. While studying how plants and animals grow, the children can check their own height and weight as well as their diet. In a study of how animals survive, the child's own safety can be stressed. Whereas an animal may be colored like his surroundings to camouflage him from enemies, the child will be safer on a dark, rainy day while crossing a street in heavy traffic if he wears something conspicuous, such as a white raincoat, rather than a black one. A study of light can be more effective and stimulating if human vision and the care of the eyes are included. Consideration of the way in which a lens works is more meaningful and more functional if the lens of the human eye and the eyeglasses that people wear serve as examples. Likewise, a study of sound becomes more significant when hearing is included. One teacher, concerned with dirty hands or worse, instituted a number of experiments to show that hot water and soap are good for dissolving grease and dirt, much better than cold water alone. Whether or not science and the health work are completely integrated in the school program, a close relationship is inherent and profitable; each can make the other more successful.

In the modern health program, emotional adjustment is an important consideration to which science can make a large contribution. A person's mental health is deeply affected by his interpretation of the surroundings. A three-year-old nursery child one morning saw a spider hanging from a bookcase. He became much excited and asked the teacher what "that thing" was and where it had come from. The teacher explained. Later that morning she heard him telling another child, almost boastfully, that he knew what a spider web is. Where understanding is lacking, the reaction is quite likely to be one of fear — dread of the unknown. One teacher tells of the nursery-school child who somehow had learned to fear animals. When a rabbit was brought to the nursery the child was frightened and withdrew to a remote corner in great trepidation. But the other children were delighted to have a rabbit, and gradually the fear was overcome, until eventually the child was feeding the animal and enjoying it with everyone else. No doubt his changed attitude extended somewhat to other animals and even to life in general.

Needless fears and distorted views may be less obvious in older children, but nevertheless are common. Even many adults fear the unknown, whereas they could quite as well approach unfamiliar situations with the anticipation and delight that one derives from the unfolding plot of a good novel. In science natural curiosity and the joy of learning are stressed, for these constitute the motivating force of scientific research, as well as the most effective means of learning for children.

After a certain first grade had worked with electricity, the mother of one of the boys came to the teacher and said that her child had been afraid of lightning storms until recently. He had been in the habit of crying and showing other signs of terror during storms. Recently, however, the mother had rushed to her son's room as a thunderstorm began and was surprised to find the boy calmly gazing through the window, showing great interest in the storm. She immediately asked why he was no longer frightened, and he replied:

"I just wanted to see the electricity jump from one cloud to another."

With the aid of science children can overcome blind, unreasoning fears and yet develop essential caution where real hazards are involved. Children can learn, for example, that salamanders and garter snakes are harmless but some snakes are not to be treated lightly. Although dry cells may be handled freely, children should learn that the house circuit can be dangerous. Adults sometimes throw kerosene onto fires, or even gasoline; in school, as children, they could have been taught reasonable caution. To impress on children the need for care — and to allay adult fears as well — the teacher should stress safety in the use of open flames, yet should not overemphasize the caution so much as to seem absurd and cause the children to react adversely. Alcohol burners should be left on a table, not carried about, for the alcohol may splash out of the burner and catch fire. Even though the alcohol spills, little damage may be done, unless panic results. The burner should be used on an asbestos or metal surface, and a large tin can full of sand should be kept nearby so that the sand can be dumped onto any flame that gets out of control. Used matches may be dropped into another jar or metal can placed nearby for that purpose. No matches should be available for the children to use without close supervision by the teacher. The use of strong acids and lye can be avoided entirely, or can be limited to teacher demonstrations. If acid is used, household ammonia, baking soda, or slaked lime should be kept nearby, ready for use in an emergency. If acid is spilled, it should be rinsed away immediately and the ammonia, soda, or lime applied to neutralize any acid that may remain. If lye is used, vinegar should be kept at hand for a similar purpose. Water should never be poured into a strong acid; and if acids are used, they should be used by the teacher with obvious care. Respect for real hazards can be taught and needless apprehensions overcome. Greater understanding gained through science should lead to greater safety and fewer hazards in the common activities of life.

SCIENCE AND MATHEMATICS IN THE SCHOOL PROGRAM

Exact measurement is essential in the advanced sciences, and complex mathematics is used in the interpretation of data. For the child in an elementary school, however, science is not exact to the same extent, being more concerned with general principles than with exact amounts. Nevertheless, there are many instances where mathematical concepts and skills should play a large role. Measurements of all sorts are involved. The sizes of the planets and their distances from the sun can be determined to scale in constructing models, and large numbers must be used in the process. The children conducting a diet experiment will need to weigh the experimental animals carefully, learn to use the metric system or the English system of weights, and record the data on charts and graphs. The results of experiments can also be shown in tables or scale drawings. The quantities involved can often be reported as fractions, as decimals, or as a percentage. The older children in performing their science experiments can learn to use simple equations. Ratios can be learned while studying the lever. The number of degrees at our latitude, the angle of the sun, and the length of shadows can be stressed while the children study the changing seasons. Astronomy gives the basis for our units of time: the day, for example, being one rotation of the earth on its axis, and the year one revolution of the earth about the sun. The month originally was from one new moon to another, and a week was the period from one lunar phase to the next. The hours of a day correspond to fractions of the sun's apparent motion in a circle about the earth and can be measured by angles on a sun dial.

The need for all sorts of computations in various circumstances will arise in science. Small children can learn to count by 2's through the use of a thermometer calibrated in the usual way, and the older children can learn to read a Centigrade scale. The averages of daily maximum and minimum temperatures can be computed each week. Whatever processes are being taught in arithmetic at a given time can be the ones stressed in science. To learn counting, adding, and other computations the numbers involved in experiments can be used. The various units of volume will need to be learned. Science experiments can give meaning to arithmetical processes and make them more functional. Problem-solving situations are plentiful in science.

SCIENCE AND THE SOCIAL STUDIES

The relationship of science to the social studies is close, for the developments of science are largely responsible for our way of life, with which the social studies are concerned.

The type of home life people lead is of great concern in the social studies. Science is definitely an element of home life today, whether the families concerned are aware of the implications and make the most of them or not. Problems of growth, reproduction, nutrition, and maintenance of health are basically questions of science. Our homes are heated, insulated, and protected from fire and lightning. In our homes we have electrically-operated lamps, stoves, waffle irons and toasters, refrigerators, radios, flashlights, fans, mixers, telephones, clocks, doorbells, and heating pads, to name but a few of the more common appliances. We also have thermostats, thermometers, and barometers; we should know how to use and interpret them. We work with sewing machines, lawn mowers, and vacuum cleaners, and we should understand the basic principles upon which they operate. A knowledge of solvents will help in cleaning or "spotting" clothes. Our kitchens and bathrooms are stocked with chemicals, and the kitchen is a veritable laboratory in many respects. In the garden, problems of plant growth are not abstractions, as any home gardener can testify. Some knowledge of insects becomes necessary for the care of both garden and house. In our homes, certainly, the social studies and science are closely related.

In the social studies we learn how man has progressed through the ages. The earliest records of life come from fossils. Science tells us how these records were formed and how they can be interpreted.

The social studies are concerned with transportation and communication, with inventions and industrial processes. Transportation involves the basic principles of aviation, the lifting force upon an airplane, the controls and the design of wings and fuselage, how weather is forecast, how instruments are used. Jet and rocket aircraft and steam, electric, gasoline, and diesel engines involve many scientific concepts, such as the advantage of gears and levers. The telegraph and the telephone have played a large role in the history of our country, and the electrical principles represented in these instruments are fundamental in science. A study of the industrial revolution may well be concerned with the transition from mill wheels to electric generators and great power developments, from hand work and beasts of burden to steam, gasoline, and hydroelectric power.

While studying about the local fire department, one second-grade class built a fire truck and a fire house of blocks and packing cases. They equipped the building with miniature lamps and with an electric bell operated by dry cells. To make their light red, like the warning lamp on a fire truck, they dipped the bulb in red poster paint. While setting up the fire bell and warning lamp, the children were learning science in addition to social studies, for they learned how a bell rings, how a lamp gives light, and how a lamp or bell must be connected to a source of current. The class also performed experiments which showed that fires must have air to burn, that some fires will start by themselves in spontaneous combustion, that some fire extinguishers smother a fire with carbon dioxide, and that smoke is composed of tiny carbon particles.

When children study pets, they may learn how the animals protect themselves, how they get food, how the young are born and cared for, and how some animals are suited to live in one place and some in another. A cat, for instance, has claws and sharp teeth with which to protect itself and to capture food. It can climb trees to escape and is quick and stealthy of movement. The coloring of many cats tends to conceal them. The fur of its body gives protection against the cold. The household pets commonly used in social studies activities can be used concurrently to develop an understanding of animal life.

Indian life is a common topic in the social studies. The Indian legends of the stars are of interest to children and can stimulate questions regarding the sky as we know it today. A study of Indian life likewise can raise questions regarding the growth of corn, the spawning of fish, and the habits of birds and other wild animals.

When farm life is studied, almost all areas of science have application and may be studied to the extent that is appropriate at the time. The farmer uses a great variety of machinery, and ordinarily today the farm is wired for electricity. The weather and climate are great factors in farming. The farmer's work is concerned with soil and rocks, with problems of erosion and flood control, with virtually all aspects of plant and animal life. Many farmers today follow scientific agricultural practices in the crops they raise and the livestock they maintain.

Because science is an important factor in our lives, having direct bearing upon our social conditions, our beliefs, our economic well-being, and our personal problems, an active science program has many implications for the social studies, and a close relationship should be developed in the school program.

MAINTAINING A BALANCED EMPHASIS AND DESIRABLE RELATIONSHIPS

Facts taught in isolation tend to lack meaning. A new fact may seem strange at first, but once its relationship to ideas already understood becomes clear, the new fact then seems to "make sense," suddenly becomes meaningful. A large share of meaning is in the relationship of one fact to another. Where meaningful relationships exist in learning situations, those relationships should be developed, not arbitrarily limited by traditional subject-matter boundaries or by a previously arranged daily schedule.

Complete integration of science with other aspects of the curriculum is possible and if well done has many advantages in that the natural relationships can be developed to their greatest extent. Some prefer to integrate science only with the social studies, with health, or with some other one area. Experience reveals, unfortunately, that integration is sometimes integration in name only, for one of the integrated areas may be neglected. Where science and social studies are combined, for example, and the teacher is more familiar with social studies, little science may be included. Although science is closely related to all areas, and those relationships should be developed, the entire program of science should not be incidental to other curricular areas. Somewhere in the program the emphasis should be reversed and placed on the science itself, with implications from other areas developed. For example, a social studies unit or a problem dealing with transportation and communication may involve science through the telegraph, the telephone, and other electrical devices, but the main emphasis is likely to be on the social studies. On the other hand, a science topic concerned with electricity and its applications also would have implications for both fields but would reverse the emphasis.

It should not be necessary to have a perfectly balanced program each day, or even each week. But over a longer span no essential area of the curriculum should be neglected.

Some of the most valuable contributions that an active science program can make to the elementary school curriculum come from situations which develop the worthwhile character traits of resourceful individuals in cooperative social circumstances. True scientific investigation in the school, as in the research laboratory, is a democratic process in which many individuals cooperate in the solution of common problems, and such problems ordinarily involve more than science.

STUDY GUIDE

1. How can science contribute to the reading program? How is science related to the language arts, the social studies, the health program, and other areas of the curriculum?
2. What are the advantages and the limitations of relating science to other subjects, such as the social studies or mathematics?
3. How should books be used in science?
4. At the library locate magazine articles you can review in class to show your classmates that useful ideas regarding the teaching of science can be found in professional magazines. Likewise review the reports of research in the teaching of elementary-school science.

6

The Materials of Instruction

For an effective program of science, adequate teaching materials are essential. Equipment, supplies, and community resources that are suitable for the purpose should be available and should be used when needed. A shortage of concrete teaching resources, as distinguished from books and other printed materials, is one of the most common problems that teachers face. All too frequently instruction is limited by a lack of resources or by failure to be aware of what could be used. Yet the materials needed to perform the experiments and other activities commonly recommended are neither difficult to obtain nor expensive. A large share of the supplies required can be gathered together at no cost at all; some items can be constructed or improvised. Other articles should be purchased. All should be on hand when the teaching situation requires their use. Collecting and organizing the essential supplies is a common and persistent problem of teaching. The solution of the problem is largely dependent upon knowing where to look for an answer.

INSTRUCTIONAL MATERIALS ARE INDISPENSABLE

The scientific method requires materials for investigation

From its inception modern science has stressed first-hand investigation, a process which requires that real materials be used. Reading and discussion alone are not enough.

The fundamental role of observation and experimentation is apparent in the origins of modern science. From the beginning modern science has been in conflict with authoritarian methods of learning. During the fifteenth century in Europe the new art of printing and the prosperity that came with increasing commerce made possible a revival of the ancient Greek and Latin writings. The classical writings were so much more scholarly than anything written during the Middle Ages that all statements made by the ancient authorities were thought to be fundamental truths. Eventually, however, some practical thinkers began to question the statements of the ancient philosophers. The most common story is one of the best examples. Heavy objects seem to fall faster than light objects, and accordingly the ancient philosopher Aristotle stated that a ten-pound weight would fall ten times as fast as a one-pound weight. Galileo, instead of merely accepting the authority of the famous Aristotle, dropped weights to see for himself how they would fall. He resorted to direct experiment rather than accept authority alone. Galileo, we are told, showed his associates at the university that unequal weights actually fall together, but the professors were only made angry and preferred to accept the classic authority rather than experimental evidence.

At a later date in Europe a great controversy raged between the experimentalists and the philosophers. Newton, by means of a prism, had separated a beam of sunlight into the colors of the rainbow. He also succeeded in recombining these colors to form the original white light, and thus was developed our present view that white light is composed of many colors. On the other hand, the European philosophers of that day, including Goethe, the German poet, assumed that white is pure, a view we still hold in a symbolic sense. Since white was assumed to be pure, Goethe reasoned that white light cannot be subdivided because a pure substance, being all one thing, cannot be separated. In such a manner Goethe's reasoning led him to the view that Newton's experimental approach was absurd. Because Goethe's intelligence is above question, the example is a good illustration of the difference in methods of solving problems. Since Goethe's time we have turned in many ways to experimental evidence for the solution of problems, but in teaching we often stress authority rather than evidence. A lack of resources for presenting evidence is a contributing factor.

Long ago Francis Bacon emphasized the necessity of using tangible materials to make direct investigations:

> Neither the naked hand nor the understanding left to itself can effect much. It is by instruments and helps that the work is done, which are as much wanted for the understanding as for the hand.[1]

[1] Francis Bacon, *Novum Organum*, quoted in Forest Ray Moulton and Justus J. Schifferes, *The Autobiography of Science,* Doubleday, Garden City, 1946, p. 119.

In scientific research when the cloud chamber, the Geiger counter, the cyclotron, and other instruments were developed, work with the atom was made possible. At an earlier date, the development of lenses and microscopes led to the discovery of minute organisms, and the knowledge gained thereby is now helping us to control diseases. In much the same way that the perfection of new instruments has helped in the acquisition of new understanding in the adult world of research, the use of suitable equipment in teaching children makes possible an insight that cannot be gained without it.

In our schools the cultural heritage of science should be transmitted to children in the stimulating spirit in which it was begun, rather than in an authoritarian manner — the very antithesis of true scientific investigation. Much as a man who vehemently denies that he is hot-tempered refutes his own words, we who teach science as so much formal content to be accepted on the authority of the textbook largely defeat our own purposes. The teacher should assist and guide the child in his natural tendency to investigate, so that he will acquire the means of understanding, will be challenged to experiment, and will experience the thrill of discovery. Suitable instructional materials are essential if children are to investigate in the true spirit of science.

Modern education requires tangible materials for instruction

It is common knowledge that abstractions are hard to understand, and teaching soon becomes abstract without objective materials. Experience indicates that real materials should be used, whether school supplies and equipment or the resources of the community. In some quarters science has the reputation of being a hard subject, even for adults, for it is taught as abstractions that are remote from everyday experience. Largely because of the difference in approach, fourth-grade children, for example, upon occasion have grasped some concepts that frequently trouble college students. Teachers visiting elementary classes where science is taught have often expressed amazement to see children dealing competently with facts which they found difficult in their own high school or college science studies and even yet may not understand.

Our knowledge of child development and the psychology of learning suggests that the use of suitable equipment and supplies is fundamental. Learning is an active process based upon the individual's own experience. Children have great curiosity about the immediate and the concrete; hence their educational experiences should be grounded in the present, but forward looking. The attention span of children is limited, but it is greater where interest is inherent and spontaneous, where there is variety within the larger undertaking. Learning

Fig. 23

Some useful teaching materials

results from the solution of meaningful problems which are challenging and real to the learner, and learning that is vivid and functional is retained longer. The more realistic the learning situation, the more learnings will be applied — transferred to real life situations.

The limitations of words. The advertising department of *Parade* magazine made a point dramatically when they asked three artists who had never seen an aardvark to draw a picture of one, based on a verbal description taken from the *Encyclopaedia Britannica:*

> The body is stout, with arched back; the limbs are short and stout, armed with strong, blunt claws; the ears long; and the tail thick at the base and tapering gradually. The elongated head is set on a short, thick neck, and at the extremity of the snout is a disc in which the nostrils open. The mouth is small and tubular, furnished with a long extensile tongue. A large individual measured 6 ft. 8 in. In colour it is pale sandy or yellow, the hair being scanty and allowing the skin to show.[2]

The results were surprising, and they clearly show the limitations of words,

[2] "Three Artists Couldn't Draw an Aardvark," *Educational Focus,* 20:16–17, September, 1949.

even for adults with a considerable background of experience. If the reader is unfamiliar with aardvarks, he may attempt a similar drawing himself before checking with the picture which follows (p. 150).

Words are useful, but words are not enough. The entire audio-visual aids movement is dedicated to the proposition that learning is facilitated by the use of sensory materials. In the broader meaning of the term, audio-visual materials are not restricted to pictures, but include all physical resources. In fact, the materials used in direct experiences, as in scientific investigations, are considered the most desirable and the most effective of all learning devices. Experience with real materials in real situations provides the substance from which abstractions are built and vicarious experiences are interpreted, regardless of the age or grade of the individuals involved.

In science particularly, instead of thinking of physical materials as aids which make reading and discussion intelligible, the teacher should reverse the emphasis. Reading and discussion should be the aids that make direct experience meaningful. Children should read to interpret the environment, rather than observe the environment to interpret the printed page. The distinction is significant and fundamental.

There is general agreement that some kind of direct experience with real materials and situations is essential for learning. Educators with no vested interest in science generally agree with science specialists regarding the necessity of suitable instructional facilities. The following may be cited as examples:

Gertrude Hildreth, an educational psychologist, has written:

> When not in school, children use an endless variety of equipment for their everyday activities. The typical back yard where active boys and girls congregate is a sort of laboratory for informal experimentation. At school, however, the resources for learning have been so largely restricted to textbooks that children have been cut off from the full range of materials they should have.[3]

The yearbook entitled *Learning and Instruction* stresses the necessity for experiences with concrete objects, especially in science, and then concludes that

> All major contemporary schools of experimental psychology have as a fundamental hypothesis the principle of learning through interaction of organism and environment.[4]

Caswell and Foshay, curriculum specialists, agree:

[3] Gertrude Hildreth, *Child Growth Through Education*, Ronald Press, New York, 1948, p. 259.
[4] *Learning and Instruction*, Forty-ninth Yearbook of the National Society for the Study of Education, Part I, distributed by University of Chicago Press, Chicago, 1950, p. 293.

Especially in dealing with the physical environment, a rich variety of instructional resources is essential.[5]

State study guides and courses of study, recognizing that the manner of learning is quite as fundamental as the content covered, uniformly advocate the use of objective materials in meaningful, active situations. Two examples are quoted here:

California: Any particular project, whether it deals with science or anything else, will fail in some measure if it is too narrow in scope or if the materials used are too limited to provide some activity for every child in the class. If a child has to wait days at a time for his turn to use tools, to care for animals or plants or equipment, or to be given an assignment of importance or responsibility, his interest and enthusiasm are sure to wane, no matter how intrinsically interesting and worthwhile the class project may be.[6]

Tennessee: One of the dangers in teaching elementary science is that too much time may be devoted to reading about things rather than to studying the things themselves.[7]

Virtually everyone agrees that reading and discussion alone are not adequate, yet all too frequently that is the basic pattern, largely because the essential resources are not at hand when needed. Because the facilities are not available, children in school commonly are not able to try even the activities suggested by their books, and soon the suggestions are passed by with no expectation of doing them, and the reading by that time has become remote from reality, remote from any purpose the child may have. In contrast, where needed resources are on hand, their presence can be a stimulus to the children and to the teacher as well, leading to an increasingly effective science program. Whereas it is true that the instructional materials available should not determine what is to be taught, all too frequently they do — as a limiting factor. Frequently teachers find otherwise desirable learning experiences impracticable because of a shortage of essential supplies and equipment.

Inadequate facilities a common problem. That teachers and school principals consider the lack of facilities one of the greatest obstacles to a really successful program of science is obvious from experience and is substantiated by studies of current practice.

[5] Hollis L. Caswell and A. Wellesley Foshay, *Education in the Elementary School,* American Book Co., New York, 1950, p. 179.

[6] California State Department of Education, *Science in the Elementary School,* Sacramento, 1945, p. 29.

[7] Tennessee State Department of Education, *A Science Program for Elementary Schools, Grades Four, Five and Six,* Nashville, 1944, p. 15.

Fig. 24

An aardvark

New York Zoological Society

Quaintance reported a survey of the problems facing teachers in Oregon, in which a lack of equipment was the problem most frequently reported:

Teachers regard the acquisition of equipment as their major problem in science teaching. Seventy per cent of teachers reported this as a problem, almost double the number reporting the next ranking problem. As a reason for units which their classes liked least, teachers reported lack of equipment as most serious.[8]

A committee for the New York State Association of Elementary School Principals, making a survey of science in the elementary schools of their state, reported the opinions of school principals regarding the difficulties found in their own schools:

The obstacles mentioned most frequently in all types of schools were lack of teacher education in science, lack of teacher interest, lack of equipment and materials, and lack of time in the day's program.[9]

A survey in Massachusetts, based on personal interviews with elementary-school teachers, was reported by Lammers:

The two obstacles most prominently mentioned as standing in the way of doing more about science in their classrooms were lack of time and lack of equipment. . . . several parts of the interview revealed that questions related to equipment

[8] Charles W. Quaintance, "Oregon Surveys Its Teaching of Elementary School Science," *Science Education,* 28:265–268, December, 1944.
[9] New York State Association of Elementary School Principals, *Science for Our Children,* Bulletin XII, Jan., 1949, distributed by Charles E. Flinn, 1152 Harrison Street, Watertown, New York, p. 40.

often brought answers that were full of rationalization. Very few classrooms were found to possess any science equipment supplied by the school system. Whatever else may be said concerning this problem, the fact remains that the schools in this study were not yet providing science supplies as a regular function.[10]

The responses of in-service elementary-school teachers in certain childhood-education classes at Teachers College, Columbia University, indicated that, in the opinions of the teachers, problems involving supplies and equipment were the most common obstacles to initiating or improving their work in science. The most common difficulty was a lack of suitable teaching materials. The teachers surveyed represented all grade levels and were from 25 states and the District of Columbia, approximately 25 per cent being from the state in which the survey was made; thus there is no indication that the problems of equipment and supplies are regional or are confined to any particular grade level of the elementary school.[11]

A study based on interviews with elementary-school teachers in Connecticut was summarized and interpreted in part as follows:

> All the teachers interviewed consider science appropriate for elementary-school work; and all the comments regarding the effect of using concrete materials were positive. . . . Fifty-eight per cent . . . reported a lack of concrete teaching materials . . . the problem most frequently reported. . . . Thirty-eight per cent reported having to purchase their own materials or do without. According to the reports, considerable science was taught . . . yet few concrete materials were used for instruction. A limited number of excursions were conducted, and good use seems to be made of children's contributions. More materials would be used, the responses indicate, if the materials were on hand, easily available. . . .
>
> For the teachers interviewed, at least, it seems evident, their science programs could be moved forward, perhaps markedly so, by providing them with adequate instructional materials to further their work, and by helping them to take advantage of resources already available.[12]

In a survey of Florida teachers in 1954, Piltz likewise found that the physical facilities were the most commonly recognized source of difficulties in elementary-school science.[13] A year later, in a study by William D. Chamberlain,

[10] Theresa J. Lammers, "One Hundred Interviews with Elementary School Teachers Concerning Science Education," *Science Education*, 33:292–295, October, 1949.

[11] Clark Hubler, "Teaching Materials for Elementary-School Science," *Science Education*, 34:218–24, October, 1950.

[12] *Ibid.*

[13] Albert Piltz, *An Investigation of Teacher-Recognized Difficulties Encountered in the Teaching of Science in the Elementary Schools of Florida*, Ed. D. thesis, 1954, University of Florida, Gainesville.

Fig. 25

Good use should be made of commonplace community resources, such as the fungus on the stump shown here.

teachers from forty communities in thirteen states indicated that their most persistent problems in elementary science were concerned with storage space and the acquisition of science equipment.[14]

There is substantial agreement that instructional materials are necessary and that the present facilities are often inadequate. If the quality and extent of science teaching in elementary schools is to be improved, the problems concerned with teaching resources must be solved. Sufficient teaching materials must be obtained and used.

The values derived through use of tangible resources. Adequate instructional materials are essential if the objectives of education in science are to be attained. Not only are *concepts* based upon direct experience, but the meanings gained are more likely to function in the lives of the individuals concerned when those meanings have been learned in functional circumstances. As everyone knows, the best place to learn how to swim is in the water — the water being indispensable regardless of the skill and resourcefulness of the teacher. Other values of science education are equally dependent upon active investigation with real materials and resources. Coordination and *skill* come from working with the hands. The extent to which *interest* is dependent upon suitable

[14] William D. Chamberlain, *Development and Status of Teacher Education in the Field of Science for the Elementary School*, 1955, Wayne University, Detroit, Michigan.

resources is apparent in the way children respond when tangible resources are used. An *appreciation* of science and of the world about us likewise can be a valuable product of work conducted in stimulating circumstances. Observation and experimentation are fundamental in the scientific method. It is futile to commend the *scientific attitudes* and ways of working and yet deny them in practice. Suitable materials for observation and experimentation are a basic requirement of any science program designed to achieve the commonly accepted objectives.

In a study of children's contributions in science, Katherine Hill reported:

> It was found that more responses were made which could be classified as representing the objectives Responsibility and Cooperation, Initiative, Application of Experience, and Skills when experimental materials were more often being used by children.[15]

The use of experimental materials contributes directly to the attainment of many broad values esteemed in education. Emphasis is shifted from routine subject-matter to functional situations in which the subject-matter learned is greater in amount and quality. Children in an active situation become responsible group members, cooperating, solving problems, developing mature self-discipline. Motivation becomes inherent in the work, and readiness for learning moral, social, and emotional values, as well as facts and skills, is a natural consequence. While a child is actively investigating, the teacher can observe his behavior in a way that makes guidance effective. Where children work together with experimental materials, the child's purpose falls more nearly in line with that of the teacher. Opportunity is provided for leadership and the development of individual talents; creativity is stimulated and initiative encouraged, and the values of a democratic atmosphere can be realized. In short, to provide a wholesome learning situation in accord with the recommendations of our educational literature, practical teaching resources are indispensable.

THE AVAILABLE RESOURCES

Many of the experimental materials needed for science can be obtained directly from the environment being studied. Some can be brought to school by the children, some by the teacher. Arrangements should be made so that many of the most commonly used articles will be on hand before the need arises, just as chalk, paper, books, and other staple items are stocked in anticipation of their use. Because experimentation is essential in science, gathering

[15] Katherine Elizabeth Hill, *Children's Contributions in Science Discussions,* Bureau of Publications, Teachers College, Columbia University, New York, 1947, p. 82.

Fig. 26

The community provides many resources that can be used in science.

Harriet Weil

and organizing the needed facilities is a fundamental step. Uncertainty regarding what to obtain is a problem, but expense is not a serious obstacle, for the materials commonly recommended are not expensive; many of the items cost nothing at all. For some articles, such as tin cans and twine, it is but a matter of gathering them and finding a way to store them. Some articles can be constructed or improvised; others will have to be purchased. Where the budget is a limitation, much can still be done to provide the resources needed. Foresight and the desire to have adequate facilities are the principal ingredients of success.

Selecting the needed materials

What facilities are required for instruction in science will depend upon what is to be taught and how it is to be taught. That is, to teach the principles of magnetism, magnets must be available. To demonstrate the field about a magnet by sprinkling iron filings onto a glass plate or a sheet of cardboard which is lying upon the magnet, a magnet, iron filings, and either a sheet of glass or of cardboard must be on hand. However, if a magnetic field is to be observed by moving a pocket compass about near a magnet and noticing the direction of the needle, the pocket compass and magnet are required. If both methods are to be used, and a variety of means is desirable, then all the items named should be available. A great many articles have numerous possible uses. But in any case, the list of necessary materials will be determined by the plans for instruction.

If the teaching plans are designed to follow a single text or course of study, a tally can be made of the materials required for the experiments and other activities recommended by the book or course of study. The task is even more simple than that, for most of the science textbook publishers have prepared a list of the materials needed and either have included the list in the teacher's manual or have printed the list on a separate sheet, which can be obtained by writing to the publisher. Limiting instruction to a single text, however, gives little opportunity for the exercise of student initiative and makes little provision for the flexibility that is essential to a vital program adjusted to the needs of particular children.

It has become axiomatic in elementary-school science that complex, highly technical equipment is seldom necessary or even desirable. Rocks, caterpillars, and weed seed, for example, owe much of their value as resources to their familiarity in the child's surroundings. A glass or old mayonnaise jar costs nothing and may be preferable to a beaker or a test tube, unless the experiment requires heating. It is easy to dismiss the action of complex equipment as some-what mysterious and remote from everyday realities. But the same phenome-non demonstrated with familiar resources is apt to seem remarkable and fascinating. Four dry cells in series attached to pencil leads and placed in salt water will produce bubbles of hydrogen and oxygen, demonstrating that water is made of these two elements. With more elaborate equipment the gases can be collected, their quantities determined, and their identity established — but for elementary work the simple apparatus is preferable, even if the other is available. Complex equipment may bring confusion instead of making the principles involved obvious to the child. Whatever apparatus is selected should be clearly suited to its purpose and preferably adaptable to the child's own ideas, rather than designed for operation in a single prearranged manner. Not only should the facilities be familiar, simple, and adaptable, but, like other equipment for children, they should be sturdy and safe enough for a child's own use.

Familiar resources in and about the school

Long excursions involving considerable transportation have been given much publicity, but not all good trips are so extensive. In the immediate vicinity of the school there usually are trees, shrubbery, and other plant life that can be inspected in connection with a study of plant growth. On foot or by means of the city transportation a pond or quiet stream may be within reach. With a dip net or improvised equipment pond life may be obtained to stock an aquarium. Zoos and museums are within reach of many schools and can be used extensively. The weathering of rock can often be observed along the bank of a nearby stream or in a road cut where the bedrock is exposed, and on the playground itself erosion may be evident where water has worn small gullies. In connection with a study of electricity, the telephone exchange or power house may be within reach, or a transformer can be observed on a nearby pole. Wires can be seen leading into the school building, and with the janitor's help the fuse box inside may be inspected and the electric switch noted. There is probably an electric motor in the building, and a variety of materials, such as old light bulbs, packing cases or other lumber, wire, nails, and window glass often can be obtained from the janitor. One class even got a rabbit from the janitor, and he built a cage for it too!

If there is a cafeteria in the building, it may be possible to get food scraps for animals, beans for seed, and a plentiful supply of tin cans, jars, and bottles. For chemical experiments starch, sugar, and baking powder also can be obtained from the cafeteria. A sink or stove somewhere in the building may be available on occasions, and there may be scales for weighing children that can be used for other purposes as well. There is a pulley on the flagpole, and there is always some kind of weather to be observed outside.

The usual classroom equipment and supplies can serve many purposes in science. For demonstrating the movement of the earth, moon, and sun, the globe already used for geography may be suitable, or balls from the playground can be used. An electric lamp will serve to represent the sun. Tools, such as hammer, pliers, tinner's snips, screw driver, and saw may be available in the building, and these can be used for constructing telegraph sets, water wheels, and other apparatus. Modeling clay, if available, can be used to model various kinds of dinosaurs or to illustrate the folding of rocks. A sand table can be arranged to show how animals live, or how they protect themselves, how they get food, and how they are adapted to live in certain places. Similar relationships can be portrayed on murals with the usual art materials. The thermostat on the wall will show unequal expansion of metals, if the janitor can be persuaded to remove the cover and point out the bimetal bar. Made of two different metals, when one expands or contracts more than the other the bar will bend and thus make an electrical contact, or by pulling away it will shut off the current. If there is no thermostat, at least there are windows to illustrate the circulation of air in a room. A beam of sunlight or the light from a projection lantern can be used in optical experiments. A seesaw on the playgrounds will illustrate some principles of the lever, and a swing is one form of pendulum. Other resources about the school will become apparent as the teacher and children learn to look for them, but those already mentioned are enough to illustrate some of the possibilities.

Borrowing from the high school

Borrowing is frequently suggested as a means of obtaining needed resources, but there are numerous difficulties in such a solution to the problem of supplies. The usual suggestion is to borrow from the high school, but the equipment suitable for high schools often is not the equipment most suitable for younger children. The equipment at the high school is intended for high-school use. For elementary schools to use the same articles is likely to result in some duplication of instruction and to lessen the subsequent usefulness of these articles in the high school. The schools are on separate budgets. The high-school teacher will have but a limited supply, though it may seem bountiful to the harassed elementary teacher. High-school science teachers often have learned to husband carefully their own limited resources, and the unexpected demands of an elementary school may deprive the high-school classes of experimental materials. It may be that just enough has been ordered for the high school and to share with the elementary will mean that the high school must do without needed chemicals or without some piece of apparatus that has been damaged. Owing to some unfortunate previous experience the secondary-school teacher may be reluctant to lend his equipment. Accordingly, the elementary teacher's request may be embarrassing to both people.

The secondary-school teacher may be meticulous in caring for equipment and may require high standards of students, yet it may seem to him that borrowed equipment invariably receives rough treatment. He may fear that the equipment will be away just when a need for it arises. Whatever the explanation, reluctance to lend equipment is common — and understandable. Borrowing science materials frequently involves more difficulties than are at first apparent.

In spite of the inherent difficulties, most people are congenial enough to be cooperative, and to promote science some people will aid the elementary schools in any way possible. But frequent borrowing is troublesome and time consuming for everyone. To prevent damage to borrowed equipment, the teacher may have to place serious restrictions on the use of it, restrictions that can hamper the work of the class. In emergencies or unusual circumstances borrowing may be necessary, but as a general policy the elementary school should expect to supply its own experimental materials.

Using audio-visual aids

All the equipment in science may be considered audio-visual aids. Films and slides, when available, help to make concepts real to children, and are especially valuable when they furnish observations which cannot be provided through still more direct experience. Often both films and direct experience can be used to advantage. For example, a class might observe a film showing how wild animals care for their young and at another time visit a zoo, farm, chick hatchery, or fish hatchery as a continuation of the study. In addition, puppies, kittens, a hen and chicks, or other pets may be brought to school for observation. Films and slides help to broaden the experiences of children and develop insights that extend beyond the immediate surroundings.

In science, as in other areas of the curriculum, full use should be made of the bulletin board. Suitable clippings and photographs from newspapers and magazines may be posted. In addition, children can profitably construct posters of their own. Drawings and posters should be made directly from the child's own observations, expressing his own ideas, not copied from a book. Direct copying seldom has much value. There are many situations in which a picture on the bulletin board is useful. Charts and graphs also are helpful. A line graph showing the effects of a diet experiment on the weights of laboratory rats was a prominent feature of the work of one class.

A child's mind usually follows his eyes, and to promote a discussion it may be helpful to have some appropriate article on which to focus attention. A soft rock on the verge of crumbling will stimulate a discussion of weathering. Stones of contrasting texture can be used to raise questions regarding the way rocks are formed. The stimulus for a lively discussion of animal life can be provided by having children gather about the cage of some animal. In addition to illustrating what is meant by annular rings, a segment cut from the limb of a tree or bush will help to promote a discussion of plant growth. The real object is even better than a picture as a visual aid.

Free or inexpensive commercial teaching aids

Some large corporations distribute pamphlets, films, and other instructional materials intended for school use. Ordinarily the materials can be obtained by writing directly to the organization concerned and are supplied to teachers at little or no cost. Various state and federal agencies also produce such materials. Federal publications may be secured from the Superintendent of Documents, Washington 25, D.C. Materials currently available are listed in each issue of the *NEA Journal* and other educational magazines. Many of the pictures, maps, and charts are excellent for bulletin-board use, and much of the reading matter may be helpful as supplementary resources. The material may be more up-to-date than the text or library books on hand, and it may supply intimate glimpses of industry, for instance, which can be obtained in no other way. Being free or inexpensive, the publications may be an asset where the school budget for books is inadequate.

Nevertheless, free materials are apt to have some very decided weaknesses. Advertising material is likely to be designed more to promote sales than to promote instruction, and much of it is too advanced for elementary-school use. The resources used in a classroom have great influence on what is taught. Some free materials tend to divert the work of the class from the goals of education to the purposes of the advertising. Government materials and some commercial publications, however, are free of any seriously conflicting motive. Where a life-insurance company, for example, distributes information designed to increase the span of life, the commercial motive is in accord with the educational objectives. Free materials may be either highly accurate or biased and exaggerated; they may be well organized or obscure. Of great importance is the question of adaptability: Can the materials be used flexibly, or must every child merely follow routine directions? A pamphlet suitable for one class or one child may not be appropriate for children of other ages, abilities, or backgrounds, and their suitability also depends upon how the material is used. The free materials most apt to be inflexible and poorly adapted to the circumstances are the commercially prepared teaching plans and outlines. Nevertheless, a teacher who is aware of the limitations still can find much free material that is useful.

The designation of teaching materials as *inexpensive* is sometimes misleading. A typical science text of twelve chapters, priced at perhaps $1.80, costs but 15¢ per chapter, and each chapter may include considerably more and better information than can be obtained in some advertising material at a comparable price when postage is included. There is a great and ever-changing variety of advertising materials, and a teacher must learn to judge which are most likely to have instructional value.

Selecting books

If the science work is to be an active program of investigation, books should be useful on that basis, rather than selected simply for reading and discussion. A narrative form, suitable for reading lessons, is an obstacle to reference use, since it is difficult to locate desired information without reading the entire story from beginning to end. The index and table of contents should be such that the children themselves can learn to locate readily the information they seek. The books selected should be those which will help to interpret familiar situations and should suggest investigations for the children, with many observations and experiments that will prove worthwhile.

For their investigations children will need a variety of books to give information relevant to the multitude of questions that will arise. In contrast to a single text, a variety of books can deal with many topics and can give various points of view, so that each child who reads can find something to tell that no one else has read. The various books should be suitable for a range of reading abilities. To obtain the needed variety of books dealing with all areas of the environment, it may be necessary to use some books in spite of their faults — because of their virtues.

So that scientific attitudes can be developed, fantasy in books should be avoided — no pixies or elves performing experiments, and no animals engaged in conversation. Books should avoid an authoritarian treatment in which some one character serves as the source of all information. The organization, as revealed in the table of contents, should stress meanings rather than encyclopedic information: "How Birds Fly," is preferable to "Blue Jays" as a topic heading. To develop and convey ideas, straightforward descriptions and explanations are preferable to any kind of artificial device.

The information presented should be correct, of course, and the whole book should be clearly and attractively illustrated, easy to read yet challenging. A really attractive book will appeal to the teacher as well as to the children, but if possible it would be helpful to place a copy on a convenient table and note the children's reactions to the book.

Books serve various purposes. In addition to those science books that children use as aids to their investigations, books of fiction with realistic science backgrounds serve a worthwhile purpose. Biographies and historical or contemporary accounts of scientists at work serve to broaden the child's outlook and may be inspirational as well as entertaining.

Contributions of the children and the teacher

The practice of encouraging children to bring articles from their homes to the school has many educational merits. The child who makes the contribution tends to identify himself with the article, and his interest is more intense. Awareness of the environment is developed when the child is constantly looking for something to bring. The child who brings something to school knows where the object came from and has some idea of its relationship to the surroundings. Bringing things to class gives the child an opportunity to share, places him in rapport with the group; and what he brings voluntarily is likely to be what he is capable of appreciating. The child is actively participating, and his participation gives the teacher some indication of how he feels and what he is thinking. Children profit by the opportunity to take responsibility,

Fig. 27

Some of the needed materials can be obtained by the children.

to plan and carry out an activity. The child's activity provides a contact with the home, and the parents may become interested. The practice also has some merit in that it provides a source of needed materials, materials which in many cases would be obtainable in no other way.

For children to participate by bringing articles of interest to school is excellent experience. However, to depend upon children's contributions as the basic source of supplies is another matter. Unless there are some supplies on hand, there is invariably some delay caused by waiting for the materials with which to work. Should the child forget or be unable to bring what he had intended, the delay may become an indefinite postponement of the planned undertakings. If the teacher must ask children to bring materials, even on a voluntary basis, the children may be insistent and inconsiderate in relaying the requests to their parents, and the results can be very poor public relations. Circumstances may be such that the busy parents will find it difficult to meet the child's demands. Perhaps a search must be made to locate the needed article, or a special trip to town may be necessary to purchase it. Even if already on hand, a pyrex dish from the home, for example, may be considerably more expensive and less suitable than a pyrex beaker or test tube purchased by the school. When Father learns that his tools have gone to school just when he needs them, and he visualizes the rough treatment they probably will receive, he may not be sympathetic. A distinction can be made between articles that have monetary value and those that do not. Children should be encouraged to bring stones, weed seed, tin cans, and similar articles that are useful, but cost nothing. Dry cells, copper wire, and adhesive tape cost money, and ordinarily they should be supplied by the school. Articles brought to school by the children serve a worthwhile purpose, but are not adequate to equip a classroom.

The teacher as well as the children can help to gather science materials, and the process of collecting useful objects can be as fascinating as any hobby. The teacher may find a cocoon attached to a low-hanging branch, or she may have a discarded alarm clock that would be useful in science. Scraps of metal, bits of twine, and discarded wooden boxes are all collector's items for the science program. The school budget, however, should make adequate provision for the commercial materials needed for science. If essential supplies must be bought at the teacher's own expense, an unjustified strain is placed on the teacher's own finances, and the amount obtainable is severely limited. Furthermore, last-minute shopping wastes time. Many hours can be lost in urgent pursuit of small items the cost of which may be less than the bus fares spent on trips to town to hunt for them. It is more economical in both time and money for the schools to obtain needed supplies in advance and have them available for classes when needed.

The conscientious teacher may decide to buy some items on an emergency basis, since no one can anticipate all the needs that may arise. But last-minute searching for teaching materials, or dependence on the articles that children can bring should not be considered a desirable means of implementing the science program. An increasing number of school systems are now stocking science materials in anticipation of use, and thus are simplifying the problem of obtaining and using elementary science materials.

Equipment and supplies furnished by the schools are not intended to replace the voluntary contributions of children, nor will they do so as long as contributions are welcomed. There always will be articles of interest for children to bring, articles not likely to be found in any supply room — a caterpillar taken off a bush near home, a pebble from the beach, or a new toy that comes on Christmas. An article that a child finds is part of his own experience and consequently never could be a mere duplication of similar materials from the school. His magnet is stronger than the one at school, a different shape — or just the fact that one is his own will make it different, set it apart. A good supply at school will stimulate interest and result in more contributions, not fewer. There need be no question of either using children's contributions or doing without them in favor of school supplies; for each source will serve its own purpose and supplement the other.

EQUIPMENT CAN BE CONSTRUCTED
OR IMPROVISED

Much of the equipment needed for work with children in science can be constructed or improvised in the classroom by the children and the teacher as the occasion demands. In some cases the construction of equipment may be undertaken merely to obtain the equipment. But often the construction can provide a learning opportunity, a way of stressing desired meanings. The child who constructs his own telegraph set out of scrap wood, a tin can, nails, and copper wire is likely to gain some insights that another child will overlook while merely using a commercial set. A device that the child himself has prepared out of familiar materials may have more significance in terms of everyday experience than a complex piece of commercial apparatus. The ball-and-ring apparatus that a child has prepared out of a large ball bearing and whatever wire he could find can be used to show that any kind of metal will expand when heated. The implications are broader when puffed rice is substituted for the traditional pith balls in static experiments, or if a toy balloon is used in addition to a commercial rubber rod, for static phenomena are not limited to laboratory equipment. When children select their own models to represent the sun, earth, and moon, they are more likely to realize the limitations of the models, and they will better understand what each represents than if they had used ready-made apparatus. The child who constructs an ant nest must learn how ants live in order to provide what is needed. Considerable reference work may be necessary while the construction work is in the planning stage. Constructing apparatus can be one means of learning facts in functional circumstances.

Ordinarily the device that a child prepares himself not only is better understood but is used with greater enthusiasm. The cage he builds is his own cage. Constructing the cage can be a creative process that brings the child considerable satisfaction. If the class is studying animals, the cage may be a real contribution to the group undertaking, and the construction of it can be one way of learning how to cooperate in a common effort. Building equipment can help to develop manual skills, skills that will be useful in countless instances. The activity helps to provide a physical basis for effective learning.

Although the construction of needed facilities may be a profitable experience in some situations, at other times it may be wiser to use ready-made equipment, rather than devote time to building what is needed. Equipment prepared by children may not be well built, and if a good product is required, purchasing the equipment is advisable. If the construction skills are beyond the child's ability, frustration is likely to result. In such cases the construction work may prove to be an obstacle to learning instead of the means of learning as intended.

The necessity of gathering materials and constructing needed facilities may delay the desired undertaking. If a hutch must be constructed before a rabbit can be brought to school, the work may be worthwhile but the opportunity to obtain such an animal for observation may be lost by the time the hutch is ready. The additional work of constructing a cage may require more time than can be spared from other studies. If cages must be constructed before a diet experiment can be undertaken with laboratory animals, the construction may become the real undertaking, rather than the experiment; thus the necessity for construction may divert a class from its avowed purpose.

There are exceptions, but ordinarily it is better not to preserve the work of previous classes for later ones to use. If the work was profitable for one, it should be worthwhile for the others also to prepare their own materials. If the teacher must do the work of building equipment, the decision to do so is usually based on necessity rather than policy, but here again there are exceptions. Something that the teacher prepares may be better adapted to the circumstances than any commercial article could be. In any case, if equipment is to be constructed, the tools and building materials must be available. Wire, nails, glass, and lumber are some of the common materials needed for building cages, dip nets, telegraph sets, and similar devices.

A few suggestions for constructing apparatus

Animal cages. Cages for animals can be constructed by elementary-school children. A good cage 18 inches square and 12 inches high, suitable for small animals, such as hamsters, laboratory rats, and guinea pigs, can be built from

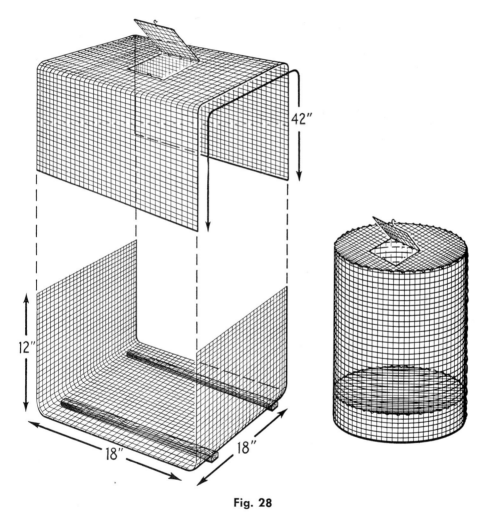

Fig. 28

Suitable cages can be constructed.

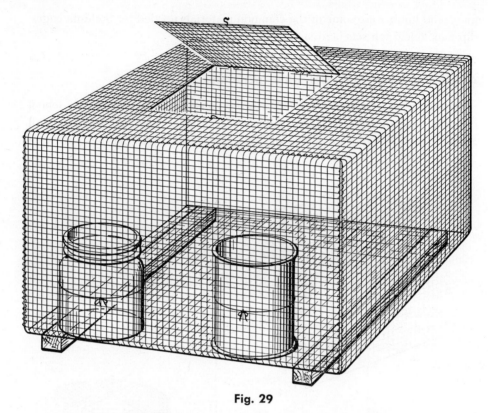

Fig. 29

A can for food and a jar for water may be wired to one
side of the cage.

two pieces of half-inch wire mesh, purchased at a hardware store. Each piece
should be 18 by 42 inches; thus both can be cut from a roll of wire 3 feet wide.
Using a board to form straight lines across each piece, 12 inches from each end,
bend the ends upward at right angles to form two U-shaped sections. One
section will form the bottom and two sides, and the other section can be inverted and fitted into the first, forming the top and remaining two sides of the
cage. A single strand of iron wire can be used to lace the sections together.
They can also be held by pressing the cut edges of one section through the
mesh of the adjoining one and then bending the ends back to hold the two
together — which also will protect children from the sharp points of wire.
Pliers will be needed for bending the ends. Before fitting the two sections
together to form the cage, attach two narrow strips of wood with staples to the
bottom of the cage so that the bottom will not touch the floor, and the cage will

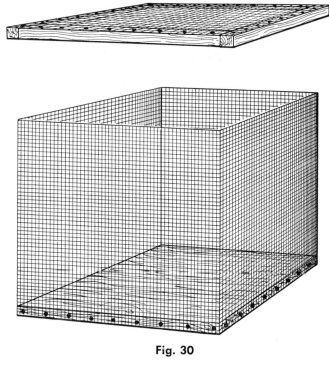

Fig. 30

A cage for insects can be made by tacking wire screen to
a wooden base.

be easy to clean. A simple way to build a door is to cut a square hole in the top, bend the cut edges back for safety, and place a somewhat wider section of wire over the hole. One edge of the cover may be wired loosely to the cage, forming a hinge. A wire hook can be fashioned for the opposite edge.

To keep the cage clean, all that need be done is to lift the cage and slip a sheet of newspaper under it, removing the old sheet and the droppings that have accumulated. So that the cage will be easy to care for, no litter should be placed inside the cage, except when an animal is about to bear young, at which time she will need cloth, paper, or something similar with which to build a nest. Lime or baking soda can be dusted onto the bottom of the cage to destroy odors. So that no damage will be done to table tops or the floor, it is wise to place a metal tray, or perhaps linoleum, beneath the cage. A simple way to supply food and water is to wire a tin can and a glass jar to the sides of the cage, each deep enough that the contents will not be spilled, yet of such a shape that the animals can reach the food and water.

Fig. 31

Two sheets of glass with strips of wood between them can be bound with tape to form an ant nest. Cotton can be used to close the opening after the ants have been added.

Cages for animals of any size can be constructed in the same manner. Quarter-inch wire mesh is available for smaller animals, and chicken wire can be used for larger ones. Another method of building a cage is to construct a wooden frame and attach the wire inside, thus preventing the animals from gnawing the wood. A third method is to roll the wire into a cylinder of convenient size and fit a top of wire, wood, or a round metal pan. For easy cleaning the bottom should be of wire mesh and should be attached an inch or so above the base of the cylinder. If the top is made removable it can substitute for a door.

An ant nest. An observation nest for ants can be purchased, but such a nest can be constructed in a number of ways. Perhaps the most simple is to use a fruit jar into which the ants and dirt, eggs, and larvae from a nearby ant hill can be placed with a trowel. A block of wood in the center of the jar will keep the animals near the glass surface, convenient for observation. The neck of the jar can be filled with cotton or covered with cloth to admit air without allowing the ants to escape. As an added precaution the fruit jar may be set in a pan and surrounded by a moat of water. When not being observed, the ants should be in darkness; an inverted tin can, preferably painted black inside and with a few small holes punched for ventilation, will serve as a convenient cover.

Another form of nest can be made from two sheets of window glass separated by narrow strips of wood and held together with adhesive tape. One edge can be left partially open for inserting the dirt, ants, and food, then closed with cotton. Molasses spread between the folds of a paper towel — so that the ants will not get caught in it — will serve as a source of food, and a bit of damp towel will be a satisfactory supply of water.

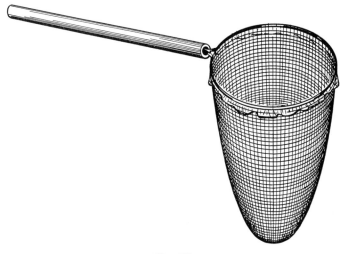

Fig. 32

A dip net can be made from heavy wire, a broom handle, and
fine-meshed netting or porous cloth.

A dip net. To construct a dip net, a cloth flour sack or other porous cloth can
be stitched to a loop of heavy wire which has been bent like a double question
mark and attached to the end of a broomstick. The loop can be shaped by
bending it about the base of a wastebasket or other cylindrical object, and the
ends can be wired to the broom handle — or, better yet, if a hole is bored into
the end of the handle the wires can be pressed into it.

A bird feeder. A device to attract birds for convenient observation can be
made from a board approximately 6 inches wide and 7 feet long. Two pieces
each 16 inches long should be cut from the board, and two other pieces should
be cut of a length equal to the width of the board. With the longer pieces
parallel and a 2-inch space between them, the short lengths should be nailed
across the butt ends of the longer ones to form the sides of a narrow box with
the ends flush on one side and projecting on the other. Another piece from the
same board may be cut of a length equal to the total length of the frame already
constructed and then nailed to the frame to serve as the bottom of the box.
Still another length may be cut from the board, this one about 2 inches longer
than the last. It will serve as a lid for the box and may be attached at the back
— the flush side — with hinges. The extra length will provide an overhanging
roof to give protection from rain. Strips of leather cut from an old shoe can be
used for hinges.

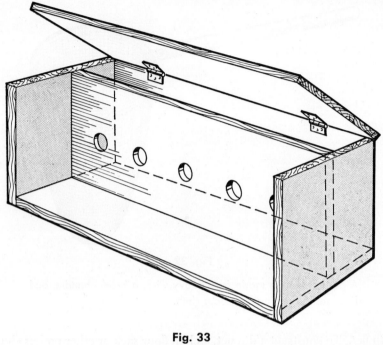

Fig. 33

A bird feeder

In effect, a box with one side recessed will have been constructed. Holes
may now be drilled in the recessed side, as in Fig. 33 (or they could have been
drilled in the board before the box was nailed together). The size of the hole
will determine how large a bird can use the feeder. When the lid is lifted, food
can be placed inside, and from the sheltered platform birds can reach through
the holes to obtain their food. Small holes drilled in the botton of the feeder,
near each end, will provide drainage. The feeding device may be mounted
somewhere outside the classroom window, preferably in a sunny location
sheltered from the wind, and accessible from the window or the ground — so
that food can be added and the hopper cleaned occasionally. The device may
be mounted on a post, a tree, or the side of the building. A few evergreen
branches, or other screen, between the feeder and the window will help to
attract timid birds. Paint will improve the appearance of the feeder.

The children may experiment to see what foods attract the different kinds of
birds. Suet, grain and nuts, fruits and vegetables, bread crumbs and table
scraps are commonly recommended.

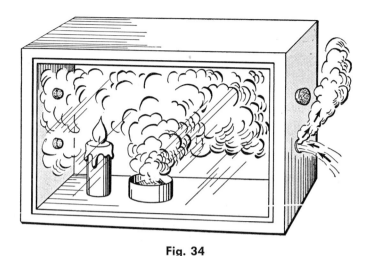

Fig. 34

A ventilation box

A modest but reasonably satisfactory feeding device can be made from a wooden chalk box with a tight lid. Holes should be bored in each side, and the box may be nailed to a board to provide a platform.

A ventilation box. To demonstrate how air circulates in a room, a ventilation box can be constructed. A tightly fitting box, approximately as large as an apple box, may be selected and made airtight with putty or weather stripping. When the box is inverted, the open top should fit tightly against the surface of the table to prevent unwanted drafts. Weather stripping tacked along the edge will help. A large rectangular hole should be cut in one side of the box and covered with a sheet of window glass slightly larger than the hole. The glass can be held in place with adhesive tape along the edges. With a smudge pot inside and a candle for additional heat, the smoke will reveal how the air circulates inside the box.

A coffee can will serve as a smudge pot, and the smudge can be paper towels or newspapers sprinkled lightly with water some hours earlier and thus slightly damp. Paper that is dry will burn freely, or if it is too damp will not burn at all. Paper towels from the wastebasket may be suitable. Paper soaked in ammonium chloride dissolved in water, when dry, will produce smoke with little difficulty.

Viewed through the glass front, smoke will be seen rising above the source of heat, a candle, and circulating to settle where the air becomes cooler. If two holes are bored in each end of the box, one above the other and spaced well apart, the holes can be used to represent windows opened at top and bottom, and the effect of proper and improper ventilation can be graphically shown.

If both the lid and the bottom of a large tin can are removed with a can opener and the side then cut vertically with tinner's snips, a rectangular sheet of metal is obtained. To reduce fire hazard, the top of the ventilation box, above the candle flame, may be lined with such metal or with asbestos.

Just as windows may be closed at the top or the bottom, or both, the openings in the ventilation box may be stoppered, or a sheet of metal may be tacked over each opening; and if but one nail is used, the cover can be slipped back and forth to change the manner of ventilation.

Additional suggestions. Further construction activities include the making of electrical equipment, weather instruments, and various kinds of models. Most such articles, however, are not kept on hand as equipment, since their value is associated more with the construction than with the subsequent use of the product. Therefore directions for the construction and use of such devices as an electric buzzer, a rain gauge, and a water wheel or turbine are given in the chapters which follow.

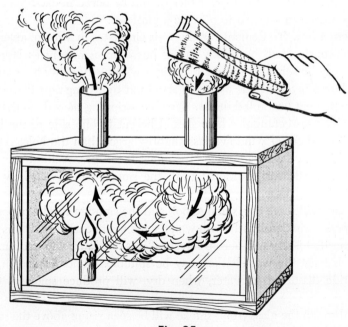

Fig. 35

A convection box

Improvising needed facilities

A convection box. A convection box can be contrived from an aquarium by placing a tightly-fitting cover over the aquarium, cutting two holes some distance apart in the cover, and placing a lamp chimney above each hole. Tin cans with both ends removed will serve as chimneys. A slightly damp paper towel in a tight roll will serve as a smudge to make the circulation visible.

An old aquarium which can no longer hold water may be quite satisfactory for use as a convection box. If no aquarium is available, four sheets of glass can be taped together to form the sides of a rectangular box. With a suitable cover and lamp chimneys added, the circulation of air can be demonstrated.

A convection box similar to the ventilation box previously described also can be made, except that two holes should be bored in the top rather than in the ends of the box, and a lamp chimney should be placed over each opening. A convection box simply shows that warm air rises and cool air sinks. A candle placed beneath one chimney will heat the air at that point. A smudge, a bit of cotton, or other lint held above each chimney will show the direction of air movement.

Aquarium and terrarium tanks. Aquarium tanks are expensive, and if funds are limited a dish pan will provide a substitute, though not as attractive in appearance. The appearance will be improved, however, if the container is rimmed with butcher paper to which an appropriate design has been applied.

A terrarium is used to represent a land surface, and so one can be assembled in a commercial aquarium which is no longer watertight. Wide-mouthed gallon jars ordinarily can be obtained from the school lunchroom or from a local restaurant. Such an empty jar laid on its side can be used to build a small but otherwise adequate terrarium. A number of such jars can be used to represent contrasting environments. The small size also will permit a number of individuals or groups to have separate terraria in the limited space of a classroom.

Ball and ring apparatus. To demonstrate expansion with heat, a ball and ring may be purchased or a substitute devised. If a metal ball, a round stone, or even a large marble can be obtained, bend one end of a thick wire into a loop just small enough that the ball will not quite fall through the loop. When the loop is heated, it will expand enough for the ball to fall through. When the wire is cooled, perhaps by immersion in water, the loop will again hold the ball or stone.

A balance. For comparing weights, a balance can be fashioned from simple

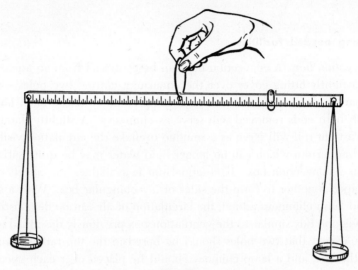

Fig. 36

A satisfactory balance can be improvised from a yardstick
and the lids of two jars.

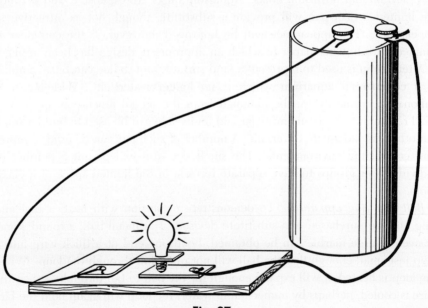

Fig. 37

An improvised lamp socket

materials. Holes may be bored an inch from each end of a yardstick and also at the center of the yardstick. The lids of two jars will serve as pans; the pans should be suspended from the ends of the yardstick by cords, three cords to each pan. With three holes punched at equal distances in the rims of the lids, the cords may be slipped through the holes and then knotted. With another cord through the center hole of the yardstick, the balance can be held by hand or suspended from some support. A paper clip or other small weight may be attached to the lighter end of the yardstick and moved along to a point where the yardstick will remain balanced while empty. Sand or objects of known weights may be placed in one pan and the object to be weighed placed in the other. Gain or loss of weight can be shown with such a device. Objects of known weight can be prepared for use with the balance by filling cloth sacks with sand. An amount of sand that just balances a quarter-pound of food — margarine, perhaps — will serve as one weight. An equal amount of sand divided into two portions that will balance will provide a one-eighth-pound weight. Divided equally again, each portion will be an ounce. Additional weights of various sizes can be prepared in a similar manner.

Lamp sockets. If no better source is available, a lamp socket, flashlight size, may be fashioned from the metal of a tin can. Using a large nail, punch a suitable hole in a strip of the metal, bend that end upward, and tack the other end to a block of wood. A second strip of metal should be tacked to the block beneath the upper end of the first, but should not quite touch it. Connecting wires may be attached by removing the insulation from the end of one wire and winding that end about a nail or screw, which then may be driven tightly into the outer edge of the metal, giving a firm contact. The second wire may be attached in a similar fashion to the other segment of metal. With a bulb in the hole that serves as a socket, and the loose ends of wire attached to a dry cell, a complete circuit should be provided. For a good contact to be made, the upper strip of metal must be adjusted to hold the base of the light bulb tightly against the lower strip of metal.

A socket also can be improvised from a coil of wire. Winding a wire about a pencil will provide a coil into which the bulb can be inserted. A strip of metal will serve as the lower contact. A third method of obtaining sockets for bulbs of flashlight size is to cut the sockets from a discarded Christmas-tree lamp cord, leaving the ends of the wires attached for making the necessary connections.

A source of heat. Obtaining a source of heat is a common problem. Candles, an electric hot plate, canned heat from the drugstore, a kerosene lamp with the chimney removed, a stove somewhere in the building, or even the classroom radiator may serve as a source of heat for experiments. Direct sunshine at the window may be good on some occasions, especially if a reading glass is used to focus the rays. But for many purposes an alcohol burner is most satisfactory. One can be purchased or one can be improvised from any flat-bottomed container, such as an ink bottle or a glass jar with a tightly-fitting metal cap. A large nail driven through the cap will provide a hole for the wick. Three strips of gauze bandage braided together will serve as a wick. The larger the wick used, the hotter the flame is likely to be. To extinguish the flame when it is no longer in use and to prevent evaporation of the alcohol, the burner should be covered. One suggestion is to set the ink-bottle burner on the lid of an empty mayonnaise jar and then put the jar down over the burner, attaching the lid. The cover and burner then can be moved about or stored for further use. A satisfactory cap also can be shaped from metal foil. Wood alcohol (methyl) or denatured alcohol, whichever is cheaper, can be used for the fuel. Rubbing alcohol is probably more expensive, but is otherwise quite satisfactory. Alcohol burners should not be carried about while in use, lest the alcohol be spilled and the flame spread. If it does spill, the flame can be extinguished by smothering.

A "buddy burner" will give a large flame and is easy to prepare. A shallow can, such as a tuna-fish can, may be filled with paraffin or the melted ends of

Fig. 38

A brooder for chicks improvised from a cardboard box and a reading lamp candles, and a coil of tag board, about two feet long and cut slightly wider than the can is deep, can serve as a wick. With scissors a fringe may be cut on the edge of the wick standing above the wax. When the wax has hardened and the wick is held firmly in place, the burner is ready for use. A strip of corduroy or other cotton cloth also will make a fine wick.

Miscellaneous substitutions and adaptations. Frequently there are a number of satisfactory ways to demonstrate the same principle. Expansion due to heat, for example, can be observed with a ball and ring; but if the apparatus is not available, a horizontal wire can be heated to show expansion. The air in a balloon will expand when the balloon is held over a warm radiator, and cold water in a narrow-necked bottle will show expansion as the water becomes warmer. Thus one way of demonstrating expansion can be substituted for another in accord with whatever resources are available. If resources are plentiful, however, it is possible to use a variety of experiments, each to reinforce the other and clarify a new aspect of the problem.

Substitutes can be used if the recommended items are not available. Plastic drinking straws may serve in place of glass tubing, and a sheet of transparent plastic may be used to replace a sheet of glass. A pocket comb and the child's own hair may be quite as satisfactory as the traditional amber or hard-rubber rod and cat's fur for producing a static charge. Blueberry sauce can be used as a crude substitute for litmus paper. Test tubes with sterile cotton in the neck of each tube are quite serviceable as petri dishes — and more easily available — for the preparation of bacteria cultures. Bouillon cubes, instead of beef broth, may serve as the nutrient. Commercial gelatin with a minimum of water can be used in place of agar in the preparation of the culture medium. For some purposes short lengths of iron wire can be used in place of copper. Modeling clay will form a bottle stopper of any desired size. Aluminum foil will provide a working surface under an alcohol burner. The foil can be a substitute for zinc in a voltaic cell, and it has a great variety of other uses as well.

Often flashlight cells can be used where larger cells and batteries are recommended, although attaching the wires may be difficult. However, a copper wire can be wrapped about the cell and twisted, and the bare end of the wire tucked under the loop tight against the bare zinc. The second connection can be made by touching another wire to the center terminal when the circuit is otherwise complete. Even better, a holder can be improvised for flashlight cells. (See Fig. 39.) Two strips of metal should be cut from a tin can and each strip bent to form an L. If the strips are spaced properly and nailed to a board, the vertical portions will make contact with the opposite ends of a flashlight cell placed between them. Wires should be attached to nails and the nails driven into the strips to permit connections with other apparatus. If the metal

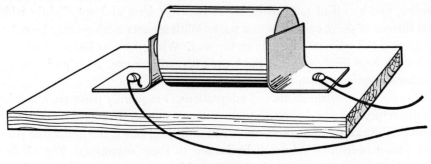

Fig. 39

A device for making electrical connections to a flashlight cell

used is enameled, the enamel must be removed wherever contacts are made.

The simple materials available for science in one locality may not be available in another; the materials representative of one environment may be foreign to another. Although laboratory rats or mice are recommended in a diet experiment, a litter of kittens may be available and can be used instead. Where a book recommends one item for use in an experiment, something else may serve quite as well. Paper can often be used in place of cloth, a rubber band or paper clip rather than twine, nails in place of iron bolts, or one kind of seed instead of another. Paper towels are a good substitute for blotters or filter paper, and a bar magnet hanging by a string, or a magnetized needle suspended by a thread, will make a satisfactory compass. A glass jar full of water will demonstrate magnification in place of a lens; an aquarium filled with water will serve as a prism; and musical instruments instead of tuning forks can be used to study the principles of sound. The metal from tin cans may be used for many purposes. (Care should be taken to avoid exposing sharp edges.) Such metal tacked to a sheet of plywood will provide a working surface, in lieu of asbestos, to protect the table top from damage.

Iron filings can be purchased, but iron filings can also be prepared with a file and a bar of iron, such as a bolt or nail. If not too coarse, the particles of metal gathered with a magnet about some milling machines may be quite satisfactory for classroom use. A tin can or glass jar of convenient size will serve as a test-tube rack, or holes can be bored in a block of wood to provide such a rack. Onions may be substituted for flower bulbs in many experiments, and adhesive tape may be used in place of gummed labels. A tin can will serve as a metal cup. Bits of paper, puffed wheat, or puffed rice on the end of a thread will serve as a substitute for pith balls in static experiments, and a glass jar can be used instead of a glass rod. Where an iron stand is not available, a wooden one can be constructed. For some experiments equipment can be attached to the classroom wall or bulletin board. A yardstick over the backs of two chairs also will provide a support from which equipment can be suspended with twine. Where plaster of Paris is recommended, slaked lime, Portland cement, or even mud may be substituted. Mosquito larvae in stagnant water or the larvae of houseflies may be quite as satisfactory for teaching the metamorphosis of insects as the more aesthetic cocoons which are often recommended. Because of the health implications, maggots and wrigglers actually may have greater value.

As teachers work with tangible resources, gradually they can learn to make full use of whatever facilities are available. Once a degree of familiarity with the teaching materials of science is attained, a teacher so inclined can improvise additional facilities which are not specifically mentioned in the books used but are needed and can be made with the resources at hand. For the children, simple materials encourage resourcefulness and stimulate learning. The child who punches holes for drainage in a tin can used as a flower pot might never have noticed the hole in a commercial flower pot, but the significance of the holes and the need of drainage are stressed when he does the work himself. With encouragement, the children of a class will have many ideas of their own, and they can profit by their own ingenuity, provided that enough resources are already available to give them a start.

STUDY GUIDE

1. Illustrate and explain what kinds of teaching materials are suitable for children in science. Show that suitable resources are necessary if each objective of science education is to be achieved.
2. Prepare an experiment recommended for children, demonstrate it to your class, and explain how the materials used were or could be obtained.
3. Prepare an experiment for children using improvised materials, and in your report indicate how practical the substitutions are.
4. Construct some item of equipment for use in science. Report how the work was done, what if any difficulties were involved, and how the item can be used as a learning device.
5. Find an experiment in a science book for children and explain how the required materials could be obtained. Should the school furnish science supplies, or should the children bring what is needed? What are the advantages of assembling needed materials in advance?
6. What resources are available in the community within walking distance of a certain elementary school? What items could the children be expected to bring? What should the teacher contribute?
7. Locate some good books in science for children, show them to your class, point out the advantages and limitations of each, and explain how the books might be used to advantage in the classroom with children.

7

Commercial Supplies
and Equipment for Science

For many commonly recommended commercial materials there are no effective substitutes. A jar of water supplements but does not replace a lens; an aquarium is too bulky to serve as a prism for all purposes — and besides, there may be no aquarium. Improvised lamp sockets, doorbells, and thermometers may serve an educational purpose yet may not be adequate substitutes for the familiar commercial items. The child who prepares an electric switch from the metal of a tin can may be unable to see its relationship to a real switch that rings his doorbell at home, unless he has an opportunity to examine a button switch the parts of which are not concealed. There is not likely to be any practical, inexpensive substitute for a test tube where heating is required, or for glass tubing and mercury where a mercurial barometer is being constructed. Rarely are dry cells, copper wire, sheets of copper and zinc, and similar items available without being purchased, yet these materials are required for the work commonly outlined in textbooks and courses of study. When they are lacking, instruction is constantly limited and is less effective than it otherwise would be.

PURCHASING SUPPLIES AND EQUIPMENT

Because the instructional materials needed are comparatively simple and because many items can be gathered at little or no expense, the total cost for the science program need not be great. Ordinarily one supply is sufficient for an entire building, with the various classes using the resources as needed. Much of the equipment, once acquired, can be used by many classes for many years.

If a comprehensive, well-balanced program in science is planned, each elementary building should have materials for work in all areas of science. The suggestions which follow may help a particular teacher or school to determine what is desirable in a specific situation. Where funds are limited, the most essential items should be selected first. On the other hand, some schools may purchase items which are not listed here, but are essential for the program as conducted in that school. Although budget limitations are certainly real, if the importance of experimental materials is appreciated, at least a portion of what is needed can usually be purchased, even in schools of limited means.

The teacher's role in ordering

Possibly the first step for a teacher ordering commercial materials is to discuss with the principal of the building the policies of the school district. If there is no established policy, it may be assumed that purchases in science will be handled in the same manner as those in other areas of the curriculum. Ordinarily the annual order is compiled in the spring for the succeeding year. Each school principal prepares a list based to some extent on teacher requests. The orders of various buildings are then pooled by the central office to gain the price-reductions and other advantages of large-scale, centralized purchasing. In anticipation of such an order, the teacher throughout the year should make a list of desired materials, adding items as the need arises. When the time for the annual order comes, the principal may circularize the staff regarding needs, and the teacher will be prepared with thoughtful, realistic requests, rather than a hastily conceived list and a lost opportunity to obtain what is needed.

Some schools will authorize the teacher to make limited purchases, but generally the purchasing is handled by the central office, the office making the purchase in response to a teacher's request made through the principal of the building. How readily teacher requests are granted varies with the financial resources and point of view of the district. In a building that has a special science teacher, for the upper grades perhaps, requests for materials are likely to be handled by that person. A science consultant or supervisor working with the elementary schools can give teachers considerable help and advice regarding requisitioning and other problems involving instructional materials.

If the teacher who needs equipment will make the request clear and definite, the probability of getting what is needed may be vastly improved. The teacher should locate a catalogue and learn to make out an order that specifies the items sought and the company from which they can be obtained. Often the schools are willing and able to meet reasonable requests, but science is a relatively new field, and procedures for obtaining materials may not be established. The principal and others who must handle the order may be unfamiliar with science and science catalogues and uncertain about what is needed or how to get it; hence if the request is phrased vaguely, the task of ordering is postponed and may never be actually accomplished. If the teacher can learn to use a catalogue, one of the greatest and most common obstacles will be overcome.

There are many advantages in the flexibility provided by a cash account for small, last-minute purchases. The unusual item required to make a creative activity practicable can be obtained, and initiative is encouraged. Even though few such purchases are made, the realization that they could be made will provide greater latitude in planning, for the activities possible are not limited merely to the resources already on hand. Perishable items can be obtained when needed, and materials can be purchased more readily from local merchants by means of a cash account. It seems advisable for each school to have a small cash account which will facilitate the purchase of incidental materials as the need arises.

Making purchases locally has certain advantages. Local materials are more apt to be familiar and to carry more meaning for the children. Baking soda, for example, may be purchased from a grocery in a familiar package that will mean more than a strange carton labeled *sodium bicarbonate* obtained from a supply house. The grocery-store item is likely to be either similar to or identical with the one on the kitchen shelf in the child's own home. In making purchases locally it is usually possible to get what is needed without delay. Buying at neighborhood stores also helps to keep local merchants informed about and interested in the schools and what the schools are doing.

But there are also disadvantages to local purchases. Some materials are unavailable locally, and since many items must be obtained from the scientific supply houses, it is frequently easier simply to lengthen the list and order virtually all items from the one source. The apparent ease of shopping locally may be more than offset by the difficulty of obtaining administrative approval for the many separate articles to be purchased in various local shops. Finding what is needed in the various stores about town may prove to be a large task and more time-consuming than ordering from a catalogue. Some of the difficulty may be overcome by trading with a department store or mail-order house, where a single order will suffice.

The purchasing department of the school, the science supervisor, or the science department of the nearest high school very likely will have on hand catalogues of the scientific supply houses [1] or can get them by writing to the companies. The elementary teacher may be able to borrow them and get help in locating what is needed. Ordinarily the catalogues will not be sent to individual elementary-school teachers, although the Central Scientific Company now has "A Suggested List of Apparatus and Materials for Elementary Science," and the list is essentially a small catalogue. The information needed for ordering includes the name and address of the company, the number or date of the catalogue used, and, for each article requested, the quantity desired, the name as listed in the catalogue, the essential dimensions or other descriptions, the catalogue number of the article, and the price listed.

No equipment should be purchased that will not be used. A record of foolish purchases makes it difficult for teachers thereafter to obtain what is needed. The materials purchased should be used economically. Copper wire, for example, may be salvaged after use, wrapped about the fingers in a convenient coil, and stored in a box to be used again when needed. Pyrex flasks need be used only where heat is to be applied, not where an old glass jar will do as well. If good use is made of the materials already available, including community resources and articles that children can gather, a strong case can be made for obtaining additional facilities when a need arises.

Today it seems that teachers and administrators alike are willing and even anxious to have an active, effective science program. The public considers it highly desirable and is willing to support it. But in a relatively new field many

[1] Cambosco Scientific Company, 37 Antwerp Street, Brighton Station, Boston, Massachusetts; Carolina Biological Supply Company, Elon College, North Carolina; Central Scientific Company, 1700 Irving Park Road, Chicago 13, Illinois; Chicago Apparatus Company, 1735 N. Ashland Avenue, Chicago 22, Illinois; General Biological Supply House, 761–763 East 69th Place, Chicago 37, Illinois; New York Scientific Supply Company, 28 West 30th Street, New York 1, N.Y.; Standard Scientific Supply Corporation, 34–38 West 4th Street, New York 12, N.Y.; W. M. Welch Scientific Company, 1515 Sedgwick Street, Chicago 10, Illinois. The business manager of the schools, or a high-school science teacher, may be able to give the names of other convenient establishments with which a good business relationship is already established. For some items, such as tools, an egg incubator, or scales, Sears, Roebuck and Co. or other mail-order houses are other possible sources of supply.

Fig. 40

Illustrative Order Form

CENTRAL SCIENTIFIC COMPANY

1700 Irving Park Road, Chicago 13, Illinois

Ship at once and bill to:

    Seattle Public Schools   Date_____
    810 Dexter Avenue
    Seattle, Washington

Signed by_____Official position_____

(from Catalog J–150)

Quantity	Description	Catalog number	Unit price	Total price
5 lb.	Glass tubing, 6 mm., 4 ft. long	14076	$ .50	$ 2.50
20 ft.	Rubber tubing, 3/16 in., medium	18220B	.07	1.40
1 pkg.	Rubber stoppers, assorted	18153A	1.10	1.10
12	Beakers, Griffin, low, with lip, pyrex, 250 ml.	14265	.25	3.00
6	Flasks, Erlenmeyer, pyrex, 300 ml.	14905	.34	2.04
6	Dry batteries, standard no. 6	79147	.70	4.20
2	Bells, electric	84010A	.80	1.60
4	Push buttons	84040	.25	1.00
2	Switches, knife, single	84315	.70	1.40
10	Receptacles, miniature	84165	.12	1.20
12	Lamps, incandescent, miniature	84420A	.11	1.32
1	Copper sheet, plain, 12 in. sq.	89085	2.35	2.35
2	Zinc sheets, 1/32 in., 12 in. sq.	89462	1.00	2.00
1	Lead sheet, 1/32 in., 12 in. sq.	89265B	1.30	1.30
1 lb.	Wire, copper magnet, cotton covered, B. & S. no. 20	89571	1.30	1.30
2 pair	Magnets, cylindrical, Alnico 180 mm. long, 15 mm. diam.	78291C	2.75	5.50
2 lb.	Iron filings	78395B	.36	.72
1	Magnetic needle	78415	1.40	1.40
1	Magnetic compass, 45 mm. diam.	78430D	.65	.65
1	Motor, St. Louis	79945	6.50	6.50
1	Telephone receiver, demonstration form	80770	2.75	2.75
1	Telephone transmitter	80800	2.75	2.75
			Total	$47.98

Fig. 41

Illustrative Order Form

CAMBOSCO SCIENTIFIC COMPANY

37 Antwerp Street, Brighton Station

Boston, Massachusetts

Ship and bill to: Camp School
                   15 Prospect Street
                   New Britain, Connecticut

Official

signature_____Position_____Date_____
                    (from 1956 catalog)

Quantity	Description	Catalog number	Unit price	Total price
2	Aquaria, 15 gal.	75–35	$17.95	$35.90
1	Animal cage, 9×9×15 in.	75–215		11.75
1	Collection, rocks, minerals, 40	700–298		8.95
3	Thermometers, outdoor	67–220	2.00	6.00
2	Thermometers, chemical, F.	33–328	1.62	3.24
1 pkg.	Acid, tannic, N.F., powder, 4 oz.			1.29
1 pkg.	Ammonium chloride, labgrade, 1 lb.			.50
1 pkg.	Benedict's sol., labgrade, 1 lb.			1.20
1 pkg.	Calcium hydroxide, U.S.P., 1 lb.			1.13
1 pkg.	Copper sulfate, labgrade, 1 lb.			.63
1 pkg.	Glycerin, U.S.P., 1 lb.			.97
1 pkg.	Iron sulfate (ous) U.S.P., 1 lb.			.61
1 pkg.	Potassium nitrate, U.S.P., 1 lb.			.81
1 pkg.	Potassium permanganate, U.S.P., 4 oz.			.70
1 pkg.	Sulfur, labgrade, flowers, 1 lb.			.64
			Total	$74.32

---

uncertainties stand in the way, so that whoever will take the initiative in obtaining suitable resources is apt to find ready support.

The science kit as a source of supplies

The usual science kit is a chest of supplies adapted for work in elementary-school science. The commercial kit may include such articles as dry cells, magnets, pulleys, and test tubes. The items vary, but they should include the materials that are most useful in teaching but not otherwise easily obtained when needed. The selection may include in one kit materials from all areas of science, or a number of kits may be used to encompass the field. Kits are usually intended for service in any grade of the elementary school as needed — one or more kits for an entire building. The materials may be used by the teacher for demonstration or by the children in experimentation, as circumstances permit.

The kit is convenient to use and convenient to order [2], in comparison to selecting the items separately from a supply catalogue. The kit can be moved from room to room with ease, and it provides a definite place for each item, where the articles can be located easily when needed. The supplies included conform quite closely to probable needs. For the teacher not already well acquainted with the field, having materials already selected may be quite helpful and suggestive of potentialities. Most of the materials will last for years. Replacements or additions can be purchased from the maker or from any scientific supply house as needed. Having supplies on hand, whatever the source, is highly desirable — in fact is essential, if good work is to be done.

As a source of supplies, however, the kit has disadvantages as well as advantages. It cannot be adapted to the requirements of a particular school as well as a list of supplies prepared by the teachers. The fact that the materials are in a kit already prepared with directions for their use tends to make the kit somewhat inflexible. Instead of the child's attention being centered upon the environment, it is apt to be centered upon the kit, as if the kit were a "bag of tricks," and the problem at hand may be simply to see what can be done with the kit. This criticism may not be entirely fair, for it is largely a question of how the supplies are used, and it may apply somewhat to the use of materials from any source. When the needed materials are gathered together for a specific purpose, however, the relationships they exemplify are likely to be clear. The fact that a kit is highly organized, with directions for use, may thus detract from its value in aiding children to interpret their environment. Although sizes vary, the amount of material in a kit is limited. Additional provisions for obtaining and storing materials will have to be made if the program is to function as it should. Nevertheless, the kit is at least a modest beginning.

[2] Science kits may be obtained from Gustave H. Kock, 204 Dexter Street, Tonawanda, New York (*Science Kit*); Standard Science Supply Company, 1232 N. Paulina Street, Chicago 22, Illinois (*Stansi Science Kit*); Tunis Baker, State Teachers College, Paterson, New Jersey (*Elementary Science Equipment Units*); Central Scientific Company, 1700 Irving Park Road, Chicago 13, Illinois (*Educational Hobby Kits*); Science Associates, P. O. Box 216, Princeton, New Jersey (*Learn-by-Doing Kits*); W. M. Welch Scientific Company, 1515 Sedgwick Street, Chicago 10, Illinois (*The Welch Rol-a-Lab,* a movable table, cabinet, and equipment).

Relative costs can be computed by figuring the prices of the items as they are listed separately in a scientific supply catalogue and comparing the total with the price of a kit. Such estimates reveal that supplies can be purchased separately for considerably less money. Whether a kit should be purchased or supplies ordered separately, perhaps with the help of a list included here, will depend largely upon the circumstances in a particular school. The kit is somewhat more expensive and is not as adaptable, but it is likely to be more convenient in some cases.

Kits are prepared sometimes by school systems for use in the various schools. Except for the item of costs, the same evaluation would apply somewhat to kits prepared locally. They tend to be inflexible, but are convenient. Kits which must be transported from a central storage place outside the school where they will be used are not likely to be available when needed, and it may be inconvenient to obtain them. If kits are used, they should be kept in the building where they are needed.

SUPPLIES RECOMMENDED FOR ELEMENTARY SCIENCE

The following are some specific recommendations for experimental learning materials likely to be needed in a well-rounded science program. The list can and should be modified in accord with local circumstances and plans for instruction. These resources should be on hand at school in a supply room available for use when needed. Locally, many of the commercial items can be obtained from hardware and automobile-supply stores, from drugstores and variety stores, from groceries and department stores. Nearly all of them can be obtained from a scientific supply house.

Materials for a study of light and the sky

To study the universe, very little special material is ordinarily used. For observing at night, binoculars, if available, are very useful; and a flashlight is a help in pointing out stars. (The beam can be seen directed toward the star in question.) A flashlight is also valuable for experimenting with light. To demonstrate an eclipse, the change of seasons, the cause of day and night, and the phases of the moon, a world globe or large ball is necessary. A tennis ball or baseball will serve to represent the moon; an electric lamp with a long cord can be used to represent the sun. For experimenting with light, a school should have at least two magnifying glasses and another convex lens that is smaller —

that is, of shorter focal length — to illustrate the principle of a telescope. A triangular prism, a concave lens, a concave shaving mirror, and a flat mirror also will be useful.

Materials needed for chemical experiments

For chemical experiments, household ammonia, cream of tartar, table salt, baking soda, starch, sugar, vinegar, and possibly washing soda can be purchased from a grocery. Other chemicals needed are ammonium chloride, boric acid, Benedict's solution, copper sulfate, Epsom salts, glycerin, iodine, iron sulfate, slaked lime, neutral litmus paper, potassium nitrate, potassium permanganate, sulfur, and tannic acid. Alum is useful in showing how crystals form. In spite of the fact that sulfuric acid is a strong acid, it is useful in teacher demonstrations. Many elementary-school books recommend it for use in constructing voltaic cells and storage batteries. The experiences are definitely worthwhile, and if the teachers fully understand the precautions to be taken, the acid can be used with safety. In addition to the chemicals, an alcohol burner with denatured alcohol, test tubes and brushes for cleaning them will be needed.

All the chemicals, the alcohol, and the test tubes can be obtained locally at drugstores, but the prices of chemicals are lower at a supply house, since a cheaper grade can be purchased there. Local purchases, however, have the advantage of coming in familiar packages. Scientific-supply catalogues list the chemicals by their chemical names; hence for convenience in ordering, the chemical names for common materials are given below:

alum	aluminum potassium sulfate
household ammonia	ammonium hydroxide
boric acid	acid boric
cream of tartar	potassium bitartrate
Epsom salts	magnesium sulfate
iodine	iodine tincture
slaked lime	calcium hydroxide
table salt	sodium chloride
baking soda	sodium bicarbonate
washing soda	sodium carbonate
sugar	sugar, cane; or sucrose
vinegar	acid acetic (is equivalent and can be diluted with water)

If the school has no supply of chemicals, many are common enough that children can bring them from home. Most of the other chemicals needed can be found in a child's chemistry set.

Supplies for a study of the earth's surface

To study rocks, soil, and other surface features of the earth, few materials need be purchased. Surface features can be studied outside in their natural setting, and a collection of typical local rocks can be made by students. To aid in developing a local collection, a small commercial collection of common rocks and minerals may be purchased. A small can of paint, preferably a flat white, will be needed for labeling the rocks — or white adhesive tape, though not so lasting, is more convenient and can be used. A dish pan, tray, or large flat pan for demonstrating erosion, also modeling clay and window glass will be needed, but may already be available. A few pounds of Portland cement can be purchased at a hardware store, and with sand can be used to show how fossils have been formed in sandstone. A quarter-pound or so each of copper sulfate, alum, and Epsom salts can be kept on hand to demonstrate how crystals are formed from solution.

Materials for studies concerned with plants and animals

To study living things some of the following materials are needed: tin cans to use as flower pots, and saucers or trays to place beneath them for drainage; broad, flat boxes for planting seed; glass jars in which root development can be seen; and flat pans, with cotton, blotters, paper towels, or sand on which seed can be sprouted. A trowel will be needed. Kidney beans and mustard seed can be obtained from the grocery; radish and nasturtium seed are also quick-sprouting and desirable to have on hand.

Thirty feet of half-inch wire mesh three feet wide, from the hardware store, will make several cages suitable for a hen, a rabbit, or laboratory rats. A few square feet of wire screen will make smaller cages for insects. On the other hand, it may be preferable to buy the cages ready-made. Grain for a hen or for laboratory rats, or pellets for rabbit food will be needed if these animals are to be kept at school for any appreciable length of time.

Ordinary gelatin, or preferably agar agar from the drugstore or scientific supply house, and either petri dishes or test tubes from the same source, a double boiler from the hardware store, and bouillon cubes from the grocery store will be needed if cultures of bacteria are to be made in connection with health work or a study involving primitive forms of plant life.

Dip nets can be made or can be purchased from a scientific supply house or possibly from a sporting-goods store. Commercial fish food and turtle food will be needed. By far the most expensive items on the usual lists of elementary-school science materials are the glass aquaria, which can be ordered from hardware stores or pet shops as well as the scientific supply houses.

For schools that can afford to be well equipped, at least one microscope capable of revealing bacteria is highly desirable. An instrument with two magnifications, 100 diameters and 430 diameters, will be satisfactory. For use with the microscope there should be a supply of glass slides, including some depression slides, and cover glasses with which to mount bacteria, protozoa, and whatever else is to be observed. A small incubator for eggs can be purchased from a mail-order house or other source, at about the price of a good aquarium, and can be very useful in studying how living things grow and develop.

Supplies for experiments in electricity

To study electricity certain supplies are indispensable. The supplies can be purchased at an electrical supply store, hardware store, or scientific supply house. Cotton-insulated copper wire will be needed, preferably a large spool of Number 20 or 22. Bell wire from hardware stores is more expensive and less convenient to use than the smaller Number 20 or 22 sizes of wire, which may have to be obtained from a scientific supply house. Also needed are dry cells, possibly half a dozen for the average school, or three as a minimum, and electric bells, flashlight bulbs with a screw-type base, porcelain sockets to match, knife and button switches, a compass, bar magnets, iron filings, a lodestone, assorted corks, and a package of darning needles. Very fine iron wire, heavy iron wire, and bell wire or a still heavier copper wire to contrast with the Number 20 or 22 already mentioned can be used to show differences in electrical resistance. Perhaps a few short lengths of such wire, enough for the purpose, can be collected without cost.

Sheet copper and zinc from the hardware store and ammonium chloride from the drugstore, or both from a supply house, will be needed if voltaic cells are to be made; and for storage cells a sheet of lead and some sulfuric acid are essential. The acid involves some hazard and must be handled with care, but the valuable learnings involved may justify its use as a teacher demonstration. If copper sulfate is obtained, copper plating can be done with the dry cells and copper sheet.

The principles of the telephone are fundamental, and to teach them effectively a transmitter and a receiver will be needed, purchased from a scientific supply house. For static experiments the following are desirable, although substitutes can be found: glass and hard-rubber rods, cat fur or wool cloth, silk thread, pith balls, balloons, and a sheet of window glass. A demonstration motor of the St. Louis type is not very expensive but is very valuable in developing an understanding of motors and electric generators.

Materials for a study of weather and related topics

For a study of air, weather, and ventilation a school should have alcohol burners and denatured alcohol, several thermometers for measuring the temperature of the air inside the building and out, and one or two thermometers that can be used in water. A teakettle or coffeepot will be needed for heating water, and pliers will be needed for handling heated materials. Most of these can be obtained at hardware stores. Candles, carbon tetrachloride cleaning solvent, and safety matches can be found at drugstores. The children can bring milk bottles, glass jars and bottles of various sizes. A wash tub, dish pan, sheets of glass, a funnel, a world globe, and a medicine dropper are useful in this area and in others as well.

The following items and many of those previously listed can be obtained from scientific supply houses: a spool of fine iron wire, a compound bar which will illustrate the principle of a thermostat, a ball-and-ring set that also will show expansion with heat, lamp chimneys, assorted rubber stoppers, rubber tubing, glass tubing and mercury for constructing a mercurial barometer. The glass tubing should be at least 32 inches long for use in a barometer; 6 mm. outside diameter is a convenient size. Rubber tubing of 3/16 inch inside diameter will fit the glass tubing tightly. An aneroid barometer is useful. A few pyrex flasks and beakers from the supply house will be needed, because glass jars and bottles cannot be used for heating. A ventilation box and a convection box for demonstrating air movements can be constructed or can be obtained from a supply house.

Miscellaneous experimental resources

Some items have been included in more than one of the previous lists. Other materials that have a variety of purposes include aluminum foil, a jar of petrolatum, gummed labels, funnels, nails of all sizes, and wood screws, including some with round heads. Tin cans, bottles, glass jars, and cardboard cartons have many uses. Wide-mouthed gallon jars should be collected for terraria, as well as for general containers. Dish pans and a number of other pans will have many uses. It is convenient to have iron stands with burette clamps and rings, test-tube clamps, and a file that can be used to cut glass tubing. Iron wire has many uses, such as in constructing cages, conducting the flame test for chemicals, and showing electrical resistance. Many books suggest the use of tuning forks in experiments. Asbestos pads make safe working surfaces. A balance or other scales for weighing is required in many situations. Pulleys and suitable cord to use with them are commonly recommended. Mechanical toys, an old egg beater, a nutcracker, and similar devices will help to show the advantages of machines and how they work.

Tools are indispensable in learning activities that include the construction of telegraph sets, cages, or other devices. Each school should have a hammer, a saw, pliers, screw driver, tinner's snips, and assorted nails. Metal may be obtained from old tin cans and wood from boxes, but the materials should be assembled ready for use.

ORGANIZING THE RESOURCES FOR CONVENIENT USE

A central supply

The supplies commonly used should be kept on hand in a supply room or closet, ready when needed from one year to the next. The facilities of the building and the wishes of the individuals concerned should determine how the supplies are handled. They can be distributed from the supply room in the same manner as any of the other school supplies, or kept in a special science room or closet. A visual-aids room, book room, or simply a cabinet at one end of the hall are other possibilities. The supplies may be kept in one of the classrooms if space permits and the teacher concerned is willing to accept the responsibility and the opportunity that goes with it. One supply ordinarily will do for an entire building, since the materials in most cases are not in constant use. One teacher may be placed in charge of the supplies; some teacher who has a special interest in and aptitude for science and is capable of acting as a consultant for the other teachers would be a logical choice. Working with the instructional materials provides a functional contact with the other teachers and their problems. If it seems necessary, the hours for obtaining supplies can be limited to prevent inconvenience for the one in charge. The teacher in charge may be able to delegate some of the responsibility to certain children. If it is not too time-consuming, the responsibility can provide a valuable experience for them.

Seeing that equipment is returned to the supply room may become a problem. Perhaps the best answer is to have students make periodic calls to pick up whatever is no longer needed. Some record should be kept of what materials are borrowed, when they are taken and when returned. A plain notebook will do, with each teacher recording what he has borrowed, giving his name and the date, and perhaps also the day that the material will be returned. If a second teacher needs some of the same items, he will know whom to consult. Small articles may be kept in boxes, drawers, or cupboards labeled according to the subject area for which the articles are most likely to be used. Copper wire, for instance, would be kept in a box or on a shelf marked *electricity.* An inventory of the resources for each area may be kept with the supplies where teachers can check to see what is available.

Chemicals should be stored in a separate compartment; fumes from the chemicals will cause metals to corrode. If the supply includes strong acids, lye, or other poisonous chemicals, those items should be kept on high shelves, preferably behind locked doors where they will not be accessible to the children. If children are sent to the supply room to borrow equipment for teachers, close supervision of the supply room will have to be arranged to prevent accidents, confusion, and loss of equipment. It may be preferable to permit only the teachers to obtain the equipment, or at least to require a note written by the teacher requesting specific items. If children have even limited access to the supply room, it is imperative that no dangerous materials be used, or that they be stored separately. Most of the equipment used in elementary schools is not at all dangerous, of course, but even safe equipment can cause trouble if treated carelessly.

Perhaps a school project, with teachers and children all helping, could be undertaken to gather and organize needed materials from the community — and from commercial sources as far as the budget will permit. Certain articles collected for one undertaking may be worth saving for future activities. Rocks, tin cans, bottles, perhaps even wire, stoppers, discarded mechanical toys, and similar items of instructional value can be gathered and will be at hand when needed. Points of interest within range of the school could be catalogued and their significance listed. For example, the banks of a nearby stream could be listed as a good spot to visit while studying erosion or the broader problem of conservation. A gully in a nearby field could be listed for the same purpose, as could a point where during a heavy rain dirt is washed off a bank and deposited in the street or road.

Room equipment

In addition to a general supply for the entire school, each classroom should begin to develop an individual supply of simple, inexpensive materials for use in science. The classroom supply may include tin cans, bottles, wire, and other articles that can be obtained without cost yet have frequent use in science and often in other activities as well. The greater accessibility may justify the inclusion of some of the less expensive commercial materials frequently used, such as pyrex beakers, an alcohol burner, or a thermometer. The storage facilities in a classroom are limited, of course, but often what is already on the shelves can be reorganized to provide space, and it may be that additional cupboards can be constructed or improvised to serve the purpose. Teachers find it less troublesome to locate resources on short notice where some are stored in the individual classrooms.

Each classroom should be equipped with a worktable, although any surface, including the floor, can be used if need be. The table need not be restricted to science work, but at times may be used for other activities as well. The worktable, or another like it, may be moved to the front of the room when demonstrations and reports are made. Movable desks and chairs, giving space for children to gather about the table, either for experimentation or to observe demonstrations, are highly desirable. A close view often adds to the interest and the effectiveness of the work. Parenthetically it may be pointed out that discipline need be no problem where children are gathered thus at close quarters. Anyone who is disorderly can simply be asked to leave the group until he is ready to stop interfering, and social pressure will help to make the treatment effective.

Some rooms fortunately are equipped with a sink and running water; in other rooms a bucket of water will be needed, and if possible a broad, flat pan over which certain experiments may be conducted. A dish pan will serve as a comparatively convenient sink, and a teakettle or coffeepot will provide the "running water." An asbestos pad, a sheet of metal, or other working surface is desirable for experiments, especially if fire is used. An extra pan of water or sand for emergency use should be at hand. The school very likely already has a fire extinguisher and a first-aid kit, and their location should be known. A tin can for used matches should be provided, and some heavy cloth, such as a portion of an old rug, should be on hand to smother any flame that might otherwise get out of control. In fact, one of the values of instruction in science is to teach children needed precautions and the control of fire. The equipment of a room should help to exemplify those precautions. Avoiding the use of fire will not teach caution; if such a policy is followed, some of the more daring children may do their experimenting by themselves, without supervision. If strong acid is used, a bottle of household ammonia water or a box of baking soda, lime, or other weak base should be nearby; the sooner the spilled acid is washed away and neutralized by applying a base, the less the likelihood of damage.

Additional worktables may be needed at times. A small table on which the teacher and children may conduct their demonstrations is desirable. Perhaps the school can arrange to provide suitable worktables that can be moved to the rooms where they are needed and taken away when no longer in use. A cabinet or open shelves where the materials currently in use can be kept will be needed, and some source of heat should be obtained. An alcohol burner or electric hot plate, which like other equipment can be moved from room to room, is usually adequate.

A science workroom

A special room for science, if available, has some advantages. More adequate facilities can be provided in a single room than would be practicable for all the separate classrooms of a building. The room also may serve as a center where science supplies and equipment may be kept. The disadvantage is that a special room tends to be remote from the other activities of the class, and work in science may be limited to periods when the room is available, with the result that an artificial situation is created. Perhaps the best way is to use the classroom for activities in science, except for those undertakings that require more elaborate facilities. In such cases, if a sink or bunsen burner is available in the special room, or if that room can be darkened for experiments, demonstrations, or visual aids that require darkness, the class may go to the special room for that particular purpose and return when the work is completed. The room could be used for other purposes also, such as art work and construction activities, provided that a part of the room is devoted to storage for each area, so that one does not infringe upon the other.

WHERE LEADERSHIP CAN HELP

Complete solution of the materials problem is beyond the scope of an individual teacher working alone. Because science is relatively new in the elementary curriculum, many teachers have had little experience in the area and little opportunity to become familiar with the instructional materials. The resourceful teacher, it is true, can accomplish much with limited equipment. But substituting, improvising, and constructing are not always as easy as they may sound. A dish pan can be adapted for use as an aquarium, but unfortunately there may be no dish pan. Ability to substitute and improvise implies versatility and familiarity with the subject and the teaching materials involved. It is not easy to be ingenious with strange materials in a strange situation. If teachers are to become resourceful, suitable resources must be available and their use encouraged. If some materials are provided, ingenuity in exploiting other resources can be learned.

Although teachers can learn to be resourceful, it remains true that even the most skilful teacher can accomplish more with adequate facilities than without them. In a bare classroom the teacher must work under a serious handicap. If a teacher has the time, inclination, and skill, some equipment can be constructed, but not always do teachers have the necessary construction skills for effective workmanship. For a teacher to spend many hours hunting for resources that could equally well be kept on hand is not a wise use of time. To devote so much time to all areas of the curriculum would be impossible. Improvising and constructing sometimes can be unproductive obstacles to learning. Science must be taught in all classrooms, not just those of the most resourceful teachers.

School policies regarding teaching facilities

For teachers to make frequent purchases either from their own purses or from the school funds is not accepted policy in most school systems. Yet too often it is assumed that somehow teachers will find the needed resources for effective work; articles from variety stores, drugstores, and similar establishments are commonly recommended in the professional literature, with no suggestion regarding how to finance or arrange their purchase. The conscientious teacher may pay for an occasional small item, but if no other provision is made and supplies are limited to those the teacher can afford, the limitation is too great. Hasty last-minute substitutes often cost more and are less suitable than supplies acquired in advance. The situation is a matter not of a school policy but of the lack of a school policy. Science will not be firmly established as an active program in the elementary schools until school policies regarding experimental resources are clarified.

Whenever purchases for elementary-school science are mentioned, some educators are apt to be disturbed by visions of elaborate technical equipment. Yet resources of some kind admittedly are necessary, and in most schools they are not being used as commonly as effective learning would require. Out of a complex environment it is difficult for the teacher inexperienced in science to determine what is significant and what is appropriate for use with children. Leadership may be required to determine needs and locate what is suitable for use. It would seem that the time has come for more school systems to include commercial science materials in the regular budget, to be obtained through the usual purchasing channels. Commonly recommended materials suitable for the program as outlined in the schools concerned should be supplied by the schools, just as other supplies and equipment are provided. If a school provides textbooks, pencil sharpeners, chalk, and art paper as standard supplies and equipment, that school also should provide the equally essential dry cells, rubber stoppers, and pyrex beakers. For the administration to provide essential resources in advance is not an infringement on the democratic rights of the teacher or the children; in fact, having resources available makes a choice possible and an active democratic program feasible. Even greater flexibility and independence of judgment can be achieved through providing a limited cash account for items not included in the standard list of equipment.

In comparison to the cost of playground equipment, art supplies, books, and similar justifiable expenses, the cost of science materials is not great, yet the items are fully as important. In one school system where there were three elementary schools and a total annual budget of $1,800 for art supplies, a proposal to allot $100 in each school for a single year to establish an active program in science was cut to $60 in one school, $40 in another, and zero for the third — reputedly because the schools could afford no more. Nothing at all had been spent for science in previous years, and nothing was spent in the years following. Many schools with otherwise adequate financing neglect to provide even the minimum requirements of science.

"Without appropriate materials, a modern educational program is an impossibility," according to the Thirty-First Yearbook of the American Association of School Administrators.[3]

Solving the problem of supplies

Purchasing science materials for children is complicated by the fact that no one store can furnish all the needed items, although most of what is sought can be obtained from a scientific supply house. The supply houses, however, are unfamiliar to teachers, and their catalogues are difficult to use. The administration can take the initiative in ordering. In most school systems someone can be found to take the lead, someone who is familiar with science and science catalogues. A committee could be selected to include individuals who know the elementary schools and their needs. Through such a group the es-

[3] American Association of School Administrators, Thirty-First Yearbook, *American School Curriculum*, The Association, Washington, D.C., 1953, p. 183.

Fig. 42

Having good equipment contributes greatly to the success of the science program.

sential teaching materials could be located and made available for all. Elementary-school orders should be pooled with those of the high school wherever possible; supply houses do not welcome small orders, since they find them unprofitable to fill. Thus an organized effort to obtain needed supplies is more economical as well as more feasible than random individual efforts.

There are many good ways for schools to solve the problems involving teaching materials for science. A standard set of materials can be determined and be made available to all buildings, just as other supplies are provided. Such a list could be based upon the recommendations of a professional publication, the local course of study, or the textbooks in use. A curriculum committee may study the problem and make recommendations adapted to local circumstances and desires. The teachers could determine their own needs and check to see what resources are already available. Meetings could be organized to help them learn how to use suitable experimental materials, and a plan could be developed for gathering and storing resources not already on hand. According to a report in *The Science Teacher,* Cleveland is one example of a city that has moved in the right direction:

> Each year a list of standardized items is sent to the schools. The blank contains the names and specifications of the articles. Each school orders what it wants within its budget limitation. The budget is determined on the basis of the school enrollment. The list of requirements from each school is sent to the commissioner of supplies. From the school requests a combined list of supplies is developed. This list goes to the purchasing department where bids are taken. The bids are returned to the commissioner of supplies for recommendation as to the quality to be purchased. Any question arising at this point is referred back to the science supervisor. The method of grouping the orders enables schools to secure better prices than individual schools could receive. The supply houses ship the materials to the board of education warehouse. In the warehouse the items are separated and sent to the individual schools. Many items are carried as regular warehouse stock and are available at all times as required, provided the request remains within the budget.[4]

Whatever arrangement is set up, care should be taken that it does not become stereotyped. Teachers should not be limited to a prearranged list, except insofar as the budget is always a limitation. Once a list is determined, it should be reviewed constantly by study groups, and it should also be subject to modification on the recommendations of individual teachers.

The influence of supplies and equipment

Equipment should not determine the school program, yet the fact remains that the available resources strongly affect not only what is taught but how it is taught. The resources can be either a limitation or an opportunity. This fact should suggest to the administration one way of helping to shape an effective program in science. The use of appropriate instructional materials frequently makes the difference between good teaching and ineffective work, or perhaps no work at all in science. If the children in our schools were provided with

[4] Grace C. Maddux, "The Problem of Supplies for Elementary Science: How One Large City Solves the Problem," *The Science Teacher,* XIX:114–115, April, 1952.

the resources for an active, interesting, worthwhile program of investigations in science, many of the disciplinary problems that take so much of an administrator's time, as well as that of the teacher, would cease to exist. A vital program helps to remove frustrations, and the child is encouraged to develop an interest in something outside himself. Although the problem is shared by all, one school principal has said:

> As a rule, it is the principal who makes requisitions for supplies and books. . . . Unless the principal is alert to the importance of such needs, anticipates them and is sympathetic to them, a good program may die. It should not be necessary for a teacher to defend requests for help and overcome administrative indifference or resistance.[5]

STUDY GUIDE

1. If possible, list the commercial resources for science that are available in a certain elementary school. If you were authorized to spend $100 for science materials at this school, what items would you select, and how would you obtain them? Explain why the items chosen are considered most essential.
2. What is the procedure in ordering supplies for the school you have cited as an example?
3. If a science catalogue can be obtained, prepare an order for the materials selected in the first question. List items which could be obtained in local shops instead of the supply house.
4. Inspect the school cited above to see where science materials are stored and how they are organized for use. If the school is not a good example, suggest needed improvements. Make specific suggestions for storing and organizing the materials that should be available.
5. What are the advantages and limitations of commercial science kits?

[5] Helen A. Bertermann, "Principals Help the Teachers," *The National Elementary Principal*, XXIX:13, February, 1950.

8

Interpreting the Sky

Astronomy was the first of the modern sciences to develop, owing to the fact that people have always been curious about the sky. Children are no exception. They have great interest in what can be seen above them, and the subject is a rewarding one to teach to children. It can be as pleasant for the teacher as for the children.

THE FASCINATION OF THE SKY

"How high is the moon — higher than the clouds?" "What's above the sky?" "Where does the sun go when it rains?" All these are questions asked by a first-grader. In the third grade one of the children wanted to know if the big dipper would ever pour down water she could drink. At Christmas time another third-grade child said, "Do stars really have points?" In the sixth grade someone asked, "Why do stars twinkle?" Another sixth-grader wanted to know what makes the sky blue. The sky is fascinating to children and is the basis of much speculation and many questions. If instruction is limited to folk tales, such as the one about Henny Penny going to tell the king the sky is falling, the children's thinking about this area of their environment will continue to be confused by many fallacious beliefs. A knowledge of the sky, or the lack of it, has great influence on thinking — perhaps more influence than any other field of science.

Facts that catch attention

There are many surprising facts about the stars and planets that intrigue children. Although light travels 186,000 miles per second — fast enough to be reflected back and forth across the United States, from coast to coast, about 75 times in a single second — the distance from us to the stars actually is measured in light years, the number of years it takes light from the stars to reach us. The North Star, for example, is reported to be 470 light years away from us. Light that left Polaris when Columbus discovered America, according to these figures, will arrive here to be seen by us in 1962. Other than our sun, the closest star visible to our unaided eyes in the northern hemisphere is Sirius, a very bright star that can be seen not far above the southern horizon throughout the early evening hours of the winter and spring months. As with all the stars, Sirius appears to move westward from month to month; in January it will be found at about 9 P.M. in the southeast, whereas at the same hour in March or April it will be toward the southwest. Sirius is not only the closest — 8.6 light years — but also the brightest star, although some of the planets appear brighter. The most distant object visible to the naked eye is the Great Nebula in Andromeda, a huge mass of stars, a galaxy, visible only as a slight blur of light. The Great Nebula is estimated to be two million light years distant, yet it is one of the closest of many thousands seen through telescopes. Each time a larger telescope is built, more distant stars can be observed. No one knows how large our universe may be.

The teacher can find many intriguing facts to arouse the interest of children in a study of the sky, and the children themselves can find many more to report. Ronnie, for instance, reported to the sixth grade what he had found about the extremely high temperatures of the stars. Someone else read a newspaper report that astronomers have now discovered that Jupiter has twelve moons, yet when the books were written only eleven were known, and a few of the older books stated that the planet has ten moons. Older children may enjoy computing how long it would take them to make a rocket trip to the moon, about 240,000 miles, at the speed of sound, about 770 miles per hour. Dividing the first number by the second will give the number of hours, and dividing this by 24 will give the number of days for a one-way trip. The children also may be interested in how long a trip to Mars would take. As the two planets, Earth and Mars, move about the sun, the shortest distance between them is about 35,000,000 miles.

If a person could live at all on Pluto he would be unlikely to live to be a whole year old, because a year there is about 248 times as long as one of ours. But if it were possible to live on Mercury, a child who is nine years old here would be 37 years old there, for a year on Mercury is shorter. Mercury, unfortunately, might not be a comfortable place to live that long, for there is no air to breathe, and with the sun always shining overhead on one side of the planet, that side becomes so hot that a person would be roasted; whereas on the other side the sun never shines, and the temperature is far lower than anything people could endure.

For children, reading is necessarily the principal source of information about the sky. It is fortunate that the reading can be as fascinating as it is. It can be stimulating to learn that directly overhead in the early hours of a fall evening is a large square of stars that the ancients thought was part of a horse with wings. The flying horse is used as a symbol by one of the gasoline companies today. Facts about the sky can stir the imagination of a child. Our earth is about 25,000 miles in circumference and turns once every 24 hours — which is a speed of more than a thousand miles an hour at the equator. The air tends to travel with us; otherwise the wind would be greater than that of the strongest hurricane. Children delight in reporting the surprising information they read. A teacher can help children to weave the facts they find into broad concepts of the universe. Facts are meaningful and interesting when used to explain something the child has observed in the sky. The Flying Horse, Pegasus, can be observed when the ancient myths are read. Information about Mars and the other planets will be pertinent when some child reports having seen one of the planets. When the children read about craters on the moon, if binoculars can be obtained the class will enjoy observing what their books have described.

Children at work studying the sky

A discussion began in one class when the teacher asked the children whether they could see farther in the daytime or at night — a question with a catch to it, something that often appeals to children. With interest aroused, more serious questions followed regarding the distance to stars, what stars really are, and how distant objects seem smaller. In another class, a third grade, a spontaneous discussion of shadows developed. One girl said that she thought only trees and people had shadows; so the class placed different objects in the sunlight at the window to show that anything which light cannot penetrate has a shadow. Someone recalled that one of the books explained how to tell time by the sun, and the class decided to experiment. In still another class, a second grade, Frances asked, "Is there really a man in the moon?" Jay said he'd heard that the moon is made of green cheese, and he wondered if that could be true. In considering these two questions the class raised additional ones and prepared a list for further study:

1. Is the moon made of green cheese or what?
2. We should learn about planets. Their names.
3. What keeps planets in place?
4. What keeps planets moving?
5. How far apart are the planets?
6. Are there people on the planets?
7. How do we learn about planets and stars?
8. How far away is the sun from the moon?
9. How hot is the sun?
10. What is the sun made of?
11. What color is the sun?
12. Is a rainbow hot or cold?
13. Is there a man in the moon?

To help answer the questions, many of the children brought books from home and from the public library. Some of the questions listed proved more helpful than others as study guides, yet even the poor ones served as starting points for the children. At night, often with the help of parents, the children observed the Big Dipper, the Milky Way, and other "star patterns" that had been discussed and read about at school. An eclipse occurred during the study, and much reading as well as observation resulted. Various children sketched on the board their impressions of the moon during the eclipse. Some children went to the science museum and the planetarium. Ruth wanted to make a planetarium at school. She and the teacher decided that they could get the same effect by punching holes in dark paper. When Ruth brought the paper to the teacher, the holes representing the Big Dipper were not very conspicuous; so the teacher held the paper up to the light at the window. The outline of a dipper stood out vividly there.

Ruth said, "I know, I'll put it in the window!" She taped it to the glass and on the window sill laid a placard explaining: "This is a star pattern. There are many star patterns. It is not hard to see it is a dipper."

A month later, at Easter, Michael used the same technique, punching holes in dark paper to depict a scene of hills topped by three crosses, "a river of Mary's tears," and a stone in front of the tomb. He wrote a story of Jesus to accompany the picture — a completely spontaneous effort, without a word of suggestion or encouragement from the teacher. The scene was most effectively portrayed and was a beautiful piece of creative art, adapting a technique developed in the boy's science work.

The class prepared a booklet listing the questions raised and the answers finally decided upon. The answer to the sixth question led to an argument. One boy opposed all the others, insisting that there are people on the planets, but offering no evidence to refute theirs. He began with an amused glint in his eye, but as the argument progressed his insistence became more serious. Certain clues in his behavior indicated to the teacher what he had in mind, and she finally insisted that he tell the class.

He said: "Well, we are all people, aren't we? And the earth is a planet, isn't it?"

So the answer recorded for the sixth question was: "Yes — on earth."

SOME INITIAL CONCEPTS

When one child said, "If I could go up there and push back that blue part, I could look right up into heaven," the teacher interpreted the statement as evidence of interest in the sky and also as evidence of limited understanding. The school can help children to understand what they see in the sky, and these explanations will be the foundation upon which the broader, more mature concepts will be built. The first goal may be simply to gain an increasing awareness of the stars, the sun, and the moon. Before a child can learn why the moon has phases he must observe that it does have phases; and before he can realize that there are such changes he must become aware that there is a moon. Gaining a clear impression of the moon's appearance now will make it possible to realize a week from now that the appearance has changed. The question *why* will follow logically and spontaneously.

Shadows and reflections

Small children often become conscious of shadows; this awareness can lead to some valuable learnings if encouraged. Through contrasting the warmth that they feel in direct sunlight with the coolness of a shady spot, children can learn that we get heat and light from the sun. The heat is greater when the sun is more nearly overhead. By observing the changing length and direction of shadows, and the direction of the sun itself, children can learn that the sun seems to move. Eventually the change will be interpreted as due to the movement of the earth. Activities such as sketching shadows of the children on sheets of butcher paper or making sun dials likewise can be directed toward developing basic knowledge of the sky and of light. Since our knowledge of the sky comes through our eyes by means of light, a study of light and a study of the sky can be closely integrated wherever desired. The lines that form a shadow in the sunlight or a beam of light in darkness show that light travels in a straight line. While the sun is shining, if a window is covered except for a small hole, a beam of light can be made visible with chalk dust. Light will penetrate some objects better than others. We see through window glass, for light will penetrate the glass, but a brick wall casts a shadow. A shadow is dark. Darkness is the absence of light.

An interesting sundial can easily be constructed on the schoolroom floor or, better yet, on the sidewalk nearby. With the footprints of a child marked on the walk, the direction of his shadow can be marked at hourly intervals with lines radiating from the center where the child stands. To use the sundial later, all a child need do is step onto the footprints and note the direction of the shadow.

The angle at which a beam of light is reflected from a mirror or other surface is worth noting. The children in one class noticed that sunlight from the school-room window was reflected from a girl's barrette onto the wall. The spot on the wall moved when she moved. In another case a boy was writing at his desk when he noticed that the sunlight was reflected from the metal band on his pencil, casting a disk of light onto his desk. He asked the teacher what had happened, and, realizing the significance of it, she had him show the other children.

Older children will learn that most of the objects we see are seen by re-flected light, and that colored objects reflect only a part of the light and absorb the remainder. White clothing is cool and black is warm, for the black material absorbs light, but white objects reflect the light to our eyes. That black is the absence of light can be demonstrated by asking children to note what color they see in a closet, at home or at school, with the door closed and all cracks blocked. One teacher took her class outside to the bicycle rack, and with a flashlight showed that the red reflectors on the bicycles have no light of their own but reflect the light from some other source.

The changing seasons

An awareness of the seasons is of value in itself, and also can lead to further understandings. A fairly common practice of primary classes is to take a short walk to a park or into the open countryside, there to observe the foliage, the animals, the temperature, the angle of the sun. At some time later another walk is taken and comparisons are made. After each trip there is often a discussion of the changes noted. Drawings are made of any sights that impressed the children, and, if any collecting was done, the materials are displayed. Leaves may show a change in size from one trip to the next; flowers may have changed to seed pods; plants and animals observed on one trip may be gone by the next. The weather will have changed; the angle of the sun and the lengths of shadows will be different. At the same time the length of day can be noted. The length of day and the angle of the sun's rays are the two factors that account for our change of seasons — but that interpretation will probably come later. At first it will suffice to establish the facts themselves, facts that the teacher knows are significant.

Changes in the sky at night

The stars appear to move across the sky each night much as the sun does each day, and for the same reason — the rotation of the earth. A child can become aware of such movement by observing the stars early on a winter evening; then some night when the child is staying up late, he can make another observation and note a change in the position of the stars. In addition to the apparent daily motion, there is an apparent seasonal motion of the stars. If children learn to locate a certain group of stars, such as the constellation Orion, at about the same hour each evening, then some months later when they look for them again, the stars will be found farther to the west, owing to the earth's eastward movement about the sun. But the interpretation should not be made until observations have established the facts. It is sufficient at first simply to note the position of the stars. The moon goes through even more obvious changes. In addition to its phases, the moon appears to move westward each night, but on succeeding nights at the same hour it will be found to the east of its previous position. If one person were circling a city block in an automobile while another individual circled it on foot, each time the first passed the second, the second would seem to fall behind, but on succeeding trips the pedestrian would be observed at an advanced position. As the earth turns eastward each day, the moon, moving in the same direction more slowly, seems to fall behind, westward; but on succeeding nights the moon is east of its previous position, because it actually is moving in an easterly direction about the earth. The interpretation is not complex, provided that the facts are clearly established by observation. Accordingly, the school may encourage children to note the position of the moon on successive nights, with the interpretation being

Fig. 43

A visit to an observatory is a rewarding experience.

made when the children are ready for it. Because the moon circles the earth in approximately a month, whereas the apparent motion of the stars takes a year, the changing positions of the moon very likely will be noted first by the children.

Observing the stars and planets

Our moon and the planets are found in only one portion of the sky: that is, near the path from east to west along which the sun appears to move each day. The visible planets are quite bright, and they do not twinkle. Twinkling, incidentally, is due to the bending of light by our atmosphere when it is unevenly heated; similarly objects seen beyond a metal roof or down a highway in the summer seem to shimmer. Though actually much smaller than stars, the planets are much closer and appear to have broader diameters; therefore the light from a planet is not as likely to be cut off by the flickering due to our atmosphere as is the narrow beam of light from a star. The positions of the planets along their east–west path change in relation to the background of more distant stars, but an almanac will tell where to locate them. Children should learn that there are planets other than our own and that their positions in the sky change.

The North Star actually is much brighter than our sun, but it appears less bright because of the distance. Some stars appear brighter than others, and some are larger than others, but what we see is brightness, not size. Stars are so far from us that even in a large telescope they are seen as mere points of light, in spite of their tremendous size. Often the brighter star is simply the closer one. Children can compare the stars to lights seen outside on a dark night when both the distance and the actual brightness of a light determine how bright it seems.

Stars vary in color from red to blue-white according to the temperature. If a fine iron wire is heated in a flame it will glow red, then orange, then yellow as it becomes hotter. In the classroom it probably will not be possible to heat a wire until it is white-hot or until it reaches the blue-white temperature. Children should be able to note differences in the colors of stars. Our sun gives a yellow color, for its temperature is a medium one for stars.

If an eclipse occurs, it should be observed. Meteors also should be noted. Though actually quite small in most cases, meteors appear as bright as stars, because they are close enough to be in our atmosphere. Children can learn what meteors are, how they glow as a result of friction with the air, and that they are not "shooting stars." Stars are much larger than the earth, but meteors are small, most of them being but a fraction of an inch in diameter. An eclipse or a shower of meteors can arouse either fear and confusion or wholesome interest, depending upon the attitude taken and upon the degree of understanding. Accordingly, it is worthwhile for these phenomena, when observed, to be discussed in the school, where the discussion will develop a favorable emotional tone based on understanding.

THE CONSTELLATIONS AND THEIR STORIES

The origins of the constellation myths date back to the obscurity of prehistoric times, but it seems probable that many complex factors were involved as people strove to make interpretations in accord with their own beliefs and customs. Psychologists today use random blotches of ink in one process of psychological analysis, the Rorschach tests. What the patient sees in the blotches is presumed to be a projection of what he has in mind. Likewise the ancients saw in the stars the outlines of gods, heroes, and animals that were meaningful to them. In the Tigris-Euphrates and adjacent regions, a shepherd lying on his back, leisurely tending his flock, had plenty of time to study the stars. The atmosphere at that latitude is exceptionally clear, and with no city lights and no industrial smoke or fog, the stars were strikingly conspicuous. Once a pattern among the stars was noted and pointed out to friends, who also could then see the figure, it was easy to assume that the figure did exist, and the phantasy gained credence as a rumor does today. Even the authorities of that day, the astrologers, could see the figures, and the limited facts that they learned while observing only served to substantiate and extend the myths.

Interpreting the constellation myths

Children can be taught that constellations and the stories of the constellations are legendary rather than true. An effective way of teaching this is to cover the blackboard with random dots, much as the stars are scattered about the sky. To emphasize the random nature of the dots, the help of several children may be enlisted to put the dots quickly on the board. Then, as the ancients did with the stars, the children can study the dots, using their imaginations to locate figures on the blackboard. Being modern children, with present-day objects and persons in their thoughts, they probably will see figures that differ somewhat from those seen by the ancients. When a child sees the pattern of an object, he may be asked to outline it on the board by connecting the dots with lines.

In a first grade, after the teacher had placed dots hit-or-miss on the blackboard to represent the stars, the children found a donkey, a sheep, and a duck. In their language lesson one of the children told a story about "How the Donkey Landed in the Sky." In the teacher's opinion the experience was creative and in no way confusing, and helped the children to understand how other people came to make up similar stories about the stars.

In like manner a third grade located a duck's head, a boot, a nut, a rabbit, and a dog — although some thought that the latter looked more like an owl. Other figures seen were a bed, a moon, a camel, a man, a pig, a swan, a candlestick, and a tree. A number of stories similar to the following were written:

How the Pig Got Up to the Sky

Once there was a pig who liked to dig. One day he started to dig a hole. He dug and he dug. Then he dug some more. When night came, he stopped. When morning came he started again. He dug such a big hole that he dug right out to the sky. He never got back to earth again.

The Owl Story

Once upon a time in a great big forest there stood a great big oak tree. In the tree there lived a mother owl and her baby owl. One day the forest caught fire and all the birds and beasts ran from all directions — from the north, the west, the east, and the south. After the fire died down, all the animals tried to find new homes, but the owls couldn't find any tree; so God took them up into the sky.

A fifth grade found that their books called the Big Dipper a Big Bear, but in their own observations the class could see little resemblance to a bear. So a discussion developed regarding the way in which stars got their names and how the stories about them grew. At the teacher's suggestion they put dots on the board and drew pictures from them to see how the ancients must have imagined objects in the sky. With great enthusiasm the children filled the board with a variety of outlines: a cowboy, a boat, a fish, a swan, a duck, a chicken, a dog, a pig's head, a peace pipe, a fingernail, a saxophone, and a rocket ship. After using all available space, the children thought of stories to explain how the various objects got into the sky and what they were doing there:

The Peace Pipe

Two Indians were smoking a peace pipe. When they finished, they kept on arguing. So one Indian said to the other, "Peace pipe no good." So he threw it so high that it landed in the sky and stuck there.

The Dog

A dog was walking along a dusty road. He suddenly stopped, for ahead of him he saw an angel. This angel told the dog that the children in heaven wanted a friend. She cast a spell over him, and he was taken to heaven to be the children's friend.

How the Peace Pipe Got Up in Heaven

There was a man smoking a peace pipe. He died and he went up into heaven. There was a pig, dog, and duck up there. The man had the peace pipe in his mouth. The duck, pig, and dog were so hungry that they ate the man up. They left the pipe alone.

The Peace Pipe

Once upon a time many moons ago a chief of a tribe died and the braves buried him with his bow and arrows, spear, and his peace pipe. On his way to heaven his peace pipe dropped but did not fall all the way to earth. And ever since then the peace pipe has been up in the sky.

The Fingernail

There was a little girl who always bit a fingernail. The fingernail that she bit didn't like to be bitten; so the fingernail broke off and ran away. He ran and

ran until he met a bird. . . . The bird took him up and put him on a star. That
is how the fingernail got in the sky.

The last story was written by a girl who was concerned about her own habit
of biting fingernails. A great deal of insight into the child's own viewpoint can
be obtained through such creative stories, and, needless to say, the children are
learning to express themselves in a situation that has meaning to them.

The constellation Orion

Today astronomers use the constellations as one way of locating stars. Orion
is a good constellation to know, for it is conspicuously bright and easy to locate
in the early evenings from December to April and includes many points of
interest. To the ancients Orion was a hunter, but to the modern child it may
look more like a baseball diamond; in which case Betelgeuse is the bright star
in left field, and the stars in Orion's belt become third base, shortstop, and
second base. Other positions also are represented clearly. About the catcher,
Orion's sword, is a bright mass of glowing gas, a gaseous nebula, that can be
seen as a haze through field glasses, and some say they can detect it with the
naked eye. Betelgeuse is on Orion's shoulder, whereas an even brighter star,
Rigel, is on Orion's foot in the southern portion of the constellation. In the
baseball analogy Rigel is a batter waiting his turn. Rigel is actually the brightest star known, 14,000 times as bright as our sun, although because of its distance, 460 light years, a few closer ones — Sirius, Vega, Capella, and Arcturus
— appear brighter to our eyes. At our latitude, about 40° N., Betelgeuse follows as the eighth brightest star to our eyes. Betelgeuse is interesting, for it is
one of the largest stars known. Being a variable star, it varies in size and
brightness. At its maximum some have found it to be the largest of all stars,
although other measurements show Antares larger. Antares is visible near the
southern horizon during the summer months. Betelgeuse is a reddish color and
is known as a red giant, whereas Rigel is much hotter, being a blue-white color.
Most of the stars in Orion are at a blue-white temperature, but if Betelgeuse
were much cooler it would not glow at all. Many of the stars in Orion are not
single stars, as they seem, but several; for example, the star near Orion's belt,
the runner off third base, is actually five stars that appear as one to the naked
eye, and the third baseman is a double star. In some cases such groups are held
together by their own gravity, but in other cases they merely seem to be together, because they are in approximately the same direction from us. If
binoculars are available, it will be interesting to note particularly the nebula in

Orion. Notice also that when the instrument is properly focused the points of light from even the largest and brightest stars are not magnified, but they do appear brighter, and more stars can be observed than with the unaided eye.

According to the myths, Orion was a hunter, tall, handsome, and skillful, but because of his conceit the gods had him bitten by a scorpion and placed in the sky. The scorpion also is in the sky but is visible only in the summer.

Some brilliant constellations of winter

Once a constellation is known, it is relatively easy to locate others with reference to the first. Thus the bright star Sirius is part of the constellation Canis Major, which is a large dog trailing along at Orion's heel. It rises each night in the east just behind Orion. Canis Minor, the small dog, is nearby — above and north of the big dog. A straight line from Rigel through Betelgeuse will lead to two bright stars, Castor and Pollux, in the constellation Gemini. The brighter of the two is Pollux. The distance from Rigel to Betelgeuse is about half the distance from Betelgeuse to the twin stars. Gemini is north of Canis Minor. North of Orion and west of Gemini is a large kite-shaped, pentagonal group of stars, Auriga, the brightest of which is Capella. Almost equidistant from Betelgeuse and Capella, but west of both, is Aldebaran, in the constellation Taurus. The most conspicuous portion of Taurus, at the head of the bull, is a V-shaped group of stars called the Hyades. The Hyades is an actual cluster of stars held together by gravitational attraction. Another such cluster in Taurus is the Pleiades, or Seven Sisters (only six, however, are visible to the naked eye). To some the Pleiades have the appearance of a small dipper. On a line from Betelgeuse the Pleiades are just beyond the Hyades. When Orion is observed in the southeast, Vega, a brilliant white star, can be seen in the northwest. Capella is yellow like our sun, and Aldebaran, somewhat cooler, is an orange color.

Using a star chart

If a star chart is used to locate the stars, it is helpful, while observing directly above, to hold the chart overhead, with the northern portion of the chart pointing north. While observing Orion in the south, the chart may be held in that direction with the southern portion down. Likewise, when looking north, east, or west, if the corresponding portion of the map is held down and in the direction under consideration, the stars will be easier to locate, for such a practice helps to compensate for the fact that a chart is on a flat paper whereas the sky

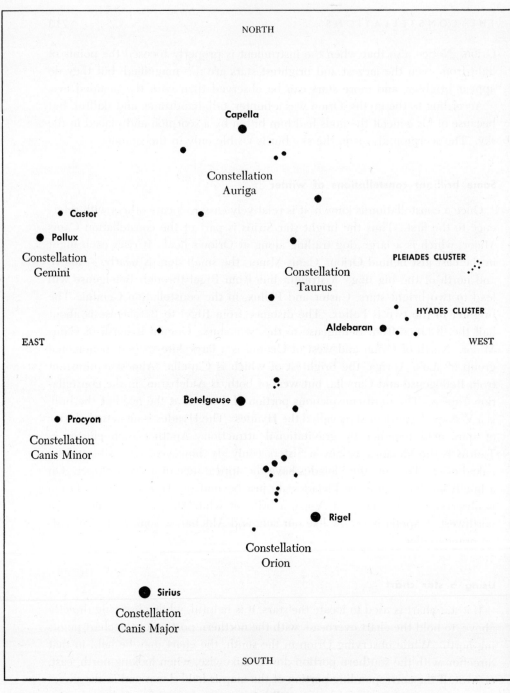

Fig. 44

The constellation Orion and neighboring stars as seen toward the south at about 9 P.M. during January and February. The constellation Auriga will be approximately at the zenith. East and West will appear in the true position when chart is held above one's head.

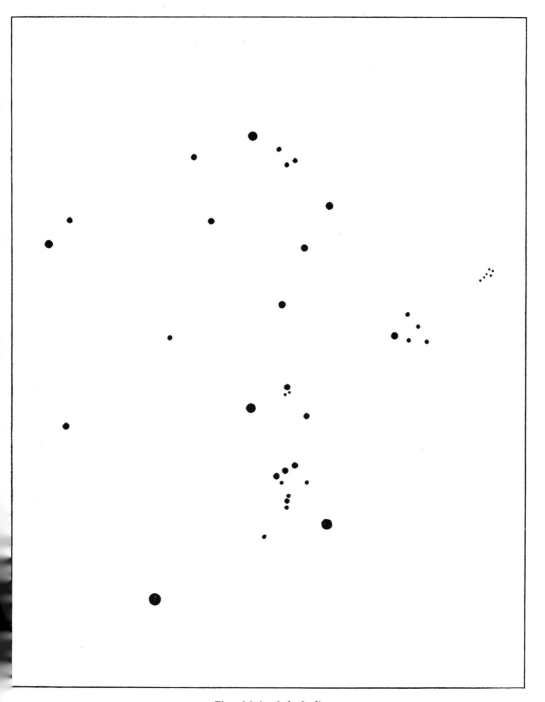

Fig. 44 (unlabeled)

The constellation Orion and neighboring stars as seen toward the south at
about 9 P.M. during January and February

itself is curved. It will also be noted that when a star is observed in the east, a westerly direction will be above the star and the easterly direction will be toward the horizon.

Reporting observations

While discussing a news item about the Palomar observatory, several of the children in the fifth grade who had looked through telescopes told about their experiences. The teacher was surprised to find that many knew the Big and Little Dippers, the North Star, Venus, and several others. Then eventually, on the first clear night, a few of the class who lived nearby came to the teacher's house. They observed the stars already discussed and also located the constellation Orion. The next day at school the group reported what had been seen and where. On the following morning other children arrived in great excitement, for they too had located these stars. Whenever the teacher can help with observations, the help will be a great asset, but in many situations the children may have to look for the stars without immediate assistance. In any case, actual observations should be made and reported to the class.

Reading and discussion should stimulate continued observation and reporting, for as more is learned, more can be detected in the observations. The children in one third grade developed so much interest that before they went to bed each night they would look at the sky and the next day would bring to class sketches of the moon and of certain stars as they saw them. The winter months are a good time to observe, not only because bright stars are visible then, but also because darkness comes early — which makes it possible for children to observe before going to bed.

To represent the stars which children report having seen, holes can be punched in a sheet of heavy, dark paper — large holes for bright stars and small holes for the small stars. The top and bottom may be removed from a large oatmeal carton, a flashlight or reading lamp placed inside, and the star chart fitted over the end of the carton facing the children observing. Or, as already noted, the chart may be placed in the window. When a star is mentioned, it can be pointed out on the chart and its position in the sky indicated. If colors are desired, the appropriate color of cellophane may be pasted over the hole.

After singing the song "Twinkle, Twinkle, Little Star," the first grade was talking about the stars, and Cappy, whose father is an airplane pilot, said that if we go up high enough in an airplane the stars don't twinkle. Susan said that the stars are little suns, but the teacher explained that the stars are large, many of them larger than our sun, though more distant. In a similar situation another teacher pointed out that in pictures the small objects are simply the distant ones, that through a window we can see houses, automobiles, trees, and even mountains — all of them actually larger than the window itself. Similarly, airplanes seen at a great distance appear to be moving slowly. The stars are in even more rapid motion, but at immensely greater distances they appear not to be moving at all, except for the daily and seasonal motions of the earth. Children are familiar with the fact that the hands of a clock cannot be seen to move, although they actually do, and the movement can be detected after a period of time. The stars are so distant that even after many lifetimes the positions of most stars in the sky appear virtually unchanged, even though their actual motion is much faster than anything a child is able to imagine, including the speeds of rocket ships.

One of the basic methods, called *parallax*, by which astronomers determine the distance to many of the stars can be conveniently illustrated by holding up a pencil and looking at it first with one eye and then the other. Note that the pencil seems to shift in relation to the background of the room. Repeat the process with the pencil held at arm's length and notice that the shift is less. Thus the amount of shifting is an indication of the distance from the eye to the pencil. Our eyes are some distance apart; thus by using first one and then the other, the observer looks first from one direction and then from another. Likewise, as the earth moves about the sun, astronomers see the stars from different positions and can detect a slight shift in the nearer stars. From the amount of shift the distance can be computed. The parallax of the stars, however, is too slight to be detected with the naked eye.

INTERPRETING THE SOLAR SYSTEM

The movements of the moon and the planets can be demonstrated with models. A suitable globe or large ball can represent the earth, a smaller ball the moon. A glass jar will serve as a base for either ball. A light bulb in a socket with a long cord may be used to represent the sun. The shades at the windows should be drawn. With such equipment the movements of the earth and moon about the sun can be shown, as well as the consequent phases of the moon, eclipses of sun and moon, the cause of seasons, and day and night. The easiest of these to understand, and hence often the first to be shown, is the cause of day and night. A bit of modeling clay holding a matchstick upright will serve to mark the location of the school on the ball or globe.

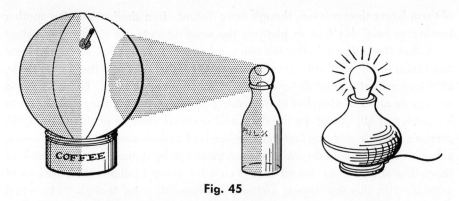

Fig. 45

Demonstrating an eclipse of the sun with a basketball, a tennis ball, and a reading lamp to represent the earth, the moon, and the sun

The cause of day and night interpreted with models

One way to demonstrate the cause of day and night is to have the class gather in a circle, and, with models of the sun and earth on the floor before them, allow the children to work out their own explanation. Someone may express his idea of what causes daylight and darkness, and if the idea is good, whether actually correct or not, he can be given the opportunity of demonstrating what he means, using the models. He should take care to stand or kneel where he will not block the view of others — directly in front of his own empty chair, perhaps; and he should be allowed to demonstrate his views without interruption. After he has finished, someone else may correct him, if the idea did not work out or for any reason is not acceptable to the class. Thus the teacher need not give a verdict of right or wrong, but may let the class work out its own solution. The second suggestion may be demonstrated as the first was, and if that needs modification or correction, other suggestions and demonstrations may follow until an acceptable solution is reached, whereupon the teacher's opinion may be added. Ordinarily the child should express his idea in words before demonstrating, for most people are unable to do both at once effectively, and the others will be unable to follow the thinking. A challenging problem situation is provided by this approach, and the children are actively participating, seeking a solution; it has proved effective with numerous classes and a great variety of age levels. Understanding is likely to be greater than if ready-made explanations are given by the teacher, and the process will arouse more enthusiasm among the children. In some cases questions may be raised that cannot be satisfactorily answered at the time. The disagreement must be resolved by recourse to further reference work and observation. Then, with the models again, another attempt may be made to resolve the problem at issue.

To demonstrate the cause of day and night, the children may locate the position of the sun locally at noon, at sunrise, at sunset, and at midnight. Then they may determine in which direction the earth must turn for the sun to rise in the east. It can be shown with the models that part of the earth is having daylight while the other side is having night. The difference in time of day between East and West also can be explained.

Interpreting the seasons with models

The children will have read that the earth moves about the sun, and if they have observed that the apparent seasonal movement of the stars is westward, then the earth must be moving eastward to produce such an effect. Someone usually will suggest that summers are warmer than winters because we are closer to the sun during the summer; but if that be true, why is Argentina having summer while we have winter? Actually, astronomers have found that we are about 94,500,000 miles from the sun in July and 91,300,000 miles from it in January: more than three million miles closer during the winter. So apparently the distance to the sun is not the main factor in seasonal changes.

Before models are used to explain the seasons, children should know that the sun is more nearly overhead during the summer, and that the period of daylight is longer at that time; both are factors that make it hotter in the summer. When a flashlight is held directly above the floor or the blackboard, the circle of light that it forms is small and concentrated; whereas when it is held at an angle the circle is large and the light is diffused. In each case the distance should be the same, perhaps the length of a yardstick. Likewise, when the sun is high in the sky the rays are concentrated, and the heating is more intense than when the sun is close to the horizon. With models the children themselves can determine how it is that the days are longer and the sun is more nearly overhead in the summer. The reason, of course, is that the earth's axis is inclined to the plane of its orbit, rather than perpendicular. With some point on the ceiling not directly overhead to represent the North Star, the children can show how the earth moves about the sun with the Pole Star always above our North Pole. By this time they should begin to see how such a movement will determine the length of the day and the direction of the sun's rays — and hence the seasons. In the summer, while the sun is overhead in the northern hemisphere, the point which marks the school on the globe moves through an area of light for more than half the distance of the globe's daily rotation. During the winter, while the earth is at the other end of its orbit, the effect is quite the opposite.

At points halfway between the two extremes it can be shown that the nights and days are of equal length, for a spot on the globe which represents the school passes through equal areas of daylight and darkness as the globe rotates. These two dates, known as the vernal or spring equinox (equal night) and the autumnal equinox, are March 21 and about September 23. The point at which the sun is most nearly overhead and the daylight is the longest of the year is called the summer solstice, and the opposite point is the winter solstice. The terms are not essential for children, unless needed to interpret newspaper accounts at the corresponding season. The point at which we in the northern hemisphere receive the most heat from the sun arrives about June 22, yet the warmer days of summer follow at a later date. Likewise, the coldest day is not December 22. The seasons lag behind for the same reason that noon, when the sun is most nearly overhead, is seldom the hottest time of day. Anyone who has built a fire in a stove to heat a cold room may realize that even with the stove red hot the room may remain cold for a time. Officially the beginning of each season is marked by an equinox or solstice; thus spring begins on March 21 and extends to about June 22.

Using the models, and remembering that stars are observed overhead at night (since during the day the sun is too bright), it should be possible to see why the stars change with the seasons. The stars that are visible will be those on the side of the earth that is opposite the sun, and as the earth moves eastward about the sun the stars appear to move in the opposite direction. With the models it can be shown that the sun shines in all directions, not only upon the earth. The movement of other planets about the sun can be represented with additional models. All planets move in an easterly direction and in approximately the same plane — that is, on the floor in this case. The actual path of the earth about the sun is marked in the sky by the apparent path of the sun each day; thus the true orbit is at a sharp angle to that used for the models on the floor. While working with the models, it may be noted that *up* is always away from the center of the earth; in the universe beyond our earth the word has no meaning.

Interpreting eclipses and the phases of the moon

The revolution of the moon about the earth can be interpreted with a lamp for the sun and models for the earth and moon. If no problem has yet been raised, one way to begin is by questioning the children to determine the extent of their understanding. Unless they can recall having seen the moon in its various phases, it will be fruitless to attempt an explanation of something that has not been observed. It may be wise to postpone the use of the models until the children have watched the moon for a time and have noticed the changes and the length of time between them. In case a child has observed a crescent moon he may attempt to explain its appearance. With the models it can be shown that as the moon proceeds in its orbit around the earth, half the moon is lighted at all times, except when the moon passes into the shadow of the earth, in which case an eclipse of the moon has occurred. However, the phases are gradual changes, not to be accounted for in this abrupt manner. As the children are gathered about the models, those who see the moon from the direction of the earth will note that ordinarily only a portion of the lighted half is visible. With the moon approximately in the direction of the sun, the dark side will be toward the earth, and the moon will not be visible; this phase is called the dark of the moon. As the moon moves eastward along its orbit, a small crescent of the lighted portion becomes visible from the earth and is called the new moon or crescent moon. With this explanation it should be obvious that the crescent moon holds no water and has no effect on the weather.

As the moon moves eastward, a point will be reached at which half of the portion of the moon that faces the earth appears lighted. This phase, sometimes referred to as a half-moon, is correctly designated as the first quarter. The moon is at a point one-fourth of the way around its orbit. Moving another fourth of the way, and avoiding an eclipse, the entire face of the moon as viewed from the earth will appear lighted. The moon is then full. With each phase it may be wise to have the children move to a point where it can be viewed from the direction of the earth. Moving along its orbit, the moon reaches the third quarter and then, again, the dark of the moon. There the moon is not only dark on the side toward us but is obscure in the bright light of midday. There is no moon at all in the sky overhead at night when the moon is dark. The moon then is on the opposite side of the earth.

While studying Indians, one third-grade class became interested in the moon and in the way Indians marked time by the moon — as to some extent we ourselves do. A month was originally a *moon* as the term was used by the Indians and by our own predecessors; but with the development of the calendar the month was adjusted so that twelve months would equal a year; hence the month is no longer exactly a moon. A week was the period from one lunar phase to the next; thus there are four weeks in a moon.

Whenever the moon, earth, and sun are in a direct line so that either the moon or sun is obscured, an eclipse occurs. An eclipse of the moon occurs when the moon is obscured, eclipsed, by the shadow of the earth; and an eclipse of the sun occurs when the moon passes between the earth and the sun, blocking the light from us. With the models it should be apparent that an eclipse of the moon occurs when the moon is full and that an eclipse of the sun occurs at the dark of the moon. As explained to this point, an eclipse of the sun should occur once each month, and an eclipse of the moon should occur equally often, but the children may realize that eclipses are not that frequent — and this poses another problem for the children. They should be helped to realize from the beginning that models do not give a completely accurate picture of the true situation. It should be explained that the sun is much farther away than the models show it, and is much larger than the earth; accordingly, the shadows cast are narrower and an eclipse much less likely to occur. Also as demonstrated here, the moon and earth are both moving in orbits along the floor, or a few inches above it, but actually the moon's orbit is inclined slightly, 5 degrees, to that of the earth. If the model of the moon is lifted somewhat as it moves between earth and sun and then lowered beneath the earth's shadow at the other end of its orbit, no eclipse will occur that month.

Direct observation of the moon itself should be stressed. Children should know that the moon is lighted by the sun. They can observe that the lighted portion of the real moon is always the side that is facing the sun. If models are used but no actual observation is done, the children may become familiar with the models but have little idea of what they represent, and thus the experience will be largely meaningless. Work should not end with the models, but the thinking should be transferred — extended to the motion of the real sun and moon as observed outdoors.

Preparing a chart of the planets

In becoming acquainted with the planets it is helpful to prepare a chart of facts as they are acquired, not for the purpose of mastering those facts, but in order that certain relationships may become apparent. As new information is discussed, it can be added to the chart, the chart being a record of progress. What facts are listed can be determined to some extent by the interests of the children and by the references available to them. The names of the sun and the planets may be placed along the top of the chart on the blackboard, on a sheet of butcher paper, or on whatever is available. Along the left side of the chart, headings for the type of information sought can be listed, including the diameter in thousands of miles, the distance from the sun in millions of miles, the length of year as compared to ours, and whatever else the children may decide should be included. Accordingly, Mercury's data would be 3 for the diameter, 36 for the distance, and ¼ for the year. Most children are interested in the possibility of life on other planets — which is dependent upon the atmosphere and the temperature. Without oxygen and a moderate temperature, life as we know it would be impossible. The number of moons, the length of a day, and other information can be added as desired. As the facts are gathered it will become apparent that the more distant planets have longer years and cooler temperatures. The distant planets are probably too cold for life; Mercury has no atmosphere. Only Venus and Mars, in addition to the earth, are reasonable possibilities, and no oxygen has been detected on Venus. The ammonia and methane that constitute a large share of the atmosphere on Jupiter would be poisonous gases for us.

Using models to show size and distance

An adequate impression of the immense size of our solar system and of the universe can hardly be gathered from reading alone. Making models to scale will help. The data gathered for the chart will provide a convenient source of information regarding the size and distance of each planet. A convenient scale for the models is 1 inch for 32,000 miles. With that scale the diameter of each planet can be divided by 32,000 to determine how many inches the diameter of the model should be. According to the scale, the diameter of the sun will be 27 inches; Mercury a scant ⅛ inch; Venus and the earth each almost ¼ inch; Mars, ⅛; Jupiter, 2¾; Saturn, 2⅜; Uranus and Neptune, 1 inch each; and Pluto perhaps ¼ inch. Circles may be cut from heavy paper or cardboard to represent the sun and the planets, then pinned to the bulletin board to show the relative sizes. A small placard may be posted below each planet giving some facts about it that are not included on the chart.

Some conception of the relative distances can be gained if the class attempts to place the models at correct distances from the sun. The earth is 93,000,000 miles from the sun, which divided by the 32,000 will give a distance for the models of almost 3,000 inches, or 250 feet — ⅚ the length of a football field! By the same scale, Pluto would have to be almost two miles away. Obviously the models cannot be spaced at their correct distances from the sun and still remain in the classroom, but the information can be included on the placard posted with each model. It becomes apparent why an adequate conception of the distances is difficult to convey through books alone, for if the distance in an illustration were reduced to the size of a page, the planets themselves, by the same scale, would become invisible. Alpha Centauri, a star of the southern hemisphere, is our closest visible star, being only half the distance of Sirius; yet by our scale a model of Alpha Centauri would need to be halfway around the earth, on the opposite side from us.

SOME EXPERIENCES WITH LIGHT

The light with which we see comes to us from the sky, much of it reaching us directly from the sun and stars, some of it indirectly as reflected from one object to another. It is only through light that we have knowledge of the stars, the sun, and the planets. Accordingly, an understanding of light is closely related to an understanding of the sky.

Experimenting with lenses

A reading glass was on the science table in a combined fifth and sixth grade. One boy happened to look through it toward the window where the sun was shining on the grounds beyond the school building. Suddenly he blurted in surprise: "Miss Silver, the trees are upside down!"

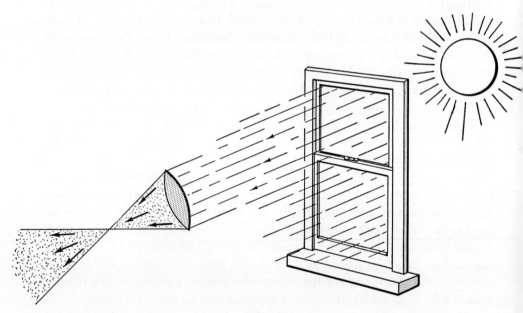

Fig. 46

Rays of light from the sun brought to a focus with a lens and made visible with chalk dust

If the children do not discover this phenomenon for themselves, the teacher may hold a magnifying glass between them and the window, and a question will be raised: why is the image inverted? Further experimentation with lenses may help to give an answer. If the magnifying glass is held in the direct sunlight, either outside or through the classroom window, the rays can be focused to a spot of intense light. A flashlight or a projection lantern can be used instead of the sun, although the room may have to be darkened somewhat, and the lens should not be held too close to the flashlight. Having the children gather in a small, compact circle about the experiment will help to cut off some of the outside light. The distance from the lens to the spot of light is called the focal length, and the spot of light is at the focal point, or focus. At any other distance the spot of light is broader. If two erasers are dusted together above the lens, the dust particles will reflect the light enough to make the beam visible, and it will be observed that the light from a magnifying glass converges toward the focal point and then broadens again. A diagram on the blackboard will help to show that beyond the focal point the rays are inverted, light that passed through the top of the lens being at the bottom of the image. With the chalk dust it will be seen that as the flashlight is brought closer to the lens the distance to the focal point is increased. Many cameras are adjustable so that by increasing the distance from the lens to the film close objects can be brought into focus. If an object viewed through the lens is closer than the focal length, the light rays do not come to a point, and the image is not inverted but magnified. The bending of the light rays by the lens gives an illusion that the points from which the rays come are farther apart and hence that the object seems larger than it actually is.

The bending of light. Children can see for themselves that a magnifying

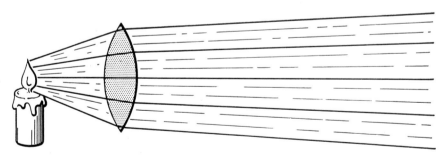

Fig. 47

If the source of light is closer than the focal length, the rays, though bent, are not brought to a focus.

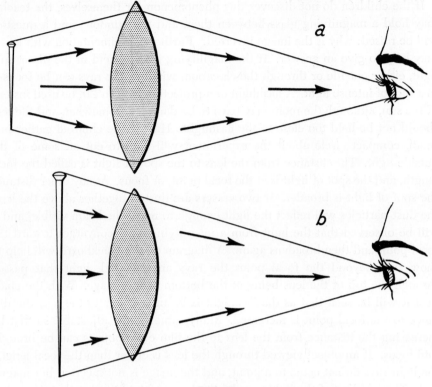

Fig. 48

The illusion of magnification. Light reflected from the pin is bent by the
lens, as in *a*, but seems to come in a straight line, as in *b*.

glass is thicker at the center than at the edges; the rays of light bend toward
the center, where the glass is thicker. A glass or jar of water will give a similar
effect. Occasionally window glass is of uneven thickness, and objects seen
through it are distorted. A yardstick or ruler in a pan of water will appear bent,
but actually it is the rays of light that are bent, not the ruler. If a coin is placed
in the bottom of a pan, and a child stands where the coin is barely visible over
the edge and then takes a step backward, the coin will be just out of sight.
Another person then should pour water slowly into the pan, taking care not to
move the coin. As the water rises in the pan, the coin will again become visible.
The water has caused the light reflected from the coin to be bent toward the
child's eye.

A camera. An interesting device similar to a pinhole camera can be con-

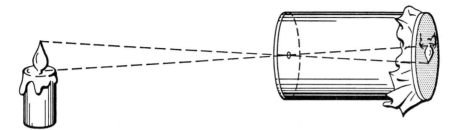

Fig. 49

An oatmeal box with a pinhole at one end and tissue paper at the other provides a simple example of a camera.

structed from an oatmeal box or other convenient carton by covering the top of the box with tissue paper in place of the lid and punching a very small hole in the bottom of the box. The tissue paper can be held in place with a rubber band, with glue, or by some other means. When the pinhole is held toward a bright source of light, such as the classroom window, a lamp, or a burning candle, an inverted image can be seen on the tissue paper. As with the lens, a diagram will help to explain why the image is inverted, but here the light travels in a straight line; it is not bent as it was by the lens. With a film in place of the tissue paper, it is possible (though ordinarily not practicable) to make a photograph with such a device, which is called a pinhole camera. The usual camera is similar, but has a lens instead of the pin hole.

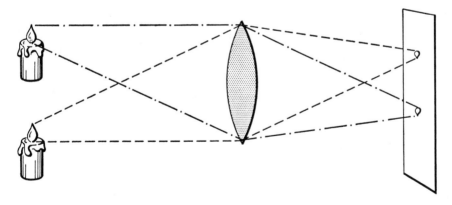

Fig. 50

Light can be brought to a focus on a sheet of paper, just as it is focused on film in a camera. The direction from which light comes to a lens determines where it is focused on the paper.

With a magnifying glass the light from a classroom window can be brought to a focus on a sheet of paper, forming a clear image of the window. The distance from the lens to the paper must be adjusted until the image is sharp, and it is best to stand in the dark part of the room, at some distance from the window. Likewise, if a camera is available and its back can be removed, it is possible to open the shutter as for a time exposure and see an inverted image through the lens. If tissue paper is placed over the back of the camera, an image can be seen on the paper as it was seen with the cardboard box.

Lenses for the human eye. If some rather strong spectacles (discarded) can be obtained for examination, the lenses for a farsighted person will be found to be thicker at the center than at the edges — that is, convex, like a magnifying glass. Lenses for a nearsighted person, however, are concave — thinner at the center. Using a beam of light and chalk dust, children can see for themselves that a concave lens causes the light rays to diverge rather than come to a focus. The human eye is similar to a camera, an inverted image being focused on the retina. In the nearsighted eye, distant objects are out of focus, the eyeball

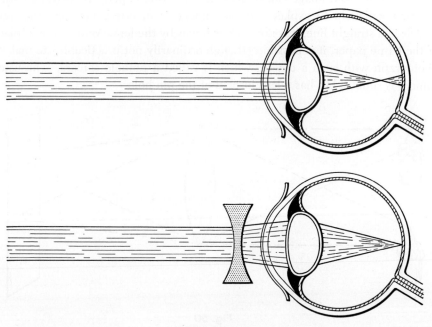

Fig. 51

Spectacles help the retina of a nearsighted eye to focus the light from a distant point.

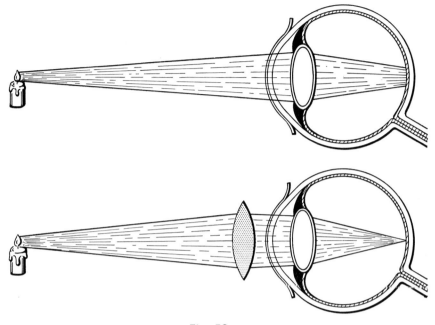

Fig. 52

Spectacles help the lens of a farsighted eye to focus the light from close objects.

being longer than the focal length of the lens; but, as already described, close objects come to a focus at a greater distance from the lens and hence can be seen by the nearsighted person. Spectacles with concave lenses cause the light rays to diverge enough for the lens of the eye to focus them at the proper distance. The farsighted eye is essentially the opposite: it needs a convex lens to assist its own lens in bringing objects to a focus at a shorter distance.

A telescope. If two magnifying glasses of different focal lengths are available, they can be used as a simple telescope by holding the short one close to the eye and the longer one at arm's length, or at whatever distance is necessary to bring objects into focus. The greater the difference in the focal lengths of the two lenses, the greater the magnification. If several lenses can be obtained, compare the magnification of one combination of lenses with that of another. The children will notice that the image is inverted. For observing objects in the sky the inversion does not matter, but for a terrestrial telescope the image must be reinverted. If asked, the children may be able to suggest that another convex lens will serve to reinvert the image. Another form of telescope, similar

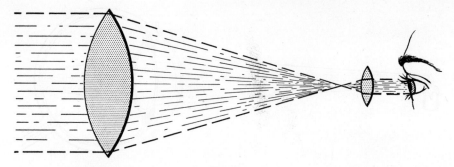

Fig. 53

With two lenses a telescope can be improvised. The large lens brings light to a focus so that dim objects, such as stars, appear brighter. The small lens projects the rays into the human eye.

to field glasses, can be illustrated with a concave lens near the eye and a convex lens a few inches away.

A prism and the colors of the rainbow

A triangular prism held in the sunlight at the window can be turned slowly until the colors of the rainbow appear on the ceiling or floor. A spectrum also can be obtained by directing the rays of a slide projector at an acute angle against the side of a rectangular glass aquarium filled with water. The aquarium can be turned slowly until a spectrum appears on the wall beyond the aquarium. It may be noted that white light is separated into colors when the beam strikes the glass at an angle; the beam is bent — some colors more than others — and the colors are separated as a result. An aquarium tank full of water and standing in the sunlight at the classroom window also may form a spectrum. When the sun strikes the tank at the proper angle, a spot of rainbow colors will appear somewhere in the room. A large tumbler filled with water and placed on the window sill, near the inner edge, in direct sunlight may project a spectrum on the floor. Try several tumblers to find one that will produce a good spectrum. Lay a sheet of white paper on the floor to show the colors clearly. One child brought to class an old chandelier crystal which served very well as a prism to give rainbow colors when placed in the sunlight. A spectrum even more like a rainbow can be obtained in the early morning or late afternoon by setting a sprinkler outside while the sun is shining and is low in the sky; a rainbow will be seen in the mist from the sprinkler.

White objects reflect all the light. Black objects reflect none, except perhaps a surface sheen, as on a highly polished pair of shoes. To show that colored objects reflect only a portion of the light — the color seen — locate some transparent colored papers. Food wrappers will do. In daylight, but not in direct sunshine, look through a blue paper at a red object. If the red object reflects only red light and the blue paper transmits only blue, no color at all will be seen. Actually, the red may be a blend of colors, and the blue may be thin enough to transmit some light other than blue; hence the object may not appear quite black. A surface sheen also will obscure the effect of the colors. Nevertheless, by experimenting with various papers and different colors, the children should be able to see that a colored object reflects only a portion of the daylight. The remaining colors are absorbed. (See also p. 373.)

Another way of showing how colors are reflected is to place a prism in the sunlight at the window and turn it until a good spectrum is obtained. (Or use a tumbler of water as previously described.) Let the colors fall onto various colored objects, such as books, art paper, or clothing. Compare these effects with the appearance of the spectrum when it falls on a white sheet of paper. Which colors of the spectrum are reflected most vividly by the various colored objects? As has been said, colored objects reflect only a portion of the light and absorb the rest. With the spectrum it is possible to see which portions are reflected.

Another source of colored light for the previous experiment can be obtained by placing colored cellophane or a transparent colored food wrapper over the end of a projection lantern — or several sheets of the colored paper may be placed between two lantern-slide cover glasses and projected just as a picture would be. Likewise, a large sheet of dark paper may be placed at the window and the shade drawn to darken the window above it. A hole cut in the paper and covered with a sheet of colored cellophane will provide a beam of colored light while the sun is shining on the window. When a mirror with a sheet of transparent colored paper on it is held in sunlight at the window, it will reflect a colored beam of light that can be used for experiments in a darkened room.

Motion pictures

In one third grade something was learned about motion pictures and projectors when a child brought to school a toy in the shape of a gun. Pulling the trigger of the gun would move a photographic film into position so that light passing through a lens in the barrel of the gun would give a magnified picture. Needless to say, the children were all very much interested, and learning was

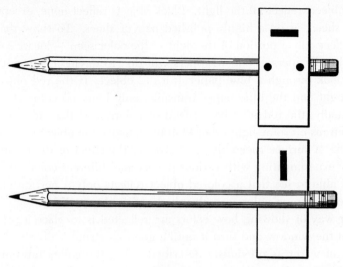

Fig. 54

Spinning the pencil will make the lines on the front and back of the card look like a cross.

easy. Toys often can serve as instructional materials. The persistence of vision which makes motion pictures possible can be illustrated by attaching a strip of cardboard near the end of a pencil so that the cardboard crosses the pencil, making a T-shaped figure. The cardboard may be attached with thumbtacks, a rubber band, or twine. If a vivid horizontal mark is made with a dark crayon near one end of the cardboard and the cardboard is then inverted and a vivid mark made vertically near the end which is opposite the other mark, the device will be ready for use. The pencil may be rolled between the hands to spin the cardboard — or, with the cardboard hanging over the edge of a table, the pencil may be rolled back and forth along the edge; and if the marks have been properly placed the two lines will seem to make a cross. The children can prepare similar devices on other cardboards. One, for example, may show a stick figure jumping up and down.

STUDY GUIDE

1. Indicate the grade with which you work, or would like to work; then explain how a study of the sky might be initiated in your class.
2. Observe the moon, one of the planets, or a group of stars; then explain how you would encourage children to make similar observations and report them. At the

library locate some of the myths and some of the facts concerning the stars and satellites observed.

3. To illustrate the probable origin of constellations and constellation myths, place random dots on a sheet of paper as children might do, then locate "constellations" and devise "myths" to explain what the figures are doing in the sky. What influence would these figures have on people, and what kind of character would a person have if born under one of these "signs"?

4. With improvised models show how you would explain the cause of day and night, the phases of the moon, an eclipse, and the seasons. What explanations would be suitable for the grade level you have specified, and under what circumstances would the explanations be made? What visual evidence do you have to support these explanations?

5. Prepare scale models of the planets, and determine where they must be placed in accordance with the scale. Add an explanatory placard, and display the models as children might do.

6. After preparing an experiment with light, present it to your class and explain what it means. Mention some practical applications of it, and explain how it might be used in work with children.

9

Chemical Changes

If dilute vinegar is heated in a tarnished aluminum pan, the acid of the vinegar will react with the metal of the pan, and the tarnish will be removed. The exposed aluminum then will form a bright, shiny surface. But with further use of the pan, the aluminum will combine with oxygen from the air or from the food, and again the surface will become dull with tarnish. Changes in which new substances are formed from old materials are called chemical changes. Both the tarnishing and the removal of the tarnish are examples. Chemical changes are by no means restricted to the laboratory, nor are chemicals found only in flasks and bottles. Any substance may be considered a chemical. The exact nature of the new substances that are formed in a chemical change may not always be obvious. A slice of bread heated in a toaster will change in both color and flavor — and if left there long enough the bread may end as charcoal. Combustion is a chemical change in which the fuel ordinarily ends as gases that escape unseen into the air.

Chemical changes account for many of the common processes that go on about us, and children should gain some understanding of such changes if they are to interpret their environment adequately. Chemical changes take place in the green leaves of trees, for example: carbon dioxide from the air combines with water from the ground to form sugar. As the tree grows, the sugar may be converted into wood. When leaves change color in the autumn the change is chemical. When the leaves fall to the ground and begin to decay, the chemical changes are continuing. Man has learned to control some of these changes; many industrial processes are based on them. Through such changes industries obtain metals from their ores and produce glass, a great variety of drugs, dyes, and perfumes, synthetic rubber, detergents, and fibers such as nylon.

The addition of vinegar to skimmed milk to form curds is a simple chemical experiment that is suitable for children, yet it represents what happens naturally in milk during digestion, and the process is similar to what happens when milk sours. From skimmed milk, chemists have learned how to produce, by means of chemical changes, the raw material used in casein glues, casein paints, plastics, cosmetics, and a great variety of other common materials. Chemistry is a large and important field with great influence upon our way of life.

Children should be taught reasonable precautions in working with chemicals. Iodine, copper sulfate, and household ammonia can be used at school and are commonly found in homes yet are poisonous if taken internally. Therefore children should not put chemicals in their mouths, and they should learn not to handle chemicals with bare fingers. Ordinarily a clean spoon may be used. If nothing more, handling will at least contaminate an otherwise pure chemical. Just as boys and girls should be protected outside the school from sharp knives in the kitchen, from the medicine in the bathroom chest, and from traffic in the street, they should be protected from hazards at school and taught essential precautions in their work with chemicals. On the other hand, a blind fear of all chemicals is unnecessary and should not be conveyed to the children.

Simple chemical experiments are fascinating to children and highly satisfactory for a program of active experimentation in the intermediate and upper elementary grades. The experiments which follow have been used with marked success in grades four to seven. Modified somewhat, parts of them have been used with the first three grades. Spontaneous combustion, for example, when demonstrated to a second grade during fire prevention week, impressed upon the children the fact that fires can start by themselves and hence litter must not be allowed to accumulate. The experiments described here have been selected as being meaningful, safe, and suitable for children to perform. They stress common materials and applications. The chemicals needed are common enough that many can be brought by the children from their homes. Most of the chemicals are likely to be included in a child's chemistry set, and they can be obtained from a high-school science department, from a scientific supply house, or from a drugstore. In virtually any teaching situation enough of the needed substances can be easily obtained so that at least a few of the experiments can be done. For convenience the names of chemicals are printed in italics to identify those needed for each experiment.

HOW COMPOUNDS ARE FORMED

Producing carbon dioxide

Many chemicals which are very common are seldom thought of as chemicals. *Baking soda* and *vinegar* are examples of chemicals used in the kitchen. Place a teaspoonful of baking soda in a drinking glass. Pour one-third cup of vinegar into the glass with the baking soda, and the two will react to release carbon dioxide. The carbon dioxide is a gas and bubbles out of the liquid. When the two chemicals react, a new material is formed, and the reaction is called a chemical change. Bread dough rises owing to a chemical change in which carbon dioxide is produced; the air holes in the bread are made by the bubbles of gas. Light a match and hold it above the liquid in the glass. Fire will not burn in carbon dioxide. The large fire extinguishers commonly found in the halls of schools and other public buildings contain a solution of baking soda in water. When the extinguisher is inverted, acid spills into the baking-soda solution; carbon dioxide is thus formed, and with the water it spews out of the nozzle onto the fire.

Fig. 55

Experimenting with chemicals brings many new insights.

Try the above experiment substituting *lemon juice* for the vinegar or *slaked lime* for the baking soda. Sea shells, eggshells, bones, limestone, marble, and some blackboard chalk contain lime and may be used in the experiment.

A compound of silver and sulfur

If a *silver coin* is covered with *sulfur* and left for a while, the coin will turn black on the surface. The sulfur combines with the silver to form tarnish. Eggs contain sulfur and will cause silverware to tarnish if the silverware is not washed soon after being used. If no sulphur is available, put rubber bands around the coins and notice what happens in a day or so. Rubber bands have sulfur in them. In this experiment two elements, silver and sulfur, combine to form a compound, silver sulfide.

Removing copper from one compound to form another

Dissolve a little *copper sulfate* in a small glass or test tube of water and notice the blue color. Pour fine *iron filings* slowly into the copper sulfate solution, stirring all the while, until the blue color has disappeared. The change in color indicates that the copper sulfate is gone, and at the same time copper has settled to the bottom of the glass. A chemical change has taken place, because copper was formed from the iron and the copper sulfate. The remaining liquid may be poured off and saved for another experiment, for the liquid contains iron sulfate that is useful in preparing ink. If the copper is then placed on a paper towel or newspaper, the copper will soon turn dark; this also is a chemical change. The copper combines with oxygen from the air. Because the particles are fine, the chemical change will take place rapidly, but the same thing happens to pennies and other large objects made of copper. Notice that old pennies are dull with tarnish but new pennies are bright. Scratch an old penny and observe that it is bright under the surface where the copper has not been exposed to the air.

If iron filings are not otherwise available, some can be made by filing a nail or bolt and catching the particles on a piece of paper. In this experiment, if the copper sulfate is in large crystals, before attempting to dissolve them in the water, grind them on a sheet of paper using a milk bottle as a rolling pin, if no mortar and pestle are available. The finer particles dissolve more rapidly. Likewise, the filings should be as fine as possible if the reaction is to proceed rapidly.

Fig. 56

Using ink made in a chemical experiment to write a report

Rust is a compound

When iron combines with oxygen, rust is formed. Rust is called a compound, because it is iron combined with oxygen. The oxygen usually comes from the air, but the iron must be moist for the chemical change to take place. To show that oxygen is taken from the air when iron rusts, put some *iron filings* in a glass jar or test tube that is moist with water. Iron filings will cling to the moist jar; hence the jar may be turned upside down and placed in a shallow pan of water. Leave the jar there for a day to see what happens. Be sure the mouth of the jar is kept below the surface of the water. As rusting removes oxygen from the air, water will rise in the jar so that it is possible to see what volume of oxygen is removed. Steel wool can be used instead of iron filings in this experiment.

Rusting is a chemical change. The product, rust, is not as strong as iron and is a different color. Bicycles and other things made of iron (which includes steel) are painted to prevent rusting. To see the effect of paint, dip one end of a large nail into paint. After the paint is dry, place the nail in a shallow jar or pan of water and leave it to see what happens.

Making ink

Dissolve one-fourth teaspoonful of *iron sulfate* in a glass with a teaspoonful of water; then dissolve an equal amount of *tannic acid* in another teaspoonful of water. There is no danger in handling the tannic acid. Notice the color of each solution; then pour the two together and see what happens. The change of color indicates that a new material is formed. The new substance is an old-fashioned ink. Put the ink into a glass and use it to write a report of the experiment.

The iron sulfate from a previous experiment (p. 237) could be used here, or if no iron sulfate is available, try any iron compound that will dissolve in water. Often the word *ferric* or *ferrous,* meaning iron, is used in such compounds, as in ferric ammonium sulfate or ferrous sulfate. The term *sulfate* means that sulfur and oxygen are in the compound. There is tannic acid in tea. Make some strong *tea* and pour into it a little of the iron sulfate solution. Note what happens.

HOW COMPOUNDS BREAK DOWN

Decay is a chemical change

When silver was combined with sulfur, the tarnish formed was called a compound. When iron combined with oxygen, the rust formed was another compound. After compounds are formed, they are sometimes broken down. Heat a small amount of *ammonium chloride* in a dry test tube (slowly at first, turning the tube to heat it uniformly and avoid breaking it). The odor of ammonia can be detected coming from the tube. The compound has been broken down; the ammonia has been separated from the remainder of the compound. When organic materials decay, the compounds likewise break down, and ammonia is one of the common products of decay.

If the ammonium chloride is not otherwise available, use some of the black powder from inside an old dry cell; the powder includes ammonium chloride. If a flashlight cell is used it may be convenient simply to break it open and heat it without removing the contents from the cell. A pair of pliers can be used to hold the cell in the flame of an alcohol burner.

When a mat of hair (taken from a comb, or perhaps off the back of a dog) is dusted with *slaked lime* or *washing soda* and heated dry for a while in a test tube, the odor of ammonia will be apparent. In this case the protein of the hair has decomposed, and one of the products is ammonia. If the odor of ammonia is unfamiliar to the children, it may be wise to dampen a cloth with some *house-hold ammonia* and let them smell it gently.

When apples rot or butter spoils or meat decays, the change is a chemical change in which compounds are broken down, decomposed. Other common examples of decomposition are plentiful. Household bleaching powders and solutions decompose in the process of bleaching. Hydrogen peroxide is unstable and breaks down to form water and bubbles of oxygen. In photography when a film is exposed to light and then developed, a compound is broken down, releasing silver which is deposited on the negative to form the picture. When fruit juice ferments, sugar is decomposed; carbon dioxide is released and bubbles from the liquid. The cracking process of converting petroleum into high-octane gasoline is a process of making small compounds out of large ones — decomposition.

Cooking involves chemical changes

Heat a little *sugar* in a spoon over an alcohol burner until the sugar turns brown. The brown substance, caramel, is a mixture of simple sugars formed from the table sugar through a chemical change. Caramel is used in candy, as a syrup, and as a food coloring. Continued heating will cause the caramel to decompose still more until only the black substance, carbon, remains. Other parts of the sugar will have escaped as gases during heating. Have the children taste the sugar, the caramel, and then the carbon as evidence that a change has taken place.

Cooking is essentially a complex of chemical changes brought about by heating. If a microscope can be obtained, examine a bit of raw potato and notice the large crystals of starch. Compare with a baked potato to see how the large crystals have been broken down. The chemical changes in cooking are mostly decomposition, because the compounds are broken down. When we digest food, other chemical changes occur, and hence the compounds are broken down still more.

Hydrogen and oxygen from water

With *copper wire* connect three or four *dry cells* in series — from the center terminal of one to the outside terminal of the next. Attach the wire from each end of the series to a separate piece of carbon. The carbon may be taken from the center of an old flashlight cell, or the lead of a pencil can be used. Pencil lead is really graphite, a form of carbon. An old stub of pencil can be notched in the middle so that the lead is exposed on one side, and the bare end of a wire can be attached to the pencil at that point. The wood will prevent the carbon from breaking easily. If the two carbons are then placed not far apart in *salt* water, an electric current will flow through the water, and bubbles of gas will appear at each carbon terminal. It will be noted that more bubbles appear at one terminal than at the other.

With more elaborate equipment the bubbles could be caught and tested. It would be found that exactly twice as much gas is released from one carbon as from the other and that the larger volume is hydrogen and the smaller one oxygen. Water is two parts hydrogen and one part oxygen. The decomposition of water into hydrogen and oxygen by means of electricity is a chemical change. Hydrogen and oxygen are elements; water is a compound. Compounds are made of elements. In this experiment, if an excessive amount of salt is used, the salt is decomposed and yields chlorine at one terminal rather than oxygen. Chlorine is prepared commercially by such means.

HOW CHEMICAL CHANGES ARE BROUGHT ABOUT

Heat is required for some changes

Heat some *paraffin* from a candle with a small amount of *sulfur*. They may be heated in an old spoon, in the lid of a tin can, or in whatever is available. An alcohol burner is a satisfactory source of heat. Notice the odor. Hydrogen from the candle combines with the sulfur to form hydrogen sulfide. When eggs spoil, hydrogen sulfide is formed. Small amounts should be used for this experiment, and it should be done by an open window or, preferably, somewhere outside, for otherwise the disagreeable odor will spread to other parts of the building.

The hydrogen sulfide was made by a chemical change. Heat was necessary to cause the chemical change. Food spoils more rapidly in warm weather because of such changes. We keep food cold in a refrigerator to retard undesirable chemical changes.

Odors defy description, but a sharply penetrating odor that is different from the rotten-egg odor of hydrogen sulfide may be obtained in the above experiment, especially if an excessive amount of sulfur is used. To identify the odor, heat some sulfur in a spoon until a blue flame appears. The irritating odor obtained is due to sulfur dioxide. The sulfur dioxide is formed when sulfur combines with oxygen from the air, and the process is another chemical change caused by heating.

Moisture may be needed

To bring about a chemical change, sometimes heat is needed and sometimes moisture. If *baking soda* and *cream of tartar* or *boric acid* are mixed together dry, there will be no chemical change; the two together are called a mixture; they have not joined. If warm water is added, the chemicals will react. The bubbling shows that a gas, carbon dioxide, is being formed and that a chemical change is taking place.

If *iron sulfate* and *tannic acid* are mixed together dry, there will be no reaction. When water is added, ink is formed. Many chemical reactions require water. Rusting is one example. To show that moisture must be present for rusting to take place, put several *nails* in water, or on a damp towel, and leave several other nails dry for comparison. Likewise, in cooking, water is added to make the desired chemical changes possible. On the other hand, prunes, beef, raisins, and other foods are dried to prevent changes, decomposition.

Spontaneous combustion

To start a fire, place a few drops of *glycerin* on a small scrap of paper. Put the paper on a plate or on a sheet of metal or asbestos. Grind some *potassium permanganate* until it is quite fine and then dust it onto the glycerin. Wait to see what happens. A bottle used as a rolling pin will serve for grinding. The finer the chemical is ground, the more rapid the reaction will be. Because of the fire, children should not do the experiment without close supervision.

When the glycerin and the potassium permanganate react, the chemical change gives off heat. The heat causes the reaction to proceed more rapidly. More and more heat is released until finally a fire is started.

Many chemical changes produce heat. The oil in oily rags left lying about the house may sometimes combine with oxygen from the air, and the chemical changes may produce more and more heat until a fire is started. Litter, rubbish scattered about the house, often in a closet or in the attic, may cause fires in a similar way. A fire started by chemical changes is called spontaneous combustion. Houses should be kept free of litter. Oily rags should be burned in the furnace or kept in tin cans that have lids.

For another illustration of the heat released by chemical changes — suitable for a teacher demonstration — secure a can of *lye*, sold in drugstores and grocery stores for opening the clogged drains of sinks. Follow the directions, pouring the lye into a convenient sink; then have the children carefully feel the pipe of the trap below the sink. It becomes quite hot with the heat of a chemical change. Handle the lye with care; it is very strong. Do not touch it with the fingers. If by chance some does touch the flesh, wash it off quickly and then rinse with vinegar; if this is done quickly no harm will result.

The influence of a catalyst

A catalyst is something that accelerates — or in some cases retards — a chemical change without becoming a part of the products formed by the change. To illustrate the function of a catalyst, use a pair of pliers, or whatever is available, to hold a lump of *sugar* in the flame of a candle or an alcohol burner. The sugar may melt, turn brown, or even turn black, but it is not likely to burn freely with a flame. However, if a lump of sugar is dipped into *cigarette ashes* so that some of the ash remains on the sugar, and then the sugar is held in a flame, the sugar will burn freely. The ash has acted as a catalyst to speed the burning.

The burning is a chemical change which converts the sugar into gases. One of the gases formed when sugar burns is carbon dioxide; the other is water vapor. The *limewater* test (p. 244) will show that carbon dioxide is formed by burning. That water vapor is one product of an ordinary flame can be detected by placing a cold glass or jar above the flame of a candle. The warm vapor from the flame will condense on the cold glass and thus become visible.

Fine particles react rapidly

Often chemical changes will occur more rapidly when the chemicals are ground into a fine powder. An iron *nail* or bolt, for example, will be unaffected by the flame of an alcohol burner. To provide a contrast, obtain a small amount of powdered iron by using a fine metal file on the bolt or nail, catch the tiny bits of iron on a sheet of paper, and then dust the particles onto the flame. There will be a shower of yellow sparks as the tiny bits catch fire and burn. The burning, a chemical change, took place more rapidly with small particles than with large ones. The same experiment can be conducted with copper from a *copper wire*, or with *zinc* from the case of a worn-out dry cell.

There are many other common examples of chemical changes that occur more rapidly when the particles are fine. In the spontaneous combustion experiment, the potassium permanganate is ground fine to speed the reaction. In fact, how soon the fire begins is determined largely by the fineness of the potassium permanganate. In the experiment in which iron filings are used to displace copper from copper sulfate, the reaction is more rapid if the iron is fine, even powdered. Iron filings will rust more rapidly than a nail. We split kindling to start a fire, for the same reason.

In some cases, as in cooking, or in the copper sulfate and iron experiment, stirring or shaking will mix the particles and speed the reaction.

SOME TESTS FOR CHEMICALS

A test for carbon dioxide

If *slaked lime* is dissolved in water, the water will be cloudy, but if left for a while it will clear. If then a person will blow through a drinking straw into the water, the water will become cloudy again. The lime in the water will have combined with carbon dioxide from the breath to form another kind of lime that, like chalk, will not stay dissolved in the water, and the water will be cloudy until the white particles have settled to the bottom. Each time a person blows into the limewater it will become cloudy again, showing that carbon dioxide is in the breath.

The particles of lime which settle to the bottom are called a precipitate. Each time lime water is used, the clear solution should be poured into a fresh container; otherwise the blowing may disturb the precipitated lime and cloud the liquid so that the new precipitate cannot be detected when it forms.

The limewater test can be used to show that carbon dioxide is one product of combustion. If a candle is burned in a wide-mouthed jar with the lid on, the fire will soon go out. The candle may then be removed and limewater poured into the jar. When the lid is replaced and the jar shaken, the limewater is exposed to the carbon dioxide and reacts with it. The cloudy appearance shows that carbon dioxide was in the jar. For comparison, the limewater test may be used on another jar, a jar in which there has been no fire. The second test may show some indication of carbon dioxide in the air even without a fire. Experiments such as this should be repeated several times to be sure of the results. Perhaps a number of children may wish to try the experiment, and a composite record may be kept.

To set a candle in a jar, hold a burning match below the lower end of the candle until the wax is soft and then press the candle into place. To light the candle, tip the jar; otherwise it may be difficult to reach into the jar with a burning match.

Food tests

A test for protein. Dissolve as much *copper sulfate* in a teaspoonful of water as the water will hold. Next, dissolve either *lime* or *washing soda* in another teaspoonful of water. Put a few drops of each solution into some milk in a glass. These chemicals will react with the protein of the milk, and the change will form a violet-colored material. If necessary, add more lime or soda.

Proteins are the substances of which lean meat is made. Try the test on peanut butter, sugar, flour, and other foods to see which of these contain protein. The food to be tested should be stirred into one solution and the other solution added as directed above. Have the children keep a record, listing the foods that have been tested and found to contain protein and those that do not.

A test for starch. Dissolve some *cornstarch* in water; then add some *iodine* and observe what happens. Try the same test on bread, milk, and other foods. If the same dark color is formed, the food contains starch. Have the children keep a record of all the foods tested that are starch and of all those that are not composed of starch.

A test for sugar. Heat a raisin in water with a few drops of *Benedict's solution.* Notice the color change. Test other foods. Those that show the same color change that occurred when the raisin was tested contain sugar. The children may prepare a list of those foods that do and those that do not contain sugar. This test will not work with ordinary table sugar, unless the sugar is heated strongly to change it into a simple sugar. Adding a drop of acid before heating will help. Benedict's solution can be obtained at drugstores.

A test for fat. The easiest way to test for fat is not a chemical test, because no chemical change takes place. Just place the food in a glass of water. Crushing it first will help. If oil appears on the water, the food contains fat.

The acid-base test

With neutral litmus paper, or some other indicator, test foods and other common substances to see whether they are acid, base, or neutral. If the material is dry, moisten it; then place the indicator in the liquid and note the color change, if any. If the litmus has turned blue, the material is a base; if red, the material is acid; and no color change indicates that the substance is neither acid nor base. The children may try such things as vinegar, fruit juices, sugar, salt, baking soda, and lime. Lists classifying the ones tested may be placed on the blackboard or a chart. The items may be checked each time a child reports his findings, a greater number of checks indicating increasingly reliable results — or, better yet, the child's name or initials may be used, giving him personal credit and responsibility for his findings. Conflicting results will call for further tests, but the total record should be kept.

Either beet juice or blueberry sauce will serve as a crude indicator if litmus is not available. In any case, using the substitute may help give meaning to the function of an indicator.

Soil can be tested with litmus by moistening the soil and placing the litmus in it. Leave the paper in the soil for about half an hour; then remove it and rinse in clear water. The color will show whether or not the soil is acid. Why is lime sometimes added to soil?

Carefully add enough vinegar to a solution of baking soda in water until litmus will show neither red nor blue. Here an acid has neutralized a base. Likewise, baking soda can be used to neutralize an acid.

Identifying elements

Chemists sometimes identify elements by their color in a flame. Bend a very fine *iron wire* in the form of a small loop; then either moisten the loop or heat it in the flame of an alcohol burner until it will hold some finely powdered *copper sulfate* when dipped into the powder. Hold the wire with the powder in the flame and observe the color of the flame. The distinctive blue-green color is due to the copper in the compound. Heat a fine *copper wire* in the flame and note the same color. The wire in extension cords is usually made of many fine strands, one of which will be good for the present purpose. To show the colors well, it may be necessary to use a hotter flame, such as that of a gas cook stove, a buddy burner, two alcohol burners held together, or perhaps an old kerosene lamp with the chimney removed.

Repeat the procedure with other substances by cutting off the end of the wire and using a clean portion to form another small loop. Try some *potassium permanganate* in the flame and notice the violet color of the potassium. Have the children try other compounds that may have potassium, such as cream of tartar, to see if the same color can be detected.

The boron in *boric acid* will give a yellow-green color, and *sulfur* is blue. When the sulfur burns, however, it combines with oxygen to form sulfur dioxide, which has a disagreeably sharp, penetrating odor. Accordingly, it should be used in small amounts and near an open window or outdoors. Zinc gives a different blue color. *Powdered zinc* can be prepared by filing some of the zinc off the outside of a used dry cell. The zinc is exposed when the cardboard is removed from a dry cell. As fine a file as possible should be used, and the filings can be caught on a paper.

SOME PRACTICAL USES OF CHEMICALS
AND CHEMICAL CHANGES

Making soap

Many industrial processes involve chemical changes. Making soap is one. Into an enameled pan put three cups of water, one-third cup of *slaked lime,* and one-fourth cup of *washing soda;* then boil the water for about five minutes, stirring regularly. Allow the pan to cool to room temperature. A chalk will settle to the bottom of the pan. Handle the solution with care, for it now contains lye. The lime and washing soda when heated together formed chalk and lye. If the solution is spilled on hands or clothing, merely wash it off quickly and rinse with vinegar.

In another enameled pan containing two cups of water melt three table-spoonfuls of shortening. Beef or mutton suet may be substituted for a portion of the shortening to produce a harder soap, but no cooking fats that contain salt should be used. After the fat has melted, allow the water to cool somewhat. The grease must be melted but not hot.

While stirring constantly, pour the lye solution slowly into the melted fat. Continue to stir, and apply just enough heat to bring the mixture to a boil. After ten to fifteen minutes of boiling, add a tablespoonful of salt. Heat and stir for another five minutes; then allow to cool. Set the pan aside until the next day. The soap will rise to the surface; it can be removed with a spoon, or the contents of the pan may be emptied into a strainer and rinsed briefly and then pressed into a cake and allowed to dry. The children may wash their hands with the soap, but not their faces, for the soap may contain traces of lye. The remaining liquid contains glycerin. The chemical change that formed the soap may be written thus:

Fat + sodium from the washing soda ⟶ soap + glycerin.

Washing soda is composed of sodium, carbon, and oxygen. In this reaction the sodium from the washing soda combined with the fat to form the soap. Table salt is composed of sodium and chlorine, and the salt is used here to supply additional sodium.

Our pioneer ancestors made soap in a similar way, but they used the potash from wood ashes instead of washing soda, and the class may prefer this method for its correlation with history. If wood ashes are obtained, the ashes can be soaked in buckets of water for several days; the water should then be poured into another container and heated until a large share has evaporated and the solution has become strong with potash. Then soap can be prepared as above,

Fig. 57

The early settlers placed ashes in a hopper and made soap with the rain
water that soaked through the ashes.

by heating with fat and salt. The pioneers placed ashes in a wooden hopper and allowed rainwater to drip through them into a trough which emptied into a kettle at the bottom.

Gunpowder

The name of the product in this experiment is exciting to children, but there is no danger if the fire is controlled by conducting the experiment in a shallow pan or plate, or on asbestos. As with any experiment in which fire is used, this one should be supervised closely. The powder should not be confined, but should be used on an open surface and in small quantities. If the ingredients are not in powdered form, they may be powdered separately, before mixing, by placing each one on a piece of paper and grinding it with a bottle used as a rolling pin. Do not grind after mixing, for the heat of grinding may cause the mixture to explode prematurely.

Thoroughly mix one part of *powdered sulfur* with an equal portion of *powdered charcoal* and with two parts of *potassium nitrate*, also finely powdered. The portions should be small, the total not more than ¼ teaspoonful. Place the mixture on a small piece of paper; be sure the whole is on a surface that will not burn. Then touch a lighted match to one corner of the paper. The explosion will be but a small flash, a disappointment to some of the children who will be expecting something more spectacular. The explosion is a chemical change in which gases are formed; the force of the explosion comes from the sudden expansion of the gases.

Charcoal can be prepared by placing used match sticks or other slivers of wood in a test tube and heating with an alcohol burner until the wood is black and no more fumes are given off. Turn the test tube in the fingers and heat slowly at first so that the heat will not break the test tube. The wood in this process is decomposed to form carbon and gases. The same thing happens in an open fire, except that with oxygen available the gases and most of the carbon will burn as they are released from the compound. If it is convenient, the needed charcoal may be taken from the charred remains of a fire, or from the soot in a chimney or stove.

Making coke from coal

Place several grains of bituminous *coal* in a test tube; then heat the test tube until a gas is given off. As the heating continues, a dark brown tar will condense on the sides of the test tube. The gas is known as coal gas and the tar as coal tar. Coal gas and coal tar are produced industrially, and from them chemists make many different products. One product of coal tar is nylon; others are the dyes which color most clothing, and the perfumes which women wear. It seems strange that beautiful dyes and pleasant odors can be made from a material as ugly and ill-smelling as coal tar. After a chemical change, however, the product may be quite different from the original substance.

When no more gas or tar will come from the coal, the heating may be discontinued. The residue in the test tube is known as coke. Coke is mostly carbon and is much like charcoal, which is made in a similar manner by heating wood. Coke is used industrially in the process of removing iron from ores.

Preparing a nicotine spray for aphids

The nicotine from tobacco is often used to destroy insects. A suitable spray can be prepared by boiling the tobacco from a cigarette in a small amount of water, perhaps two tablespoonfuls, in a small beaker or tin can. If a pan must be used, and thus more water, the amount of tobacco can be increased proportionally. Allow the water to boil for about five or ten minutes and then filter the solution by pouring it through a paper towel into a clean glass. Add a few drops of liquid soap from the washroom, or allow a fragment of soap to dissolve in another two or three tablespoonfuls of water and add the solution to the nicotine extract. Dilute with water to make about half a glass of spray. The soap is not entirely essential, but it helps to spread the spray. With a small spray gun or aspirator, spray the solution on some plant that is infested with aphids. Notice what happens to the aphids. A second spraying may be needed later as more aphids develop.

SOME TERMS USED IN CHEMISTRY

Distinguishing compounds from mixtures

An element, such as iron or sulfur, is all one substance; it is composed of nothing else. A compound, on the other hand, is made of elements and can be separated into its elements by means of a chemical change. Water is a compound, for example, and can be decomposed into its elements, hydrogen and oxygen. Conversely, hydrogen and oxygen will join to form water.

But substances may be together without actually joining. Iron and oxygen together are not rust, unless the two actually combine. Two substances that are together without being joined are called a mixture. In a chemical change in which two or more elements combine, a new material is formed, but salt and sugar stirred together as a mixture are still salt and sugar.

When elements join to form a compound, they combine in definite proportions. In the case of water there are two parts of hydrogen and one of oxygen. The proportions in a mixture may vary, but in a compound they are always the same.

Iron and sulfur can be used to make clear the distinction between mixtures and compounds. Thoroughly mix equal portions of *sulfur* and *powdered iron,* perhaps half a teaspoonful of each. Iron filings, if used, should be as fine as possible. Place some of the mixture in a test tube and heat the tube until a red glow spreads throughout the contents. A very small test tube should be used — preferably an old one that has been stained by previous use. To get enough heat it may be necessary to use two alcohol burners, or perhaps a buddy burner that will give a large flame. The test tube should be heated gradually and uniformly. Turn the tube and move it about in the flame, especially at first, so that unequal heating will not cause the test tube to crack.

After the test tube has been removed from the flame and has cooled, the tube may be broken to remove the contents. Compare the new material with the original mixture, some of which should have been set aside without heating to be used for comparison. Iron and sulfur have joined to form a new compound, iron sulfide. Iron sulfide resembles iron rust and is quite different from the mixture of iron and sulfur. Note that in the mixture the iron and sulfur can be seen as separate particles but in the compound the material is uniform throughout. Have the children examine both with a hand lens and compare them. In a compound the elements are not just mixed but have actually joined to form something new.

A chemical precipitate

To see what a precipitate is, dissolve some magnesium sulfate, *Epsom salts,* in half a glass of water. Dissolve some sodium carbonate, *washing soda,* in another glass half full of water. When both glasses are clear, pour the two together and observe the white cloud formed. The magnesium of one compound has joined with the carbonate portion of the other to form magnesium carbonate, which is not soluble in water. The particles of magnesium carbonate are small, but they will gradually settle to the bottom of the glass. Where the product of a chemical change is insoluble it is called a precipitate, because it has been precipitated, which means literally that it has fallen down suddenly.

The chalk formed in the carbon dioxide test is a precipitate. Ink and soap are precipitates, and the color changes in the sugar and protein tests are likewise due to precipitates.

To obtain a colored precipitate pour some household *ammonia water* into a solution of *copper sulfate* in water. A solution of *baking soda* in water or *washing soda* in water may be used in place of the ammonia water — or the children may like to try all three.

Symbols, formulas, and equations

Chemists use symbols for convenience in referring to the elements, the symbol ordinarily being an initial; thus H represents hydrogen, O means oxygen, and C is carbon. In some cases another letter must be used. Ca is the symbol for calcium, and Cu for copper, because C is used for carbon. Likewise Fe is the symbol for iron, based on the Latin word *ferrum*, which means iron, because I is used for iodine, and F represents fluorine.

When elements combine to form a compound, the letters are used in a formula to show what elements are in the compound, and numbers are used to indicate the proportions. Thus in water, H_2O, there are two parts of hydrogen and one part of oxygen. Copper sulfate is $CuSO_4$, one part copper, one part sulfur, and four parts oxygen. Magnesium sulfate, $MgSO_4$, has the same proportions, but with magnesium instead of copper. Likewise, the formula for rust is Fe_2O_3, and the formula for hydrogen sulfide is H_2S. Since the smallest possible amount of any pure substance is called a molecule, the formula represents the proportions in a single molecule. Accordingly, NH_3 is a molecule of ammonia, composed of two elements. The ultimate particles of an element, the units which enter into chemical compounds, are called atoms. A molecule of ammonia is composed of four atoms, three of hydrogen and one of nitrogen. Baking soda, $NaHCO_3$, has six atoms in each molecule, one of sodium, one of hydrogen, one of carbon, and three of oxygen. A molecule of washing soda, Na_2CO_3, likewise has six atoms, but it is composed of only three elements.

The reactions in some of the preceding experiments may be written thus as chemical equations:

$$Fe + S \longrightarrow FeS$$
(iron) (sulfur)   (iron sulfide)
$$2H_2O \longrightarrow 2H_2 + O_2$$
(2 molecules of water)   (2 molecules of hydrogen, 1 of oxygen)

$2Ag + S \longrightarrow Ag_2S$
(silver)   (silver sulfide)
$Fe + \quad CuSO_4 \longrightarrow Cu \quad + \quad FeSO_4$
            (copper sulfate)   (copper)   (iron sulfate)
$Ca(OH)_2 + \quad CO_2 \longrightarrow CaCO_3 + H_2O$
(slaked lime)   (carbon dioxide)   (chalk)

The formula for calcium hydroxide (slaked lime) indicates one atom of calcium and two each of oxygen and hydrogen.

STUDY GUIDE

1. Try several of the experiments in this chapter; then demonstrate and explain each one to your class. Point out the practical applications in each case and explain how the experiment might be used in work with children.
2. How is a study of chemicals related to studies in other areas of the curriculum and to the experiences of children outside school?
3. How might a study of chemical changes be initiated and conducted in some particular classroom with which you are familiar?
4. What are some of the values that can be derived from a study of chemical changes?

10

The Rocks and Soil
of the Earth's Surface

Knowing the origin of our landscape and the forces at work on it not only is fascinating in itself but helps to develop a sense of perspective, of time and change. Children should gain some insight into the changes that result when rock is exposed to the weather, some understanding of how a farm can be cut away by the action of a stream in flood. Earthquakes and evidence of volcanic action are common in some regions, and in all areas are fascinating to children who hear of them. The changes that have been wrought through ages past to produce our familiar scenes are of general interest, and knowledge of these changes helps to develop the broad outlook and insight of an educated person. It is worthwhile for all citizens to know something of geological forces so that the resources of our earth may be conserved and used wisely. But even more vital is the interest and personal satisfaction that comes from understanding the world in which we live.

An interest in rocks developed in one second grade when a child found some pebbles on the playground and showed them to the teacher. The teacher fortunately was able to see that the interest could lead to worthwhile learnings and so encouraged the child to continue her investigations. Several other children exhibited interest in what had been found. They commented that one stone was rough, another smooth, a third pretty with many colors in it — elementary observations, but first steps on the road to learning. The class had become aware that rocks are interesting to investigate.

Many questions were asked about the rocks, and a number of the children turned to books for information. One book was especially useful, for it described the characteristics of various kinds of rock. By comparing their pebbles with the descriptions, the class discovered that several of the rocks were stratified. The book gave an interesting account of how such rocks are formed. The next day one girl brought in a rock that had large crystals of mica, and the children found that the mica not only glistens but is unique in that it will peel in thin sheets. The class had taken a first step toward learning that rocks are made of minerals and that minerals can be identified by their properties.

OBSERVATIONS OF ROCKS AND SOIL

In working with children, observations that contribute to basic understandings should be stressed. Significant initial observations of rocks may include noticing whether a pebble is smooth and rounded or jagged and rough. The rock may be granular, colored, or transparent. Any lines in a rock are likely to be significant, and these can be observed with interest long before terms such as stratification, joints, and veins are understood. Likewise, the weight of a stone in comparison to its size may be noted. That rocks are rusty, or dark and crumbling on the surface, in contrast to the interior, is indicative of weathering. Some rocks are soft and easily broken; others are hard and resistant. The color and texture, even the taste and odor, may have meaning. The mere fact that there is a great variety of rocks can be of interest to a child and can lead to further understandings.

Rocks may become worn and rounded

Any rock which can be brought to the classroom has at one time been broken off a larger formation. The broken edges may still be in evidence, or they may have become rounded. Either condition is significant and may be stressed by the teacher when children seek information about the rocks they bring to school. To see how pebbles are formed, a rock which is not too hard may be broken and the rough edges examined. Care should be taken to avoid flying particles when the rock is broken. The children may observe that if the

Fig. 58

There is no effective substitute for firsthand observation.

pieces are rubbed together the edges will gradually become somewhat rounded. When rocks are exposed to the weather, the surface eventually crumbles; pebbles in a stream are tumbled one over the other, and this abrasion tends to round the sharp edges. In a similar way pebbles are worn somewhat flat at the beach; and in dry, windy regions wind-blown sand causes the rocks to become worn. On or near the surface, scattered about the fields and hills of the northern states from New England to the Pacific Coast, are loose rocks of various sizes which have been worn and shaped by the ice that once covered much of North America. The ice extended as far south as a curving line from Puget Sound eastward approximately along the Missouri and Ohio rivers to Long Island on the Atlantic.

If a stream is nearby, perhaps it can be visited for evidence of how rocks become rounded, and some of the pebbles may be brought to the classroom. Can glacial rocks be located nearby in the fields or empty lots? In dry regions rocks worn by the wind are likely to be found. Those who live near the coast or visit there may be able to bring rocks that have become worn and flattened by the surf.

Joints in the rocks

The bedrock that makes up the earth's crust, beneath a relatively thin mantle of dirt and loose rock, is commonly divided into segments by cracks which are called joints. When lava cools it shrinks, and joints are formed throughout the mass of rock. Similar joints are formed in sediment as it dries, shrinks, and eventually becomes hardened as rock. Similar cracks can be found in mud that has dried but has not consolidated as rock. Movements of the earth's crust, though mostly gradual, place a strain upon the rocks and may cause jointing. The intersecting cracks which divide most solid rock into irregular blocks are easy to see wherever the bedrock is exposed. The children may observe joints in the rocks if there is a hillside near the school where bedrock is exposed. Or the bedrock may be exposed along the banks of a stream, in the excavations on a building site, or where a road has been cut through a hill. In the classroom, mud cracks can be demonstrated by allowing mud to dry in a pan.

The weathering of rock

When water seeps into joints in the rocks and freezes, the crevices are made larger by the expansion of the ice in freezing. The process is repeated each time the ice thaws and then freezes again, until finally the rocks are broken apart. The roots of bushes, trees, and other plants can be found growing in the crevices, helping to force the rocks apart. At the foot of a cliff there is often an accumulation of broken stones as evidence of the process. Since many rocks are quite porous, water can soak into the rock itself; then alternate freezing and thawing cause the moist surfaces to crumble.

Chemical changes cause rocks to become soft and crumble, just as iron will rust and buildings weather when exposed to the air and moisture outdoors. Moss, lichens, and other plants can be found growing on rocks, hastening the process, for plants produce carbon dioxide, which becomes a weak acid in water. Certain elements from the rocks will combine chemically with oxygen and water when exposed to air and moisture, causing the surface of the rocks to crumble. Iron from rocks, for instance, combines with oxygen and water to form the familiar rust, which gives a yellow-brown or somewhat red color to the surface of the weathered rock. That the color is only on the surface, where the weathering occurs, can be revealed by chipping the rock with a hammer. Iron is common in rock, and therefore in many areas the yellow, brown, or red colors are familiar. In Wyoming, New Jersey, the Connecticut Valley, and other localities, the sandstone and shale were formed from weathered sand and mud containing iron; hence the rocks are red not only on the surface but throughout.

About the school and about their homes, the children usually can find some evidence of how rocks are weathered and worn. They can see the joints in rock, plants growing on or about the rocks, the roots of some wedging the crevices apart. If there is a cliff, broken rock may be found at its base. Even pebbles brought into the classroom are frequently a yellow-brown color on the surface as a result of weathering, and a stone which has long been exposed to the weather is plainly softer on the surface than beneath. Children can make firsthand investigations of such rocks.

To see how water freezing in the joints can split rocks, a sturdy bottle with a tight screw-type cap may be filled with water and placed outside during freezing weather or put into the freezing compartment of a refrigerator. In a refrigerator the bottle should be wrapped with cloth so that fragments of glass will not contaminate the food. The water in a rock will expand in freezing, just as the water in a bottle will. Such expansion may cause the wet surface of a rock to crumble or cause joints to be wedged apart.

If a fragment of porous rock is placed in water, air bubbles will appear as the water is absorbed, forcing the air out. Can the pebble be taken out and wiped dry? Any water which remains will expand upon freezing and cause the surface to crumble. In warm weather the moisture helps to bring about chemical changes which further the process.

Some rocks and minerals weather more rapidly than others. Limestone, for instance, weathers rapidly, and thus valleys are often formed where limestone is found. The weather-resistant kinds of rocks remain, and these usually form the hills. If some child reads that acids in the air and the soil slowly dissolve certain kinds of rock, a way of observing the process may be suggested: When a pebble of limestone or marble is placed in strong vinegar it will react with the weak acid of the vinegar, and the surface of the pebble will show the effect, as in weathering. The reaction will proceed more rapidly if the pebble and the vinegar are warmed by being set in the sunshine at the window or placed above the radiator. If limestone is unavailable, marble, some kinds of blackboard chalk, or even eggshells and sea shells also are composed of lime and can be used. Other kinds of rock may be immersed in vinegar for comparison.

Soil is formed from rock

Rocks such as granite are made up of several minerals, some of which are more resistant to weathering than others. As rocks crumble and are worn away, some of the harder, more resistant particles remain and become grains of sand; the finer particles become soil. For example, feldspar, the white or salmon-colored mineral in granite, weathers to become clay; the glassy particles of quartz are harder and more resistant and thus remain as grains of sand after the feldspar has crumbled from around them. Mica, which often is the third mineral in granite, also weathers to form clay. The mica is easy to distinguish. It may be light or dark, but it glistens, and it can be split easily into thin sheets, with either a fingernail or a pocket knife.

A mixture of sand and clay is called loam. Samples of clay, sand, and loam very likely can be located near the school and can be displayed in labeled glass jars. When plants grow they take certain minerals from the soil, but they return those minerals in a more usable form when the plants die and decay. Unless restored by means of fertilizer, soil may become impoverished because the minerals are removed in the crops that are harvested. Decaying plant material is called humus; soil that contains much humus is darker and richer than clay or sand. Plants can use only those minerals which are dissolved in the water absorbed by the plant. To show that some minerals contained in soil are soluble, water may be allowed to soak slowly through the dirt in a large flower pot and then filtered through a cloth or a paper towel. When the clear water that comes through is allowed to evaporate in a shallow dish, any minerals in the water will be left as crystals on the dish. A similar amount of water taken directly from the tap may be evaporated for comparison; the minerals in the tap water also come from soil and rock. If some rainwater is caught in a pan, the rainwater too may be allowed to evaporate for

Fig. 59

Rocks that have been exposed to weather readily crumble to form soil.

comparison. Likewise, water may be allowed to soak through soil rich in commerical fertilizer and the crystals remaining after evaporation examined.

To see which kinds of soil are best for crops, corn or other seed may be planted in sand, clay, and a dark loam. Commercial fertilizer may be added to the soil in a fourth container. Flower pots, or tin cans with drainage holes in the bottoms, may be used for the various soils, and all should be given identical care. A schedule of not too frequent watering will help to demonstrate one weakness of sand as a soil, for it will not hold moisture long. At first little difference may be noted, since the young seedlings gain their initial nourishment from the food stored in the seed, but before long the advantage of one soil over another should become apparent.

Humus is dark, ordinarily, for the same reason that ashes are usually black. Some of the carbon from the wood or other plant material may be left behind as the plant is destroyed, whether by fire or by decay. A partially-burned twig or other plant material may be brought to class as an illustration. Coal is black for the same reason, coal being formed from plants.

To observe how rocks crumble to form soil, the children may rub some weathered rocks together, and the particles which fall may be caught on a sheet of white paper. The children may notice that some rocks are harder than others and not so easily worn down. It should also be emphasized that the production of soil includes the chemical changes that take place in the fine particles. Badly weathered rocks may be brought to school as examples, and the class may go outside to observe other rocks that are crumbling. It is possible to observe all the various stages of decomposition in one location, except where water has washed away the particles.

Rocks are composed of minerals

Most rocks are a mixture of several minerals. Granite, for instance, contains crystals of quartz, feldspar, and either mica or one of the dark minerals hornblende or augite. The quartz has a glassy appearance; the feldspar has a white or salmon-colored luster similar to that of porcelain. The mica may be dark or rather light, has a distinct sheen, and will peel in thin sheets; the hornblende and augite are usually a rather dull black. In granite the individual crystals of the minerals are large enough to be distinguished easily, especially with a magnifying glass, but in many rocks the crystals are much smaller. The grainy appearance of a freshly broken surface is due to the crystalline composition of the rock. Crystals are formed in lava or other molten rock as the rock cools, much as crystals sometimes form in home-made candy, giving the candy a grainy texture. Just as candy which is overcooled may have large crystals, so will rocks which cool slowly have large crystals. Thus granite or other igneous rocks with large crystals must have been deep in the earth when formed. A lava, which pours out onto the surface, cools quickly; hence there is little time for crystals to form, and the grains are small. The size of the crystals in an igneous rock is indicative of the depth at which the rock was formed.

Water that contains abundant minerals is commonly known as hard water or mineral water. When the water evaporates, as from a teakettle, the minerals are left behind. In the teakettle evaporation is rapid, and the crystals left in the teakettle are small. Where evaporation is slow, the crystals tend to be larger. Crystals of quartz and calcite are common; both are formed by the evaporation of water. Perhaps someone will have such crystals to show the class.

To see how crystals develop, children can dissolve as much as possible of alum or copper sulfate in a small amount of warm water. Either the alum or the copper sulfate, the latter sometimes called blue vitriol, may be obtained at a drugstore. The solutions may be poured into glass jars; and as the water evaporates, crystals will be formed. If a portion of one solution is poured on a plate, more surface will be exposed, and evaporation will be more rapid than from the jar, but the crystals will be smaller. If the dish is placed in the sunshine or over a radiator, evaporation will be rapid and the crystals small. The children may experiment with different rates of evaporation to see what determines the size of the crystals, and thus learn why the crystals are larger in some rocks than in others.

With a bit of cloth some of the solution may be brushed onto a sheet of glass, leaving only a thin film. As the water evaporates, crystals will be formed like frost upon the glass. If a few drops of glue are stirred into the solution, the crystals, when formed, will cling better to the glass. Epsom salts make especially good crystals in this manner.

If the crystals are examined, it will be noted that each mineral forms a particular shape of crystal. Minerals can be identified by the shape of the crystal they form. Frequently, however, the shape is modified because of crowding. Even so, the shape of the crystals along a freshly broken surface is likely to be distinctive.

The fissures in rocks below the surface may be filled with minerals from water which seeps into them, forming what is known as a *vein* of minerals. Valuable minerals, called ores, are often found in veins. Gold, silver, and copper veins are rare and valuable, but quartz or calcite are more common and can be located somewhere near the school in most communities. Both quartz and calcite are likely to be a milky-white color. The quartz is hard, but the calcite is soft and is easily scratched with a knife.

CHANGES IN THE EARTH'S SURFACE

The surface of our earth tells a fascinating story of changes which have taken place in ages past, and similar changes are continuing even today. From New England to the Pacific there is evidence in sight of almost every school that massive sheets of ice once covered the northern portion of our continent. Even farther back in the distant past, rocks show that the areas where the Appalachians and Rocky Mountains are today were then under the sea, and at various times much of the Midwest was likewise submerged. The land near the coast from New Jersey to Texas is relatively flat, because in comparatively recent times it too was submerged. At one time a lofty mountain range extended along what is today our Atlantic coast, and our Eastern states contain vast amounts of sediment washed off those mountains, which have long since been worn flat. About Great Salt Lake and also about the Great Lakes of our Midwest, old shore lines reveal that the lakes were at one time far larger than they are today, and much of today's excellent farm land was once a portion of the flat lake bottom. Along the Pacific Coast evidence of recent change is provided by the volcanic peaks, lava fields, recurrent earthquakes, rugged mountain ranges, and sea cliffs. Rivers have cut through the rocks to form canyons, and great depths of sediment have been deposited in the valleys.

Changes in the land continue today. Erosion, floods, irrigation, electric power, and waterways are of public concern, as are the conservation and wise use of our mineral resources. Not only are broad national policy decisions involved, but, in many cases, the problems and opportunities of local communities and particular individuals. In any locality there is abundant opportunity for studying evidence of changes in the land. The work can be meaningful and stimulating for children.

How rocks are formed

When children find rocks they are often curious about where the rocks may have come from, and this interest can be capitalized upon by taking as a problem for study the question *Where do rocks come from?* The pebbles in the road, for example, if they are rounded, may have been dredged from a nearby stream. Similar pebbles can be found in almost any stream, and they can be traced back to their origin as broken fragments of the bedrock somewhere up-steam. Gravel is sometimes quarried where it was deposited by a stream that today no longer flows; if such is the case, there may be other evidence of an old stream bed that is now dry. If the pebbles from the road have sharp, broken edges, they very likely have been blasted from solid rock and crushed at the quarry. But the story can be traced even farther. The children can go to the quarry to observe the bedrock and can use their books for information that will help to interpret what they have seen. The books will explain that rocks are formed in three general ways: from sediment that hardens; from lava or other molten material that cools at the surface or somewhat deeper in the earth; or from other rocks through changes due to pressure and heat.

Streams carry sediment from the mountains and deposit it in the lowlands. The particles of sediment may eventually become cemented together to form rock. Such rocks are called *sedimentary*. In the classroom a handful of sand may be mixed with a little Portland cement, in the proportions of about six to one, and water added to make a paste. In a few days the mixture will have hardened; the resulting concrete, though artificial, will be similar to sandstone.

Fig. 60

Bedrock may be in layers (strata) — which indicates that the rock was formed from sediment.

If lime is used instead of cement, the artificial sandstone will not be so hard. But natural sandstones vary too. Gray sandstone, in which silica is the cement, is harder than red sandstone, in which iron rust is the cementing material. The grains of sand in a sandstone, it may be noted, are usually somewhat rounded — in contrast to the angular crystals in a rock such as granite. The grains in sandstone may have become worn by tumbling downstream or by the action of waves at the beach before becoming cemented together as sandstone. Another common sedimentary rock is shale, formed from mud. As in sandstone, the particles in shale have become firmly cemented. Shale when moist smells like mud, but it is not just dried clay. Dried clay will dissolve in water; shale will not — a test quite suitable for children to make. Another common sedimentary rock is limestone, which can be identified by the fact that it will bubble if acid is dropped upon it. Even vinegar, if warm and reasonably strong, will serve for this test. In sedimentary rocks, especially sandstone and shale, lines of stratification often are easily seen. The lines are due to the way in which sediment tends to settle out of water in layers (see p. 266). As it weathers, a sedimentary rock is apt to split along the lines of stratification.

In many areas the rock most commonly crushed for use on roads is a dark, almost black rock known as basalt or trap. Trap is formed from lava or similar molten material that has cooled and hardened on or near the surface of the earth. Granite also is formed from molten material, and hence is classified with basalt as an *igneous* rock.

The slate of which blackboards are often made is an example of rock that has been changed by heat and pressure. Marble, gneiss, and schist are rocks that have gone through similar changes. Such rocks are called *metamorphic,* because they have been changed. Metamorphic rocks ordinarily are formed deep within mountains where the pressure and temperature are great, but subsquently the surface rocks and soil may have been eroded, leaving the metamorphic rocks on the surface. Commonly the crystals of metamorphic rocks are somewhat flattened and form wavy layers. Such foliation often can be seen in schists and gneisses, rocks that are common in mountainous regions. The rocks with which children should become familiar are the few that are most common in their own locality. Those common rocks can be used to illustrate the ways in which all rocks are formed.

The wearing away of the land

After the weather has caused rock to crumble, wind or water may carry the particles away. The process by which rocks and soil are worn down and the

Fig. 61

The earth's surface has been shaped by erosion.

particles removed is called *erosion*. It can be demonstrated in the classroom by placing a mound of earth in a dishpan and allowing water to trickle down over it. The water may be poured slowly out of a bottle, and the stream that results will wear a gully in the mound of earth. To show that erosion is more damaging at flood time, the water may be poured more rapidly for a time. The sediment will be deposited in the bottom of the pan. Fast-moving streams cut their channels in a similar manner, and the sediment which was removed is deposited in the lowlands; plowed fields on hillsides lose much soil during heavy rains, and frequently gullies develop. Children should become concerned with what is being done to prevent the soil from being washed away along the banks of local streams and on nearby farms. How shallow the good soil is can probably be observed along an embankment by the roadside. Evidence of erosion and deposition should be easy to locate within sight of most schools, even in cities, especially after a hard rain.

The minerals we eat come from plants, or from animals that have eaten the plants, and the plants get their minerals from the soil. The minerals are dissolved in the water that comes through the roots. Only minerals that are soluble in water can be used by plants; hence the minerals which a plant can use are also the minerals that are most easily carried away by water. Fertilizers are used because they contain minerals that are readily available for plant use. Perhaps some farmer or the county agent may be induced to talk or answer questions about what is being done locally to enrich the soil and prevent erosion. As much as possible children should do more than become aware of the problems: they should expect to do something about them. The knowledge gained should be functional.

How moving water picks up sediment can be demonstrated by placing a handful of dirt, another of sand, and a few small pebbles in a large glass jar of water. When the water is stirred, it can be observed that finer particles are picked up first. When stirring is discontinued, the heavy particles settle first; the finer particles settle only after a period of time. During the dry season the water in streams moves slowly and will carry only fine particles, but during floods larger particles will be moved and the finer ones carried farther than usual before being deposited. As the seasons change, different kinds of sediment may be deposited at any one place, thus forming layers of varying material. As a result, rocks made of sediment are commonly stratified. Sediment is deposited horizontally in most situations; but owing to movements in the crust of the earth, sedimentary rocks may be found in slanting layers or even in folds. To show how strata develop through the deposition of varying materials, dirt may be stirred into the water in a glass jar and allowed to settle; then, without disturbing the dirt, powdered chalk can be stirred into the water and allowed to settle onto the dirt. By repeating the process, alternate layers of chalk and dirt can be built up to simulate the formation of strata. If sufficient dirt or chalk is used in each layer, the strata will be thick enough to be seen easily through the sides of the jar.

No activity in the classroom is quite as effective as observing the real thing outdoors, even though on a small scale. Heavy rainfall may have cut gullies across a field; a stream may be wearing away its banks; or perhaps the best evidence at hand can be found on the school grounds. Has the rainfall recently washed dirt out of the flower beds onto the sidewalks? Are roots of a tree or a bush exposed where water has washed away the dirt? Notice that the greatest damage has been done on steep banks where there is little vegetation and the bare dirt is exposed. In most locations where the dirt and rocks beneath the surface are exposed, children can see that the rich topsoil is but a thin layer, easily lost. On the banks of a stream, in a gully, or wherever soil is cut away by running water, the finer particles have been removed, yet heavy rocks tend to remain. Likewise, at the foot of the slope, coarse particles are deposited first, whereas finer particles are carried farther.

As the higher ground is worn away — slowly at times, more rapidly at others — the sediment carried away is deposited in the lowlands. If there is a pond nearby with a stream emptying into it, the children will be able to see that sediment has been deposited along the bottom of the pond, especially near the mouth of the stream, where the swiftly-flowing water first slowed down. If the process has been going on for some time, the deposits of sediment will have formed a delta extending from the mouth of the stream out into the pond. The same features may be seen on a small scale even in a puddle where water trickles into it. At the point where water empties from the pond or puddle, the water moves more rapidly and tends to cut deeper. As the spillway is lowered and sediment deposited along the bottom, the water in the pond or puddle becomes more and more shallow. Eventually a pond will become filled, forming first a swamp and then a meadow.

If the bed of the stream is examined it will be seen that where the water flows more swiftly the bed is being cut away, but in quiet pools the sediment is deposited. It may be noted also that the water in the stream flows more swiftly after a rain and is muddier, carrying more sediment than usual. In dry seasons the reverse is true; thus strata of varying sediment are built up in the pond or wherever the sediment is deposited.

Movement of the earth's crust

At many points along the Pacific Coast it is evident that former beaches are now high above the water. Sea shells are found in solid rock high in the Rocky Mountains. Below the soil of most of the Midwest are sedimentary rocks which indicate that the area was beneath the sea while sediment was being deposited. The channel of the Hudson River once extended out into what is now the Atlantic Ocean, for the coast line was then far to the east of its present location. Gradually the land sank beneath the water, and even today the old channel can be located where the stream once ran. Evidence can be found almost everywhere that the level of the land has not always been the same. There is pressure on the rocks of the earth's surface which causes some to be forced upward, others down. Some areas, such as the Midwest, have been lifted gently; in others, mountains have been formed, the rocks broken or folded by the great pressure. The youngest mountains in the United States are along the Pacific Coast. At some points these mountains still may be rising, although it is difficult for geologists to be certain, for the movement ordinarily is slow and gradual where mountains are being uplifted. Such motion commonly can be detected only by changes that become apparent after a long period of time.

Geologists are not all agreed as to the cause of the pressure which builds mountains, but that such pressure does exist is obvious. One factor is thought to be the shifting of weight when sediment is eroded from one spot and deposited in another. Although most crustal movement is gradual, occasionally the rocks will yield suddenly to the pressure, producing the tremors we call earthquakes. Volcanoes also are abrupt disturbances, and as such are of great interest to children.

The formation of mountains can be demonstrated in the classroom by placing several thin layers of modeling clay one upon the other and then pressing in upon the sides, causing the clay to fold. If cracks are formed in the clay, they correspond to joints and faults in rock. Clay is more realistic, but if it is not available, paper can be used. If it were not for mountain-building forces causing the land to be uplifted, our mountains eventually would be worn down to the common level, and in the past some mountains have been worn flat. But at other times the land is lifted more rapidly than it is eroded, and mountains are formed. If the bedrock is exposed by a road cut or by a stream in the vicinity of the school, the children, especially in a mountainous region, may be able to see clearly that some of the solid rock has been tilted or folded.

Volcanoes are found in regions where pressures that lift mountains are great. With the shifting pressures, molten rock is forced to the surface, forming a volcano. Perhaps the most realistic practicable way to demonstrate how a volcano is formed is to fill a deep pan with mud and leave it until a hard dry crust is formed and then press down on the surface until the still-fluid mud from below is forced to flow out through fissures in the crust. Mauna Loa of the Hawaiian Islands and many other volcanoes are of the effusive type, similar to the mud illustration. The more spectacular and dangerous volcanoes that explode and hurl ashes for many miles are similar. Where the rocks of the earth's crust are highly resistant, the pressure may increase to the point that an explosion will result. An overheated pressure cooker, for example, will explode; whereas a kettle will merely boil over, because the cover of one is more resistant than that of the other.

Fossils provide a record of the past

At Aberdeen, Washington, a sixth-grade class visited a spot near the harbor, within walking distance of the school, where sea shells were found embedded in solid rock, indicating that the land there had been uplifted. In many cities, classes may visit the museums to see the fossils on display there. It is sometimes possible to find, in sedimentary rocks especially, the bones or shells of animals, footprints, and prints of leaves or other parts of plants. Such remains of prehistoric life are known as *fossils*. Sedimentary rock may take a long time to harden, but children can simulate the process by using some material which hardens rapidly. Portland cement with sand and water forms a material similar to sandstone. Lime or plaster of Paris with water may be used to cement the sand. Clay is good, too, and corresponds to shale; however, clay will dissolve in water and is not considered a rock even when dry and hard. While the simulated sandstone or shale is still soft with water, though not too soft to hold the impression, a leaf may be pressed into it. After the cement has hardened, the leaf may be removed — in real life it probably would be removed by decay — and the print will remain. Other prints may be made in a similar manner. A cat or other pet may be used to show how fossil footprints are made. Again, bones or seashells may be pressed into the material and left there for the cement to harden about them, thus simulating another kind of fossil. Chicken bones or fish bones, being small, are good for such a purpose. The bones of dinosaurs and of primitive men have been found thus in rock. Petrified wood also is a fossil, but, as with the fossil prints, none of the original material remains, except for traces of carbon in some specimens. The wood has not changed to stone, but has been replaced by minerals as the wood gradually decayed. Sometimes on a concrete wall, in a similar manner, the print of the wooden forms can be seen on the concrete. The concrete has taken the shape of the wood. The grain, knots, and cracks can be seen, even though the wooden forms have been removed.

Fossils provide a record of the animals and plants that lived on the earth in ages past; and once that record is known, inferences can be made regarding changes in the land as well. Where the sixth grade found sea shells in rock near the Pacific Coast but well above the water, the land at some time in the past must have been lifted out of the water.

Fig. 62

Children can prepare artificial "fossils" much like the real ones shown here.

ORGANIZING AND CONDUCTING INVESTIGATIONS OF THE EARTH'S SURFACE

Small children who become aware of the rocks and other surface features of their surroundings have taken their first steps toward the desired objectives in this area. The child who brings to school a handful of pebbles and asks questions has begun his investigations.

In the kindergarten a rather poorly adjusted boy went over to a bucket of water and began to drop various articles into the water, apparently to see which would float. After a while he began to stir the water with his hand, going faster and faster. He became quite excited to find the water spinning higher on the sides and lower in the center. He also observed that everything he had dropped into the bucket had risen from the bottom and was being carried along with the moving water.

Having seen evidence of erosion outdoors, the children in a first grade

270

brought a soft, badly weathered rock into their room, obtained a pail with a hole in the bottom, and hung the pail so that water would drip from it onto the rock. After a short interval, quite a depression was found eroded in the rock. One boy said seriously to his friend:

"I wonder — if I stood under my shower, would I begin to wear away after a while?"

The concepts were still incomplete, but these children and the boy who experimented with the vortex were developing some basic meanings that are essential for a mature understanding of erosion, and erosion can be a socio-economic problem of major importance. The enthusiasm associated with these experiences was at the same time helping to develop wholesome, constructive attitudes in the children. With children investigating spontaneously, the teacher needs only to stimulate and assist them, guiding their investigations in worthwhile directions.

A third-grade study of local rocks

Interest developed when several children brought their collections of rocks to school. When the teacher saw this evidence of interest, she made a tour of the area about the school, located a bank of rock, and brought back a fragment of the rock. A text was found that contained descriptions of various rocks, and the rock was identified as conglomerate. After reading and discussing what the book said, the class visited the bluff of conglomerate. They had planned to find stones that interested them, stones they could take back to class for further study. One of the children found two that he liked. When he rubbed the two together, one made a white line on the other. To the teacher the child said:

"This is like chalk that we use on the blackboard. It makes a mark like it."

He was discovering that some rocks and minerals are harder than others, and he had hit upon the method used by geologists to determine the relative hardness of minerals, as a means of identifying them. The teacher considered his discovery significant and suggested that he report to the class upon their return to school.

One of the girls exclaimed, "I've found a mineral!" It was a small lavender glass-like object with somewhat rounded edges. She said, "Do you think it could be some kind of stone from a ring?"

The teacher was not sure. Back in the classroom, the object was examined carefully. It was found that a knife would scratch it and that it would not scratch a piece of window glass. A reference book indicated that the fractured edges were typical of glass, and it was decided by all that the object was merely a bit of glass. By then the class was interested in minerals and wanted to continue testing others for hardness, for their ways of breaking, and for other qualities described in the text the class was using. As the work continued, many more stones were brought to class from the school grounds and elsewhere in the community.

The sixth-graders study their region

At the beginning of the term the sixth grade, in planning their work, decided that they would like to study the rocks and surface features of their own community, which was located on the lava fields of the Columbia Plateau in the state of Washington. The class listed a number of questions that puzzled them and made plans for study. One of the girls brought her rock collection and showed the various specimens to the class. The great variety of rocks and minerals was stressed and some of the distinguishing features considered. In addition to crystals of mica and quartz, and rocks such as sandstone, quartzite, and obsidian, the collection included petrified wood and stream-rounded pebbles.

The class went on foot to see the rocks exposed along the highway above the river, a relatively small stream flowing through the town. On their way the children were able to see basalt rock that had once been lava. It was possible to distinguish successive layers of lava, each a separate flow from the volcanic vents, with a weathered surface between them making a line which indicated that some time had elapsed between eruptions. At some points the class found "bubble holes" in the rocks where volcanic gases or steam had escaped from the still-hot lava. Freshly broken rock was compared with old weathered surfaces. Along the joints weathering had left a brown rust. The thin soil on the surface above the rocks was noted. One crevice was filled with a weakly cemented sandstone. A vein of quartz was found, including a few small but well-formed crystals. The children gathered specimens that showed freshly broken surfaces and bubble holes, and they collected badly weathered pieces that would crumble in the hand.

Back in the classroom, the children read from a variety of books in search of information about rocks. They labeled their specimens and displayed them on the work table. Each rock was placed on a card that had upon it not only the name but whatever information about the rock the child had found and thought significant.

When the class revisited the bank of rock another day, they were able to see and understand more than on their initial trip. Additional specimens were

Fig. 63

Sixth-graders study their region.

gathered, and the class moved on to an older cut in a nearby hillside. The features observed were similar here, but the weathering was more extreme. The children saw successive lava flows, jointing, and plants growing from crevices in the rocks. The class followed an old road and found rocks so badly weathered that they had the appearance of clay and would crumble when touched. At some points where clumps of grass and bushes were growing there was no clear distinction between rocks and soil.

Later a trip was made to the stream, and there the action of the water was observed. As in all streams, the current was swifter at some points than at others. Where the water was swift, all the smaller pebbles, the clay, and the sand had been carried away, but in the quiet pools silt was found along the bottom. Most of the stones in the stream were basalt like the bedrock along the highway, but here the edges had already become somewhat rounded. Two isolated pieces of river-worn granite were located. On the way back, a mass of broken lava, breccia, was found protruding from the hillside.

At the classroom the children found additional information about volcanoes. They read how volcanoes erupt, how joints are formed when molten rock cools, and how rock weathers to form soil. The information was used to explain how the rocks and soil of their own region were formed. Rocks gathered on the trip and afterwards were added to the displays. In some cases the placards explaining them were revised as new insights were gained.

Motion pictures were used to show volcanoes in eruption and to show lava fields in other parts of the world. A number of experiments were performed.

273

When crystals of table salt, copper sulfate, boric acid, and the like were formed by evaporation of their solutions, the crystals were added to the display on the work table. One of the girls brought a travel folder with pictures that revealed stratification in the rocks, weathering, and the erosion of canyons. Other children told of trips they had made and what they had seen that now had new meaning. Throughout the work each child kept a written record of what he had done and learned. The discussions helped in the clarification of ideas and thus in the preparation of the records. Individual help and occasionally some group attention was given also to the grammar, spelling, handwriting, and other skills involved in composition. At the end of the study the class prepared a general summary of what they had learned about rocks and about the changes in the region since the days when lava flowed out over the land.

A fourth grade reports

There are many ways that children can report their investigations. A fourth-grade class in New York, while studying the earth's surface, prepared a display in the hall cabinets. The display pictured a number of the topics or themes studied in reading, discussions, experiments, and field trips. Stones were displayed that showed the effects of weathering. A large piece of granite and separate specimens of quartz, mica, and feldspar were exhibited, with a placard explaining that granite is made of those three minerals and that all rocks are likewise made of minerals. In the classroom the children had placed a mound of sod and another of soil in a large flat pan and subjected the two mounds to erosion by running equal amounts of water down over them. The results were placed on display with an explanatory placard. Another display was prepared to show fossils and how they are formed.

While the class was studying fossils, the teacher had been able to show some to the children. A trip was made to the museum, where many were on display. The class prepared some fossils artificially from sand and cement. One Monday morning, when one of the children returned from a week end in the country, he brought with him a stone containing numerous seashells. Since he had found the stone on a hillside along the Hudson River, his discovery indicated that that region had once been under the sea. Some uncertainty remained, because the stone was not freshly broken from the bedrock and might have been moved from where it was formed. Later, however, after the study had been concluded, another child brought to class a stone taken directly from bedrock near the Hudson, thus substantiating the interpretation and also indicating that the child's interest was persisting and his understanding was functional.

Reporting provides an immediate purpose, a social stimulus for adequate preparation, in addition to providing information. A display is actually one means of reporting. Oral reports are likely to be especially stimulating if informal rather than routine, and if they include actual demonstrations of the materials and phenomena discussed. The fourth-grade class referred to above made oral reports, displays, and prepared a written record for the group as a whole. That real interest and some understanding resulted was apparent one day during the noon recess when the teacher came upon a group of the boys part way up the steps with a boulder that must have weighed as much as any one of them. They had found the stone on the grounds and were bringing it in because of the large crystals it contained. The interest in rocks spread from this class to others in the building until eventually even the smallest children, fascinated especially by the glistening bits of mica, were bringing in fragments of the schist that is common in New York.

Little equipment is required for the study of the earth's surface. The resources for active investigation are readily available in any locality. The work not only is stimulating but has marked cultural value, and the understandings gained add enjoyment to outings and travel.

STUDY GUIDE

1. Make a collection of common rocks, group them to illustrate ideas that would be meaningful to children of a given age, and prepare a display with explanatory placards. Explain why the ideas illustrated are considered significant.
2. Prepare some crystals by evaporation from a solution. Add these to the display to show one way that crystals are formed, or how minerals often can be identified by the shape of the crystal. The crystals also can be used to explain why some rocks are coarse-grained and others are fine, or merely to point out that rocks are made of minerals.
3. Prepare some artificial "fossils" and add these to the display. If real fossils can be obtained for the display, the artificial ones can be used to explain how fossils are formed.
4. Locate some of the places within walking distance of your present location where geological principles are exemplified. Describe the features observed; explain what they reveal and how they could be used in work with children.
5. See if your home-town library has information regarding the geological history of your own region. If so, what are some of the changes that have occurred? Can rocks be obtained and displayed to exemplify those changing conditions?

11

Experiences with Living Things

A study of living things deals with the realities of a child's life. While learning how seed are spread, a third-grade girl — on the school grounds at recess — called to the teacher with evident excitement and satisfaction:

"Oh, look, that dog is carrying a bur just like we studied in science!"

Living things are obvious and prominent in our environment. Anyone who walks outdoors, even in a large city, comes in contact with a variety of plants — and animals, too. For the teacher, living things are likely to be somewhat familiar; for the child, they may be novel, and the constant movement and change associated with living things attract and hold the child's attention so that learning is pleasant and rewarding. Activities such as constructing an ant house, culturing bacteria, and assembling a terrarium appeal to children. There is ample opportunity to observe and experiment. Children are delighted to report how they saw a spider spinning his web or watched a bluejay scold a house cat lurking nearby. Collecting and displaying galls, egg sacs, and cocoons, caring for baby chicks in the classroom, and watching seed sprout on a damp sponge are examples of direct experience which can lead to understanding and appreciation.

WORK THAT STRESSES MEANINGS

To avoid the confusion of random activities, experiences with living things should be organized to stress relationships. Studying "all about turtles" or "taking up a study of robins," for example, is likely to result in the acquisition of isolated facts — yet effective learning comes from dealing with actual turtles and robins, rather than with generalities. In the following case the second grade worked directly with particular animals, and from these experiences recorded their own observations and developed their own meaningful generalizations.

After observing their aquarium over a period of time, the children came to the following conclusions and recorded them in a science notebook:

Snails live in the water. Fish live in the water too. A snail lives in a shell. A fish has scales. Fish breathe different from other animals. Fish swim with their tails. They have fins too. A snail moves along by its foot. He has a head with feelers. He goes back into his shell. A fish swims away. Fish eat different from other animals. A snail has a mouth too. He has a tongue with many rough things on it.

In another example the children of a certain fifth grade had decided to study animals, and each person chose some particular animal to investigate. Their study consisted of reference work and of direct observation at the zoo, at the museum, about their homes, or wherever the animal chosen could be located. The work began well, but the enthusiasm soon diminished. The teacher noted the disorganized nature of the discussions and the lack of interest in reports on the various animals. No one seemed to care about the animals that other members of the class were studying. So a new organization was undertaken in the discussions. Each discussion was arranged in terms of some question or theme. At one meeting the children considered how the various animals protect themselves, how they are able to survive. Comparisons were made. The rabbits and deer, for example, depend primarily on running to escape and upon coloring that makes the animal obscure against the background. Since it was wartime, the children were familiar with the idea of camouflage. Cats have sharp teeth and claws, have protective coloring, and can escape by climbing. Crayfish have pincers; horses have hoofs and cows have horns with which to defend themselves. Turtles have shells; porcupines have spines, skunks their odor, snakes and bees their venom. Some animals, such as rabbits and fish, produce so many offspring that even if some are lost others survive. Birds have sharp beaks and claws; and the females and the young also have protective coloring. A mother bird may feign injury to direct attention away from her young. Many birds fly south to survive the change of seasons; frogs and other animals hibernate deep in the ground, below the surface cold. These and a great many other points were made in regard to the survival of the various animals studied. Each person had something to contribute about the animal he had studied, and a stimulating discussion was the result. Other discussions were concerned with how animals get their food, raise their young, and are fitted for their particular way of life; and one discussion was concerned with ways that the various animals affect each other and people. The discussions that were organized in terms of some theme proved to be not only meaningful but stimulating for everyone concerned.

Learnings oriented to personal and social needs

Personal and social problems which stem from the environment, as they commonly do, often may stimulate investigations and at the same time may provide the themes upon which the investigations of children are centered. An activity that has no real purpose should be avoided. Making leaf prints, learning names, and collecting and pressing flowers, for example, should be avoided unless directed toward an objective that is clearly worthwhile. Seed should not be collected in the fall just to build a collection, but to develop meanings, such as the concept that seed are spread in various ways. An aquarium or a potted plant can be useful in a room, as well as beautiful, but the mere presence of the plants and the aquarium does not constitute a worthwhile science program. In terms of science learnings, it is difficult to see the purpose of making flower cut-outs, tracing and coloring the outlines of leaves, or playing the squirrel-and-nut game.

The natural curiosity of children may be profitably directed toward a matter of personal or social concern, such as encouraging the choice of better lunches in the cafeteria or better care of the school grounds and nearby picnic areas — problems that may be classified within the broad areas of health and conservation. The teacher may perceive that particular experiences have value in building an understanding of broad social problems and may guide the children with these remote values in mind, but it is of questionable value to have children deal directly with a remote problem that is beyond their comprehension and appreciation. Conservation in the broader sense, for example, will probably have little significance to a small child, unless a local drought, flood, forest fire, or other immediate occurrence brings the problem within the range of his own experience. A current issue, such as whether or not the waste products of a local factory are destroying the fish in that vicinity, may bring conservation into focus for the children.

An example of planning for work with living things

A sixth grade began their study of animals by listing what they would like to learn. Six points of concern were noted:

Animals

How do they get food?
Where do they live, and how are they able to live there?
See how they grow.
See how many kinds of animals there are.
How do they defend themselves?
Are they good for us or harmful?

The group then suggested ways in which they could find out about animals. Virginia pointed out that in a book she had at her desk there were some chapters about animals and that other books in the room would have more. Kent said he had a good encyclopedia at home and there were good books in the school library too. Somebody mentioned the city library as another good source. George said he could bring a hen. Another boy knew where he could get minnows from a stream nearby. Grasshoppers, salamanders, and turtles were suggested; and then Dorman said there were all sorts of insects in the grass of the empty lots down the street. One of the girls said she knew where there was a robin's nest in a cedar tree, close enough that the class could visit it. Once the bird nests were mentioned, other members of the class recalled seeing the nests of several sparrows, one in a tree and two under the eaves of a nearby building. At the front of the school building itself someone later found a wasp's nest along the ceiling of the porch, and this was added to the list for observation. Plans also were made to visit the museum, where various animals were on display, and ways of recording observations were considered.

Helping to plan their own work enables children to see meaningful relationships and is a stimulus for the work which follows. As a result of planning, children can see ahead, and thus can help to gather materials and otherwise aid in achieving the purposes of instruction.

OBSERVING AND REPORTING

Observation is a fundamental procedure in science and also in the behavior of children. Two preschool girls, apparently uninfluenced by any schoolteacher,

Fig. 64

Children can be diligent observers and effective reporters of what they see outdoors.

were heard and seen enthusiastically observing a bee in the flowers of a neighbor's back yard. Within the hour these same girls came by with an earthworm in a glass jar, where they could watch it conveniently.

Observations reported by individuals

Children are diligent observers. With encouragement they can observe independently whenever an opportunity presents itself, and later, during an appropriate discussion period in school, can report what they have seen: the behavior of ants along their runways or in their nests when disturbed; a cat stalking a squirrel in someone's back yard; a bird building a nest or feeding its young. Such observations should be welcomed at all times, but they should be given a special emphasis when they are pertinent to a study undertaken by the class. If the reports of direct observation are enthusiastically received and are used in a way befitting their significance in science, the effect will be to stimulate further and more careful observations. Many classes already have a time set aside, frequently in the early morning, for discussions of current interests or events and for sharing spontaneously whatever may be intriguing to the individuals concerned. Whatever the occasion, opportunity can be provided somewhere in the day for children to report their outside observations, and the time will be well spent.

Observing mammals. Ordinarily the most conspicuous animals observed in common experience are the mammals. On a farm children can see horses, cows, pigs, and sheep. In the woods and fields there may be gophers, woodchucks, porcupines, or racoons — perhaps a weasel or a fox. About houses and gardens, even in the city, some animals are common: dogs, cats, mice, moles, and squirrels. A great variety of mammals can be seen at a zoo or museum — animals such as elephants, tigers, giraffes, bears, and monkeys. One of the values in a study of living things, especially the mammals, is the understanding of human beings which can be developed. Children can learn that kittens, calves, and baby elephants — like human beings — are born alive and are nursed by their mothers. In contrast to fish and frogs, for example, these animals are warm-blooded. Eventually the concept that such animals are classed together as mammals will be developed.

A child who has opportunity to observe a rabbit, either domestic or wild, might observe and report the animal's behavior: how it sniffs about, cautiously examining whatever may be strange, or how if frightened it may thump the ground with its hind feet, a reaction that serves to warn other rabbits of approaching enemies. The large, movable ears apparently help to give the rabbit a keen sense of hearing; children may attempt stalking a rabbit to see how close they can come to the animal without being noticed. Someone may be intrigued with the way a rabbit nibbles its food, and the diet of rabbits can be noted as helping to determine where they live and how they are able to live in great numbers and whether or not wild rabbits may become a nuisance to farmers. Perhaps the newborn young may be observed in a hutch, and repeated observations will reveal not only their behavior and the mother's care but also the development of the animals as they grow, much as children change while growing larger. Similar observations of other animals will serve to provide comparisons from which generalizations applicable to many animals can be drawn.

Observing birds. In observing birds, feeding habits are among the points worth noting. Some eat grain, others insects, others a combination of the two. Ducks find their food in the water, and hawks number rodents among their prey, whereas the magpies devour much carrion. Flycatchers dive through the air to catch insects; robins walk along the ground in search of worms and insects, and cedar waxwings are often found in the trees when cherries are ripe. Ducks have wide bills for scooping up whatever can be found in the water. The nuthatch and the downy woodpecker have long bills with which to probe for insects; the English sparrow and the grosbeak have sturdy bills suitable for crushing the seed they eat. The eagle's beak and talons are suitable for tearing flesh to be devoured, and even the barnyard hen uses its beak and claws in fighting. Children may notice the way a hen cocks its head to watch and listen; the position of the eyes and ears may be contrasted with that of our own. Many birds gather in flocks, as do numerous other animals. The location and type of nest may be worthy of note, for the location is indicative of the bird's way of life, and the bird's manner of protecting the nest from marauders is a factor in the survival of the species. The fact that male birds are colorful and the females drab is a frequent source of humor but also is a factor in the survival of birds; the male's color apparently makes him attractive to his mate, whereas the drably-feathered female is less conspicuous when sitting on the nest. If a record is kept of birds seen during each month, comparisons can be made to provide a basis for the discussion of migration. A large number of the birds that were on an early list will not appear on a later one. Where have they gone? Observing geese in flight also will help to establish the concept. Keeping a migration record necessitates identifying the birds, and this can help to show that some of the distinguishing features of birds are size, color, body contour, type of bill, song, and manner of flight. Pictures will help in identification. Bird-naming need not become an end in itself, but the names should be used as circumstances require.

Observing water animals. Animals that live in or about the water also may be observed by children and the observations reported at school. When some first-graders saw fish jumping in a Florida canal they reported their observations at school. As a result, books were read for information about fish. Charts were made to record the conclusions reached, and in the process the children learned to recognize a number of new words. A seventh-grade girl reported watching sea gulls along the Pacific Coast fly aloft to drop clams on the rocks below, thus breaking open the shells. Sometimes before the gull could fly down to reach the opened shell and eat the contents, other gulls lurking nearby would attempt to steal the morsel, and the first gull, while swooping down, would scream loudly in protest to frighten away the intruders. Considerable wrangling and scolding would follow before the issue was settled — only to be repeated a few moments later.

A sixth-grade boy and an eighth-grade girl returned to their classes after a summer at their family's cottage on the Connecticut shore. Each told how they had collected soft-shelled crabs, had found the jelly-like masses of eggs of certain shellfish, had dug for clams, had seen miniature crabs scooting along the sand and had watched the barnacles on the rocks and seen their appendages moving in the water to gather food. The two children reported finding live starfish and watching sea anemones along the shore.

A second-grade boy, after a week end at the beach, came back with clamshells and explained how moon snails had drilled the holes in the shells. Another child in the same class told how he had seen turtles at the pond attack ducks swimming in the water. He also had seen bubbles coming to the surface of the pond, but wasn't sure whether they were from some animal or from the decay of vegetation. A third boy from the same class had been fishing with his father and uncle, and he reported on the eating habits of various fish: which fish would jump for flies and which were accustomed to feeding along the bottom — information obtained largely from the adults but based upon observation as well.

Other opportunities for reporting may come when a child has seen fish cleaned and has observed the internal organs and the eggs inside the female. Dragonflies and damsel flies are often seen over ponds and swamps; occasionally a muskrat may be sighted. On a fishing trip with parents a child may locate a beaver dam. Water striders, backswimmers, and various nymphs may often be found in the water or on the surface, crayfish and mussels along the bottom. In the Pacific Northwest when the smelt or salmon are running — traveling upstream to spawn — they may be observed in dense schools, and are easily caught. For people who live near the streams the run is as much a topic of conversation as the weather. The herring runs in Maine and New Hampshire are similar. The effect on the runs of sewage or industrial waste in the water, of hydroelectric dams, or of excessive commercial fishing are issues often discussed. Close observations of water life can be made in a municipal aquarium, zoo, or fish hatchery, and small specimens from a pond may be brought to school; but to understand many relationships it is best to observe the animals outdoors in their natural habitat.

Observing insects and spiders. Insects and spiders are a common part of daily experience, but many of the observations that children can report are not easily duplicated at school. With the stimulus that reporting gives, children become aware of these animals and observe what otherwise might be overlooked. If a lamp is placed in a window at night during the warmer weather, a variety of moths and other insects can be observed closely and to advantage on the glass against the background of darkness outside. A nest of ants in the woods, mosquito wrigglers in stagnant water, a hornet nest in a tree, or muddaubers in the eaves of a building give opportunity for observation. When a farmer, in harvesting, disturbs a yellow-jacket nest in the field, a subject for discussion is provided. Farm animals react violently when insects attempt to deposit eggs in their hides, and the resulting excitement may stimulate the child to consider the life cycle of insects. Observing spiders on the basement wall, cabbage moths or tomato worms in the garden, Japanese beetles on the rose bushes, tent caterpillars on a limb by the roadside, maggots in the garbage or other refuse, fireflies in the back yard at night — these and similar occurrences when reported at school can lead to worthwhile understanding of such animals in our daily experience, a knowledge that is essential in the control of harmful insects and will contribute to an appreciation of the helpfulness of others.

Observations of plant life. Especially where excursions for the entire class are difficult to arrange, pupils may report their individual observations of the plant life being studied. If the great variety of plant life is being stressed, children can report the various kinds of trees they have seen and where the trees are growing. Willows, for example, are common along the banks of streams. Many children may not realize at first that moss is a plant. They may not be aware of fungi, such as the bracket fungus, toadstools, and the mold that grows on bread. Cattails and skunk cabbage may be observed in a swamp or at the edge of a pond or stream. Someone may bring to class the green scum from a pond. Other children may find lichens, ferns, or flowering plants. Children may tell of the annular rings they have counted on a stump or of the sap they have seen flowing. Farming practices may be reported. The way strawberries, quack grass, Canadian thistle, or other plants are spread may be noted. Someone may have visited a nursery or may have seen a tree grafted. The temperature or amount of moisture necessary for the growth of various plants in a greenhouse may be reported. In the spring, when parents are gardening, the class may consider which plants require an acid soil and which should have lime. The plants used by the highway department to check erosion along road cuts may be noted, and children can compare the plants they have found growing in sunny spots with those found in shady locations and contrast the plants seen on trips with the ones found locally. Flowers may be observed opening at one time of day and closing at another in response to the light. Seed may be found spreading in various ways. Perhaps someone has noted the pollen of a poplar or a willow spreading with the wind, or has seen pollen ejected by a mulberry tree.

Children should be encouraged to report phenomena exactly as observed, not as a book says they ought to be or as someone may expect them to be. The difference may be significant. Even small children can observe independently and report their observations informally in stimulating circumstances.

Observation in the classroom

Seeing is believing, and a large share of the learning in daily living is gained from direct observation. Living things brought to class or raised in the classroom can be examined in detail and over a period of time to note changes. Everyone in a class can observe for himself at one time or another and not have to depend entirely upon a verbal description by someone else who has made the observation. Having animals and plants in the classroom, whether briefly or over a longer span of time, provides a common experience and the stimulus for group undertakings.

Instead of depending entirely upon the blackboard and the printed page for their facts, a seventh grade in a small Ohio town each year has a local bee-keeper install a hive outside the classroom window. An eighth-grade class in Ohio, while studying the human eye and vision, obtained the eye of a cow from a slaughterhouse. The eye was cut open and examined by members of the class. A sixth-grade class in the state of Washington on one occasion used the eye of a salmon recently caught by one of the parents. Learning how the eyes function, how they should be cared for, and what spectacles do to help can be stimulating in such a setting.

Encouraging close observation. If a child's natural interest in his surroundings is encouraged, many of the living things he observes he will bring to class for closer scrutiny, perhaps in connection with his report of outside observations. In one case a seven-year-old child came to the teacher on the playground one day with a small yellow-green bug. The child asked what it was, and when the teacher said she didn't know, they decided to place the bug in a jar and take it into the classroom to see what could be learned about it. In another case, when a third-grade boy caught a squirrel and brought it to school, he was encouraged to show it to many of the other classes in the building. He ex-

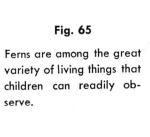

Fig. 65

Ferns are among the great variety of living things that children can readily observe.

plained how he had caught it, and told what he had learned about squirrels. The children in the various classes asked many questions and showed a lively interest in what the boy could tell them.

Close observation is encouraged if the observations are discussed and recorded. A second-grade girl came to school excited about a starfish she had found. When she brought the starfish to school, it did not take her long to gain the interest of her classmates. The children began asking questions and inspecting the starfish, and the teacher helped them to find additional information in reference books. It was decided that the class would prepare a book of its own about starfish. The observations reported were recorded on the blackboard. Information obtained from references was added. The record then was duplicated to form a "book," and each child got a copy:

The Starfish

It looks like a star.
It has five points.
If one of his points breaks off, a new one will grow.
It takes about a year to grow a new point.
He has suckers underneath his points.
They help him turn over and move around.
The starfish likes to sleep among the rocks.
The starfish keeps the water clean.
He eats oysters and mussels. . . .

In another second grade, observations made in class and also at the beach were recorded when sea shells were brought to school:

One is an oyster shell.
Oysters live inside of them.
And Frank has seen them stick their heads out.
So has Madeline at the shore.
Their heads look like tongues.
They have a very smooth shell. . . .

Animals in glass jars and cages. Small animals brought to class can be kept in glass jars with cloth over the top. One day a second-grade child brought to school a land snail in a paper bag. There was a glass jar with a metal top in the closet. The child got some leaves and grass from outside and placed them with the snail in the jar. Then holes were punched in the top of the jar to provide air. In the same class, when a small snake was brought to school, it was placed in another jar where the children could observe it without undue excitement.

In a fifth-grade class, when a popular magazine came out with colorful pictures of various insects, interest was stimulated, and the children brought to class an assortment of insects in glass jars. Some rather detailed observations were made, reported to the class, and recorded.

Somewhat larger animals, such as chickens, rabbits, guinea pigs, and laboratory rats can be kept in wire cages for observation. One class, a first grade, had planned for a hamster; on the day it arrived the children came prepared with an excess of lettuce, raisins, and carrots with which to feed it. The comments of various individuals were recorded while the children gathered about the cage:

Hey, he's cute!
What's his name?
Look at his fingernails.
I got some food.
Don't feed him yet.
Look at him drink!
He's soft. He's got a lot of fur.
In the winter they grow a lot of fur to keep warm.
He's eating *my* food! Look, he likes raisins.
If you get your hand in there he won't eat as well. . . .
You be careful with him. Pet him with one finger.
Don't squash him. Give him air.
He's getting big. He's got the mumps!
No, those are his pouches. He carries food in them. . . .
I didn't get to touch him yet.
Give him a rest.

Aquarium, terrarium, and incubator. An aquarium (see pp. 312–13) can show that a great variety of plants and animals live in water. It can reveal the relationship of one to the other, and the characteristics of the various species represented. The way fish are able to breathe in water and their dependence upon plants for oxygen can be graphically demonstrated with an aquarium. If there are no fish to destroy the young, the growth and development of polliwogs from eggs can be observed. In one first grade, where a suitable tank was available, the children brought in sand; the teacher contributed some goldfish; and one child brought some snail's eggs from his aquarium at home. The eggs were allowed to develop for a while in a separate container before being put into the aquarium with the fish. One child, who previously had shown little interest in any subject, brought in many underwater plants he had found in the creek behind his house. From that time on he was ready and willing to take care of the fish and to read and discuss subjects involving fish, and his achievement level in general showed marked improvement. A third-grade teacher reported that the children asked questions continually about the life in their aquarium. One girl wanted to know how the goldfish were able to breathe, and then the whole class began to discuss how fish live where they do and how they get their food. Someone wanted to know if fish are asleep when they remain motionless in the water. Through watching the fish and reading whatever material on the subject could be found, many of the questions were answered. The movement of the gills was observed; the motion of the tail and fins in swimming was noted. One reference stated that fish do not really sleep as people do but at times remain quite motionless, resting. One of the children wanted to know if the snail had a tongue. With a reading glass she studied the animal closely and saw what appeared to be a tongue move in and out. The numerous questions, the hurrying to look, the air of excitement while observing, and the obvious satisfaction derived from the discoveries served to reveal that interest was high and learning effective.

A terrarium can be another center of interest, the source of many profitable observations (see pp. 313–14). When Henry brought a frog to his second-grade classroom the other children were delighted and were eager to provide a place for it. An old, leaky aquarium was obtained and was filled with moss and stones from a nearby wood lot. A small enameled pan was placed near one end and filled with water. The frog thus had what the children called a "water place" and a "land place." The frog even had a "jumping off place" — a large stone near the water.

One class, a combined first and second grade, was given a small incubator by one of the parents. Some of the eggs were opened periodically to see their development. Others eventually became baby chicks, and the children cared for them. There was much reading and many discussions, all very earnest and enthusiastic. Reports were prepared in the form of books with pictures. Pictures with captions were prepared every few days to record changes. Each child devised his own statement, and the sketch was his own also, although help was given where needed.

Recording and interpreting the observations

Maintaining a continuously high level of interest in observations that extend over a considerable period of time is not to be expected, but interest can be revived when change is noted. Excitement reigned in the fourth grade when someone discovered that the tadpole had developed a new front leg, and again when the turtle laid eggs. Later the class was thrilled to discover that a butterfly had emerged from the chrysalis they had cared for throughout the winter. Until this happened no great interest had been shown since the day the caterpillar disappeared and a cocoon was found in its place. The children in a fifth grade each week made sketches of their bean seedlings to record the changes. A second grade used their crayons to show the progress of the crocus bulbs they had planted. A third grade prepared a booklet of stories and pictures recording the development of their narcissus from bulb to flowering plant. Another fourth grade made sketches to show how the leaves of their potted plants turned toward the windows, and how the roots of seedlings were growing toward the water. The same class periodically recorded the height of their seedlings in plant-growth experiments.

Recording, measuring, and sketching in preparation for reporting stimulates careful observation. The accuracy and skill revealed by the records should increase with the maturity and experience of the individuals. Drawings should be made while the specimen itself is being observed, so that detailed inspection is possible. A sketch prepared after a lapse of time, with the situation changed and the specimen removed, will be vague and inaccurate. In such a case the sketch will not serve its purpose as a means of learning. A drawing copied from some book likewise has limited instructional value. Sketches should be based on direct, immediate observation. Although children can be encouraged to sketch their observations, the work should remain largely voluntary. Overemphasis on the quality of a drawing can become an obstacle to observation and can dampen the child's enthusiasm for sketching. In all sketching and reporting children should be encouraged to describe objects and phenomena exactly as observed, not as it may have been assumed they should be. If the differences seem to be significant, they can be discussed, and this may lead to further observation and reference work.

Observing plant and animal life in the field

Field trips can play an important role in a study of living things. The suggestions which follow should indicate some of the possibilities and help in the organization of worthwhile, meaningful excursions.

Observing plant growth. In a study of plant growth, a sixth grade visited the park nearby to learn how trees grow. It was spring, and the new, lighter-colored tips at the ends of the branches — the new growth — were examined on a variety of trees. On subsequent trips it became obvious that the lengths of the branches were increasing and that some trees were growing more rapidly than others. Trees grow by adding to the tips of their branches. In the spring, growth begins with the bud at the tip of each branch. New branches develop from other buds along the sides of older branches. The children found that the growth of several earlier years could be distinguished by the color of the bark between the scars (*nodes*) where terminal buds had been. They compared the length of new growth with that of previous years. A tree grows taller by adding to the tips of its branches, but how does the trunk become larger in diameter? With a pocket knife a cut was made through the bark to reveal the green cambium layer where the growth occurs. The instructor asked why some trees have a smooth bark, whereas others are thick, rough, and cracked. Growth occurs beneath the bark. On fir trees, pines, elms, and others, the dead outer bark, the cork, is cracked by the outward pressure of the growth, forming deep fissures along the trunk. On other trees, such as the sycamore and birch, the outer bark peels and is sloughed off as the trunk grows larger. The small rough spots on the bark of a birch prompted questions by the class, and it was explained that these are *lenticels*, openings in the bark through which gases may pass. Lenticels were then easily located on a flowering cherry and on other smooth-barked trees. Attention was called to the winged fruit of the maple and elder, and the class began to look for other evidence of seed developing. The cones of a pine were examined to locate the seed forming in them. Also located were the developing fruit of a mulberry, the seed pods of a Kentucky coffee tree and of a honey locust, and the acorns of several oaks.

If trees grow taller by adding new growth at the tips, the instructor asked, what has become of the lower branches? The lower branches of some of the larger trees were all higher than even the top of a seedling tree nearby. By examining the trunks of several large trees, the children could see where some of the limbs had once been. But now the bark was growing out over the scars. Being shaded by the limbs above, the lower ones commonly die. Even in a park it could be seen that trees shaded by their neighbors grow tall and spindly. In the classroom some of the bean seedlings raised had been overcrowded and likewise had grown spindly. Back on the school grounds the class looked with new interest at the roots of a tree exposed by erosion. A few days later a clover plant was carefully dug up with a shovel and the dirt washed away to expose the root system, including in this case the nitrogen-fixing nodules of bacteria. No stump was found on the trip to show annular rings, which reveal the growth of the tree, but later one child brought a block of wood and another brought a small limb — each of which showed the annular rings quite well. The structure of the limb was compared with that of a cornstalk, a sunflower, and a number of other plants the children brought to school.

Another class, in a similar study, marked certain limbs of bushes on the

Fig. 66

Observing new growth at the tips of branches

grounds and at regular intervals recorded measurements of the new growth. The rapidity of the growth was surprising to the whole class. The girth of a tree was likewise measured and recorded for comparisons.

Identification and the great variety of living things. In a certain fourth grade that showed considerable interest in the identification of trees, the general principles of identification were developed through visits to a nearby park. It was pointed out that some trees are identified by the general shape of the tree, an elm, for example, being referred to as *umbrella-shaped.* The bark varies considerably, the bark of the sycamore, beech, and birch being especially distinctive. A great variety of leaves were found, the variation in leaves being helpful in identification. The type of flower and fruit is often distinctive. Whether the branches on a limb or from the trunk are opposite or alternate is a feature used in identification. In alternate branching each branch forms a Y, but in opposite branching two or more limbs branch from approximately the same point. This

291

class found in their library several books which gave the details of identification and classification. Although a large number of trees were identified in the process, the emphasis of the study was on learning how trees are identified. Had the class desired it, the identification of trees could have been part of a broader topic, such as the great variety of living things.

In addition to the trees, shrubs, grass, and other conspicuous seed plants, a field trip can reveal a multitude of other living things, such as ferns, moss, and lichens — the lichens commonly found on the surface of otherwise bare rock. Fungus growths include the bracket fungi found on dead logs or stumps, toadstools, puff balls, and even the mold that appears on bread. In northern forests club mosses are often found creeping along the ground. Horsetails are sometimes found growing in the sandy soil beside a pond. At a pond a great variety of plants may grow, including cattails, reeds, pond lilies, and underwater plants. Several kinds of brown or green scum, algae, may be located in the water. A dip net will reveal a diversity of animal life in a pond, except during the cold winter months, when most types are dormant. In the fall, after cold weather has begun and the usually numerous pond animals are no longer in sight, if a bit of the mud is scooped up with some water and taken back to school, it can be placed in an aquarium, diluted with fresh water, and left for observation. In the warm classroom a variety of living things may develop from the eggs deposited in the mud.

Worms and insects can be found under stones and other objects on the ground. A multitude of other living things can be found by examining a shovelful of sod. Ant hills, spiders, hornet nests, cocoons, galls, and caterpillars, as well as birds, rodents, and other small mammals can be located in the woods, or even in an empty lot. A stream or pond is usually a very good place to visit while studying the great variety of living things. Many classes have also visited museums and zoos in making such a study.

Identification of particular plants and animals in practice is often stressed as an ability to be cultivated for its own sake. The work is more coherent and meaningful, however, if identification is secondary and emphasis is placed on developing broad meanings. If not overdone, the principles of identification may constitute one such broad meaning. Some identification is necessary if children are to learn from observation how birds migrate or how plants are adapted to live in certain environments.

If learning that some plants or animals can be harmful is to be of functional value, the children must learn to identify at least a few that are dangerous. Going outdoors to see poison ivy, so that children may know and avoid it, is worthwhile. Ragweed and goldenrod, notorious as causes of hay fever, may be of interest. The life cycle of wheat rust ordinarily requires that the rust live for a time on the barberry; accordingly, in farming communities especially, the barberry is identified as a potential disease carrier. Children who can recognize wheat rust and the barberry will be able to understand the relationships better and know what adults are talking about. Whatever pest may be a threat to the gardens or farms of the local community may frequently be discussed by adults in the presence of children, and the children will become interested. Common examples may include the Japanese beetle, aphids, mealybugs, ticks, mites, tomato worms, and gypsy moths. Death camas, loco-weed, purple foxglove, and other plants which are dangerous to animals that eat them may be of interest to children.

A variety of possible trips. For the city child especially, a visit to a farm will provide new insight into scientific principles affecting plant and animal life. A chicken hatchery also is worth seeing. A conservatory or greenhouse may serve to illustrate hot and humid climates in which much vegetation will thrive: the dry and hot climate ideal for cacti and the cool but moist conditions better for certain other plants. A garden plot may be of interest to small children. One second-grade teacher, while visiting a garden, commonly stresses the fact that we eat the leaves of spinach and lettuce, the stems of celery, and the roots of carrots, where in each case the food is stored by the plant. In one school a fifth grade visited the zoo while studying animal behavior and adaptations; the fourth grade visited it while studying how animals protect themselves. When the second grade went to the zoo they were concerned with baby animals, a phase of the broader subject of how animals grow and develop.

Especially in the early grades, field trips concerned with seasonal changes are common. Classes commonly note the presence or absence of birds, frogs, or other animals. Cocoons, galls, the cottony masses in curled leaves, tent caterpillars, nymphs from a pond, or the eggsacks of a spider or a mantis may be brought back to the school for observation of the changes that will take place. What can be observed or collected will vary with the season. In April perhaps frogs' eggs can be found. Later the eggs will have developed into tadpoles, still later into frogs. Flowers can be seen in the spring, seed pods in the fall. Other evidence of change in the vegetation may be noted, in addition to the temperature, the height of the sun, the length of shadows, and the number of hours of daylight. A record of observations should be made to stress important points. This record should be kept for comparison with the records of other trips made at later seasons. Such comparisons will help children to become aware of seasonal changes.

When material is collected on field trips, if everyone in a large class gathers

Fig. 67

Children visit the zoo while studying how animals grow and develop.

specimens there is danger that the area examined will be denuded. The absurd extreme of refusing to take any specimens from any place is unnecessary, but care should be exercised so that the outdoors will not be damaged. A little carelessness multiplied by the number of people in a class can readily damage the very resources that are most admired. Conservation must be practiced if it is to be taught.

Work in the field, whether it be an extensive trip or merely a visit to an ant hill in a nearby woodlot, lends reality to a study, provides a stimulus, and helps to make meaningful relationships apparent. Living things are close at hand even in an urban community; hence often the principles being studied can be exemplified without leaving the school grounds. The purpose and organization of a particular trip should be determined, of course, by the study being undertaken. The preceding illustrations are but a few examples. Where direct observation is not practicable, or where a supplement to the excursions is desired, suitable films can be of great value. A film which pictures animals in the wild, for example, will provide a view that is unattainable by more direct means. Time-lapse photography, by showing the growth process at a more rapid rate, reveals what may not be apparent through direct observation. In spite of the value of a film, however, there is no completely adequate substitute for seeing the real thing.

EXPERIMENTING WITH LIVING THINGS

In an active learning situation questions will arise, some of which can be solved by experimentation. The text and other references may suggest suitable experiments that can be adapted to solution of the problems, or experiments may be devised to suit the purpose. Experimentation by no means need be restricted to the directions in a manual. Whenever a child devises some tangible means of actively testing his ideas, the work may be considered experimentation. The techniques and skills, of course, can be expected to improve with increased insight and experience. A problem that is challenging for one child may be overwhelmingly difficult for a younger, less skillful child. For a child with greater experience the solution may be obvious. Thus the grade placement of experiments will be determined by the maturity and experience of the children concerned.

Plant-growth experiments

One kindergarten began working with plants when a package of seed was sent them by a dealer. Their interest aroused, they planted the seed in tin cans, each child being expected to care for his own can. Some of the seed grew, but some did not; and as a result the children were confronted with a real problem. Too much water, not enough sunshine, and similar explanations were proposed by the children; then they began to devise experiments that would determine what conditions are favorable for plants.

A third-grade investigation. When the third grade brought seed for planting, there were questions regarding what is inside a seed that makes it grow. The class began to examine a variety of seed. Someone asked what the "little eye" on a bean is for. Fortunately, a store near the school had some green beans, and a few were obtained for the class to examine. By seeing the beans in the pod the children were able to answer their question. The next step was to open a bean seed to see what was inside. The children found the beans difficult to open; so the seed were soaked in water for a day. Upon opening the seed the children readily located the germ, and someone said, "How does this little plant get food?" The question was soon answered when another child decided: "From the same place we do when we eat beans!"

At this point it was decided to plant some of the seed and watch them grow. The seed were placed on wet blotters in a pan. After three days it was evident the seed were sprouting. Some were opened, and the incipient leaves, root, and stem could be detected. This class also planted some of their seed in various kinds of soil and compared the results. The class decided that their seed had grown better in the darker soil.

When one boy saw his father preparing to plant potatoes the boy brought one to school and explained how it should be cut for planting, with one or more eyes on each piece. The other children at first did not know what he meant when he referred to the eyes on the potato. Nevertheless, a rather deep box was obtained and filled with dirt as the boy said should be done. Some of the class thought it would be all wrong to cut the potato. They felt sure that the potato would die rather than grow. However, they eventually agreed to experiment. The potato was cut into three parts; one had no eyes, one had two, and the third section had several. All three sections were planted in the same box and given identical care. The class waited to see what would happen. In addition to the potato cuttings, the class had planted beans and onions and had recorded the dates of the plantings. The onion came up first, after one week. The bean seedlings appeared after nine days. The potato cutting with two eyes and the cutting with many eyes produced sprouts that appeared on the fourteenth day. At the last report the class was still waiting for the cutting with no eyes to sprout.

A fifth-grade investigation. The fifth-graders put a few radish seed, beans, and calendula seed on moistened blotting paper in a dish and covered the dish with glass. In a few days the seed had sprouted. The children became interested in the roots, especially the root hairs, examining them closely with a hand lens. From their books they learned that it is through the root hairs that plants take in water. In discussion time the children traced the way that water moves through the tubes in the stem, and eventually through the leaf veins to the cells of the leaves. So a fresh stalk of celery was obtained and half an inch of the

Fig. 68

Bean seedlings can be used for plant-growth experiments.

base removed with a sharp knife. Red food coloring was added to a jar of water and the celery was placed in the colored water. Within an hour the children could see plainly how the red water had risen in the stem, and they understood that the so-called "strings" of celery are really the tubes which carry water through the plant.

The beans sprouting on moistened blotting paper were examined in various stages of development, and the following observations were recorded by the class:

1. The outside splits open first. 2. The seed has two parts and the germ. 3. The root comes out first. 4. The leaf is folded inside the bean even after the root begins to grow. 5. When the bean leaf began to grow, the bean was on the stem for quite a long time, but finally dropped off.

The children concluded that a seed provides food for the baby plant until the roots can become established.

Ann and Brenda each planted radish seed. Ann put hers on the window sill in the sunlight; Brenda left hers in a far corner where no sun would reach it. The teacher and most of the children expected the ones on the window sill to show the most growth, but on returning to school on Monday they were surprised to find that the ones in the corner were more than an inch tall, while the ones on the window sill had been burned by the sun. The conclusion reached was that temperature also is an important factor in plant growth. The two girls replanted, being careful not to expose their seedlings to excessive heat. This time one group of seedlings was placed in a dark closet, and the others were left on a table in the classroom. Within three days a marked contrast was noted. The plants from the closet already were spindly and pale. A group of boys undertook a similar but somewhat more elaborate experiment. Seed were planted in four boxes. Two boxes were left in the room; one was placed in the dark closet and one in a cold, dark place — a refrigerator. The teacher thought this experiment almost a repetition of the one conducted by the girls, but the boys were enthusiastic, and she let them proceed. Their experiment helped to confirm the idea the children already had: that both heat and light are required for plant growth. Repetition of experiments is characteristic of children, and it can help to develop the desired understandings. Scientists likewise repeat experiments; the findings of one scientist are either confirmed or rejected on the basis of other independent investigations.

In order to learn more about roots the class went to a neighboring field one day with a trowel and a shovel. The boys dug up many kinds of weeds and other small plants. They learned that some plants have a large tap root, whereas others have a mass of branching roots.

To show that plants must have good soil, John and Francis each planted some beans. John put his in sawdust, and Francis placed his in good soil. Both boys took good care of their plants. At first both the seed in the sawdust and those in the soil did rather well, but in a short time the ones in soil began to outstrip the ones in the sawdust. The boys concluded that at first the plants were using food stored in the seed and that the difference in soil became apparent later as the seedlings began to depend upon the soil for nourishment.

Throughout their experiments with plants the fifth grade kept records of the growth and of the conditions being tested. Drawings were made of the plants at various stages of development, with the date of each drawing noted.

In a similar study another class brought in a variety of flowers, and a number of them were cut open lengthwise to reveal the developing seed at the base of the blossom. Previously the children had not been aware of the relationship between a flower and the seed pod which appears later in the season. Daffodils, tulips, and other large flowers with conspicuous parts may be examined at intervals to find how seed are produced.

Further investigations of plant growth. Controlled experiments can be conducted to show the effects on plant growth of heat, light, moisture, or type of soil. The children can determine the effects of overcrowding, as contrasted to thinning of the seedlings. The optimum depth for planting can be determined by experiment. Various fertilizers can be tested in controlled experiments. Having had more experience, older children may come to realize how some of the factors which influence plant growth are interrelated. Thus the optimum depth of planting is dependent upon the size of the seed and the amount of moisture. Experiments can be devised to determine such relationships.

To see where the new growth occurs on a seedling, the tips of stems, the tips of several roots, and a number of other selected locations may be marked at one-eighth-inch intervals with waterproof ink. Where growth occurs, the marks become further separated.

That plants can be propagated from cuttings may also be taught in the classroom. Coleus and geranium plants are used for this purpose by many teachers. They cut a stem that will include both new growth and some of the old, remove the larger leaves, and place the cutting in a glass of water. When roots have appeared, the cuttings may be planted in a pot of moist soil. The runners of strawberries and the rootstocks of Canada thistle and Kentucky bluegrass — or of any plant that has underground stems from which new plants spring — may be used to show other means of propagation.

Seed differ considerably in the length of time required for germination. To show the difference, various kinds of seed may be sprouted on a moist surface of sand, on a sponge, or on paper towels. A record should be kept of the planting date and the dates when sprouts first appear. Several seed of a kind should be used, and the median length of time for each kind may be used for the comparison. In this experiment the temperature and amount of moisture should be the same for all, but other experiments can be conducted to show how temperature affects the germination.

Seed must have air for germination. To illustrate this, place a handful of beans on a moist sponge or towel in the bottom of a fruit jar and then place a tight lid on the jar. Put another handful of beans on a moist sponge or towel in an open bowl. The sprouts use oxygen and emit carbon dioxide just as animals do. The sealed jar will lack an adequate supply of oxygen, and growth will be inhibited. After the seed in the open have sprouted, lower a burning match into the jar to test for oxygen. Because the oxygen in the jar has been used by the seed, the flame will be extinguished more rapidly than another flame lowered into a similar but empty jar.

A study of plant growth may include the observations reported by individuals and also may include field trips, on which an entire class can see growing plants in their natural setting. Observations in the classroom, often combined with experimentation, likewise should have a prominent role in a study of plant growth. If seed are collected, for example, some may be used to prepare a display; others can be used for experimentation.

The seed of a maple and the seed of a dandelion are spread by the wind. The seed of fruit and nuts are spread by the animals that eat them. Burs become attached to animals. Some seed are spread by water; the class can experiment to see which are light enough to float. A display may be prepared to show how seed are scattered.

A class studying how plants grow may include a variety of plants in their investigations. Mold can be induced to grow merely by leaving somewhat moist bread exposed to the air at room temperature. Experimentation with various temperatures and various amounts of moisture and light may reveal what conditions are most conducive to the growth of mold. The algae from a pond can be kept at school in gallon jars. The effect of light on its growth can be studied by placing some in direct sunlight and some in the dark; another jar may be placed where the light is good but indirect. Moss can be raised in a moist terrarium. The moss, the algae, and the mold can be studied closely with a reading glass, and if they are examined at intervals, changes due to growth will be observed. The spores in a puffball or on the lower side of a fern likewise can be examined.

Experiments concerned with the behavior of living things

Some fascinating investigations can be made with a microscope if one is available. Even with a hand lens children will be able to watch the minute water animals in the aquarium, see the breathing tubes of an insect, and resolve an argument about whether or not butterflies have mouths for eating nectar.

If the stems and tendrils of a bean vine are examined, it will be seen they wind about poles or other objects in one direction only. To see what will happen, children may unwind the vine and twist it around the pole in the opposite direction. The children may experiment with other vines also to see how they attach themselves and climb.

Response to moisture, obstacles, light, and gravity. If a planting box with one glass side can be devised, the influence of water on roots can be observed. If only one end of the box is watered — and that not excessively, so that the opposite end will remain dry — the roots of seedlings planted close to the glass will show the response to water. A flower pot submerged in the dirt with the bottom plugged may be filled with water to provide a constant source of moisture through seepage, without wetting the entire box. To be sure that the pot itself is not affecting the result, another similar pot may be submerged in the dry end and filled with dirt rather than water. To provide the box, a hole may be cut in the side of a planting frame, and glass may be placed inside to cover the opening. The dirt will hold the glass in place. An old aquarium, especially an old leaky one with good drainage, should be highly satisfactory for the purpose. Suitable equipment also can be purchased from a scientific supply house. Bean seedlings are ideal for this and other such experiments; and if the need is anticipated, it is easy to provide the seedlings.

With the equipment already described, the way roots respond to an obstacle which impedes their growth may be observed. Rocks may be submerged in the dirt near the glass side of the box and the seed planted above them. Bean seed should be quite satisfactory. Even glass jars may be reasonably satisfactory for the container, although no drainage is provided.

The way plants respond to the light can be observed simply by placing potted plants at locations in the room where the light comes predominantly from one direction, such as beyond the casing at one side of the windows. Or seedlings may be covered with a heavy cardboard carton in which a single small hole has been cut. The seedlings will turn toward the light and may eventually grow out through the hole.

The response of a plant to gravity is similar. If a blotter is rolled into a cylinder and placed inside a glass jar, and beans or other conveniently large seed are placed between the jar and the blotter, the sprouting of the seed can be observed. The blotter must be kept moist by occasionally adding water to the jar, but excessive watering will encourage the growth of mold. Sunlight will inhibit the growth of mold if the experiment is conducted near the classroom windows. A few drops of carbolic acid or a commercial seed dis-infectant added to the water also will help. As the seed begin to sprout, it will be observed that regardless of how the seed were placed, the roots turn down, the stems up. If the jar is inverted for a day or two, it will be observed that the plant growth also will be reversed so that again the roots grow down and the stems up. The blotter must be kept moist while the jar is inverted. Two sheets of glass with the blotter and seed between them can be used instead of the jar and blotter for this experiment. Tape or twine can be used to hold the glass sheets together. To keep the blotter moist, the glass sheets may be placed on edge in a shallow pan of water.

The effect of temperature on animals. Mammals and birds are warm-blooded, the interior of their bodies maintaining a fairly uniform temperature; but insects, reptiles, and fish, for example, are cold-blooded, the temperature of the body varying considerably with that of the surroundings. The effect of temperature on cold-blooded animals can be observed by placing a turtle, a frog, or a goldfish outside on a cold day. After the animal has become adjusted to the temperature, a record of its movements in a given period of time may be made. The animal's responses to stimuli, such as splashing the water near the fish or touching the frog, also can be recorded. Comparative observations can be made with the animal inside where the sun will shine through the window onto it, or with a reading lamp placed where it will warm the animal. Similar observations may be made with a warm-blooded animal, such as a hamster, a rabbit, or a chicken. If the weather is warm the tests can be conducted with a turtle, for example, by placing it in a jar and then chilling it in a refrigerator. The animal can be removed momentarily at prearranged intervals to check its responses to stimuli.

Moisture and oxygen from plants. To see the water given off by a plant, set a wide-mouthed gallon jar over a potted plant or seedling. Set the plant on a table near the window, or elsewhere in the light, and as water is given off by the leaves, drops will condense on the glass jar. So that water evaporating from the soil need not be a factor, cover the soil about the base of the plant with aluminum foil. To show that the water comes from the plant and not from the air or the soil, set up another jar in the same way, but without the plant. Water given off by plants provides a large share of the water that eventually falls as rain. The water given off also helps to make possible a movement of water, the flow of sap, from the roots to the leaves.

To show how the sap moves through a plant, cut the top off a fresh carrot and scoop out a small hole where the top was. Set the carrot in a jar filled with red ink. Fill the top of the carrot with a dark ink. If in a few hours the carrot is cut open, the colors will show where the sap flows up and where it flows down.

That plants use the energy of sunshine to produce sugar, giving off oxygen in the process, is a rather advanced concept, but a significant one. To detect the oxygen given off by a plant, invert a large glass funnel over some aquarium plants, such as Elodea, in an aquarium or a glass jar of water. Fill a test tube with water, and with a thumb or a piece of paper held over the mouth of the tube, invert the tube and place the open end under water; remove the thumb or paper, and, with the open end still under water, slip the test tube over the stem of the funnel. Some practice may be necessary to avoid bubbles of air in the tube. Raise the funnel a bit by placing a pebble under the edge. With the apparatus standing in the sunlight, bubbles of oxygen should rise gradually into the tube. If a good supply of oxygen is secured, it can be identified by inserting a glowing splinter into the tube. In recovering the test tube from the water,

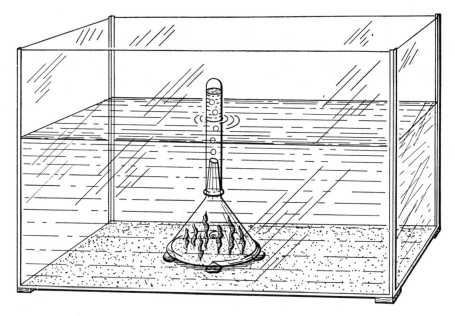

Fig. 69

The oxygen released by aquarium plants can be trapped in a test tube.

right it quickly and cover it with a thumb or a stopper until the glowing splinter is inserted. If the gas is oxygen, the glowing splinter will burst into flame.

Another means of investigating the same process is to place in the bottom of a wide-mouthed gallon jar a small flower pot or tin can with several bean seedlings in it. Moisten some steel wool and drop it into the jar beside the seedlings; then cover the jar with a tight lid. Seal the lid with grease to make the jar airtight. As a control, seal another jar with moistened steel wool inside but without the plant. In each jar oxygen will be removed to form rust. After leaving the apparatus in the light at the window for a few days, lower a lighted match into each jar. The jars should not be moved while open, and strong drafts should be avoided so that the air inside the jars will not be disturbed. If a match will burn in the jar that contained the plant, but not in the other jar, the plant must have replenished the oxygen supply. The experiment can be repeated to verify the results.

A similar arrangement of equipment can be used to show that plants produce no oxygen while in darkness. Or the apparatus can be used to show that plants in the dark do emit carbon dioxide. To detect the carbon dioxide, omit the steel wool and place both jars, one containing a plant and one with no plant, in a dark closet for a day or two. In the meantime, prepare a bottle of limewater by stirring into water as much slaked lime as will dissolve. After the water has cleared, pour the clear solution into another container. After the plant and the empty jar have been in the dark for about two days or more, gently lift the plant from its jar. Pour about a cup or so of the clear limewater into each jar; cover the jars and shake them so that the limewater will be exposed to the air inside. If the limewater becomes milky, this indicates the presence of carbon dioxide. Some milkiness may show in the empty jar owing to the presence of whatever carbon dioxide was in the original air. If more is found in the jar that has the plant, the gas must have come from the plant.

While studying the changing seasons, a child in the third grade asked why leaves fall in the autumn. In considering the problem, the class decided that the leaves had become dry. One of the girls said that leaves are "juicier" in the spring and summer.

"When you squeeze a green leaf in your hand, sticky stuff comes out," she continued, "but autumn leaves just break up in little pieces."

The class decided it is the sap that keeps a leaf alive. In cold weather the sap does not flow. Plants that are kept in a warm house continue to grow, but many garden plants die.

To show how the sap rises in a plant, a paper towel was suspended above a pan of water, with one end dipping into the water. Before long the paper was wet; water had risen in the pores of the paper. The process is called *capillarity.*

As was stated earlier, a seventh-grade boy devised one way of showing what is meant by capillarity. He placed two sheets of glass upright in a shallow pan of water. With but a minute space between the two sheets of glass, the water rose in an arc between the sheets, but if the sheets were held too far apart or pressed too tightly together, the water would not rise. Wads of paper between the sheets of glass served as spacers. The best results were obtained by holding the sheets of glass firmly together before dipping the lower edge into the water. Where the space is small, water is attracted to the glass and is thus drawn upward. In this manner water rises through the conducting tissues of a plant.

Experiments in the principles of health

Often a child is his own best example of the scientific principles he is studying, and such human applications can be a stimulus to learning. In turn, the insight that science brings can develop new interest in health. Diet experiments, for example, not only show children why a proper diet is important but also stimulate a desire to eat the right food. Instructions for the care of the eyes are more meaningful in conjunction with a study of light and lenses. Conversely, the study of light and lenses is more stimulating in terms of the human eye and spectacles.

Bacteria cultures and cleanliness. To develop a concern for cleanliness, one teacher used an experiment with bacteria cultures. The fourth grade obtained four clear plastic containers with covers, containers that once had been filled with cream cheese. An unflavored commercial gelatin was prepared according to the directions on the package, except that to obtain a firm gel less water was used, and to provide additional protein a cube of bouillon was added. (Other classes have found it more convenient to use nutrient agar from a drugstore or scientific supply house.) Enough of the solution was poured into each plastic container to cover the bottom; the lids were put on and the dishes stacked in the top of a double boiler. After being sterilized for an hour or more, the dishes were removed and allowed to cool, the gelatin to harden. With the class gathered about, one dish was opened and a boy was permitted to touch the surface of the gelatin. One of the girls touched the gelatin in another dish. The two remaining dishes were left unopened for comparison. The dishes were sealed with adhesive tape and left on a table away from the window, out of the direct sunlight. A hand lens was placed on the table with the cultures, and the children frequently stopped to examine the growth that began to appear. One child, while examining the cultures, was heard to say: "Just look at what all that dirt will do!"

In the lunchroom, one said proudly, though perhaps not accurately: "Look at my clean hands, Edith. If I keep them clean as that dish that didn't grow bacteria, neither will my hands grow any."

A diet experiment. A diet experiment was a conspicuous part of the food study carried on by a second-grade class. The teacher had been concerned about the hot lunches the children were selecting in the cafeteria. The school rules required that milk and a hot dish be consumed, before a dessert could be purchased. But the children had little sympathy for the rules and sought to avoid the restrictions on desserts. The teacher felt like a combination spy and taskmaster while trying to enforce the rules. The homemaking teacher, in the capacity of a consultant, had said earlier in the year that laboratory rats for diet experiments could be obtained without cost from the New England Dairy Council. So arrangements were made to obtain a pair of the laboratory rats.

When the children were told they could experiment with laboratory rats, the response was immediately enthusiastic. In the discussion that followed, it was suggested they could find out what would happen if the rats ate nothing but dessert, as Bobby had wanted to do at lunch that day.

Someone else suggested, "We can give one a good lunch and one a bad lunch and find out what happens."

From the science teacher in the upper grades they borrowed weights and a balance. The class chose a number of committees. One committee was responsible for cleaning the cage each morning; another committee fed the animals. Each morning a committee obtained the menu from the lunchroom and from it planned both good and bad lunches, posted them on the board, and explained their choice to the class before noon. The good lunches consisted of a portion of everything on the menu; the bad lunches for the experiment stressed desserts. On the blackboard one committee daily recorded the weight of each animal and also the gain or loss in grams. A pound of butter and several other pound or quarter-pound packages were brought in for the children to handle and compare with the gram weights. The diet and the weights were copied from the blackboard into a record book.

As the experiment proceeded, the graph had to be extended, for no one had anticipated the great divergence in the weights of the two animals. Originally each line on the graph had represented 5 grams, but when the children were unable to understand the units, each was changed to one. The outline of a rat was cut from paper and used to mark the current position on the chart. In functional circumstances the children learned how to construct and interpret graphs. For convenience each rat was confined in a gallon jar during the weighing procedure. In the process the children became acquainted with the gallon as a unit, and they learned much during the weighing. Accuracy was essential. A jar on each side was necessary for the scales to balance; and because a lid was added to one side when the animal began to climb out of the jar, it was necessary either to subtract the weight of the lid or to add a lid to the other jar. Many individuals and whole classes came to see the rats and hear about the experiment. The children had so many opportunities to tell about the experiment that eventually they began to lose interest in repeating the story. At the end of the allotted three weeks the children did not wish to give up the rats; so a plan was devised to continue the experiment, giving both animals good diets to see if the weight of the weaker animal could be restored and to learn what permanent damage would remain. Throughout the experiment the weight of each child also was recorded and pictured on a bar graph in order to stress the significance of diet to the children themselves. Each child prepared his own record book and recorded his own meals, his weight, and his height. Further mathematics was involved when the children learned to record fractional weights on their bar graphs. The children planned their own report to the parents. The parents received written invitations, and when they came they were able to observe the usual weighing, recording, and planning of diets. In accordance with a committee's plan for the meeting, various children explained what was being done and the purpose and significance of each step. While the cages were being cleaned, for example, the need for cleanliness was stressed; and while the weighing was being demonstrated, someone was pointing out the need for accuracy in experiments and explaining what a gram weight is. The children expressed their own views freely throughout the reporting. In addition, a number of selections relating to nutrition were read.

In evaluating the work, a number of observations helped to suggest that the undertaking was successful: The number of hot lunches and bottles of milk sold to the class after the instruction was three times as great as at the beginning. The dishes selected by individuals showed a better balance and were more likely to include a salad. The compulsion formerly required was no longer needed. The lunches brought from home also were of better quality.

One child said, "Since we've been studying about good lunches, I always get my mamma to put lettuce in my sandwiches." Earlier that same mother had told the teacher that the child did not eat well and seemed to want only bread and jam.

Some of the children had been afraid of the animals at first, but as the following indicates, their attitude changed. There was a fire drill one day while the experiment was in progress. The children were a bit disorderly, and afterwards the teacher admonished them for talking during a fire drill, but one of the children explained:

"We were worried about the rats. We kept on going because it was just a drill, but wouldn't it be awful if the rats got burned?"

One child reported with puckish satisfaction that his mother had said that if he didn't quit talking about rats at the dinner table she wouldn't let him eat at all.

After it became apparent that the experimental animal was not strong, his hair no longer sleek, there was considerable informal discussion which showed that the children were able to see the relationship of diet to their own strength and appearance. The limitations of an experiment involving but two animals were considered, and much was learned about experimentation in general. While laboratory rats are useful in experimentation, the children understood that common rats frequently spread disease.

Some member of the cleaning committee customarily would hold each rat while its cage was being cleaned. After fondling the rats each day during the cleaning period, Patricia came to realize that the experimental animal was nervous and easily disturbed whereas the control animal on the good diet was easy to handle. She thought about it for a time; then one day, while reporting, she explained the situation and said, "I can sing the 'good' rat to sleep in three minutes, but the one on the bad diet takes seven minutes."

Although such diet experiments usually are conducted with older children, the diets used should be simple enough to be fully understood. One class fed colas, cookies, candy, and other sweets to one animal, a balanced diet to another. In another case one animal was fed only the finest cake flour and the other was fed graham crackers to show the advantage of a whole flour over a highly milled one. Brown rice and white rice can be used for the same purpose. Older children can use a diet deficient in protein in contrast to a balanced diet Or a diet deficient in a single mineral or vitamin can be contrasted with an adequate diet. The effect of a specific deficiency may be more apparent in one kind of animal than in another. Guinea pigs, for example, are especially susceptible to a vitamin C deficiency.

A variety of experiences. A great many experiments can be carried out in the various phases of health instruction. The functioning and the care of the ears can be stressed in a study of sound. Body movement can be included in a study of levers and other machines. The cooling effect of evaporation can be demonstrated experimentally, possibly in connection with a study of air and the weather, and the effects of sitting in a draft or of coming to school with wet feet may be considered.

Observing mosquito wrigglers or the maggots of houseflies can be considered health work as well as the science of growth and development. For convenient observation the wrigglers can be maintained in a jar of water covered with cloth, and maggots likewise may be confined in whatever state they were found.

Chemical experiments may include food tests. In addition, if a raw potato is examined under a microscope and then compared with a cooked potato, it can be observed that the large crystals of starch are broken down by cooking; thus cooking is shown to be an aid to digestion, which continues the process of decomposition.[1] Many health books have directions — or plans can be devised to suit the purpose — for evaporating milk in a tin can or other container until only the solid residue remains. Further heating will burn the protein, fat, and milk sugar so that only the minerals are left. One function of minerals can be demonstrated by soaking a chicken bone in strong vinegar to remove the minerals. How long the bone should remain in the vinegar will depend upon the size of the bone and the strength of the vinegar. When taken from the vinegar and rinsed, the bone, with the minerals removed, will have little strength and will bend easily. Dilute hydrochloric acid, if available, will

[1] See also pp. 240, 244–45.

remove the minerals more rapidly. Hydrochloric acid is a strong acid, however, and if used should be handled by the teacher with care.

The fuel value of food can be demonstrated by burning a piece of very dry bread on a metal or asbestos surface to show that, like other fuels, the bread releases heat energy when burned. In the body, bread and similar foods provide heat and the energy for motion, just as oil gives a diesel engine power to move a passenger train and oil in a furnace can heat a house.

TOPICS THAT REQUIRE CAREFUL TREATMENT

The process of reproduction, matters which involve religious beliefs, and other subjects with emotional overtones must be handled with care if any progress is to be made. Simply to avoid all controversial areas is no solution, for the areas avoided are likely to be among the most vital and those in which instruction is most needed. Approaching these topics with complete scientific objectivity, examining the factors and possible conclusions, making no attempt to sell a preconceived opinion, is the best way to overcome the difficulties in areas of emotion and controversy.

Sex education

Reproduction is an inherent part of growth and development, and when taught in the broader context is likely to have more meaning and less emotionalism. The little child characteristically makes inquiries into all areas of living; and if adult emotions are not transmitted, the child's inquiry regarding reproduction is little different from his curiosity about the weather, the rocks of the field, or anything else with which he comes in contact. One reason for beginning instruction of the right sort early is to develop in the child a calm, sympathetic understanding of growth and reproduction, an understanding which will control and direct his emotions as they develop. Instruction given at a later date may have to overcome a snickering, negative emotionalism.

One day Patricia's mother called to invite all the children from the kindergarten to see the brand-new kittens. When the children arrived four kittens were lying in a basket, being nursed by the mother cat. The children were excited and enthusiastic. They watched intently and made remarks such as "Where did they come from?" "Why are they eating there?" "Aren't they tiny! The mommy is 'bout five million times as big as the babies." Obviously fundamental relationships were graphically portrayed for the children, along with a constructive, sympathetic attitude and no implication of shame. Kittens, puppies, and baby chicks have been brought to classes for a similar purpose. One class, observing baby animals on a visit to the zoo, stressed the close relationship between mother and offspring. The baby is much like its mother.

The seventh- and eighth-grade science classes in an Ohio junior high school were in the habit of bringing to class a variety of insects, salamanders, frogs, snakes, hamsters, mice, and plants. One of the mice gave birth to a litter of young on the second day of her stay in the classroom. This phenomenon captured the attention of everyone. Innumerable questions were asked regarding the development of living things. The students looked for charts showing the internal organs of the human body, but found only small ones in books. Purchasing suitable charts was considered, but funds were limited, and an even better plan was decided upon when large-sized drawings were suggested. Volunteers soon began to prepare the sketches. The children worked in small groups. Neatness and accuracy were the principal requirements. All the drawings were good. Discussion and extensive reading played a large role in the study. A heart and an eye of beef were brought to class for close examination. A visit to a slaughterhouse or farm where an animal has just been butchered would have been helpful. Seeing the internal organs of any mammal — from a rabbit to a pig or cow — would have been highly satisfactory; even a freshly butchered chicken would have been useful. Sex education here was taught in a broad context which included a study of many internal organs and their fuction in the body.

In the third grade, a boy said, "Will that fish turn into a frog?"

Characteristically, the teacher answered, "What do you think?"

He was uncertain, so the teacher helped him locate a book about fish.

Later the child came to the teacher and said proudly: "Miss Sullivan, this is a polliwog here." He pointed to a picture in the book. "Our fish won't turn to a frog, because it's a sunfish. It might grow bigger as it gets older, just like we do. Do you know how to tell a mother fish? You just look at its stomach, and if it's getting fat, then it has eggs in it, and it is a mother fish. This book says that some fish are prettier than others, and that is another way of telling."

Conflict with established beliefs

Contrary to a common assumption, it need not be presumed that there is any inherent basic conflict between science and religion. Both science and religion seek the truth, whatever it may be. The Holy Spirit, referred to in the Bible by Christ, was designated as the "Spirit of truth." [2]

2 *The Holy Bible*, King James Version, John xiv:26; xv:26.

Christ said: "I have many things to say unto you, but ye cannot bear them now. . . . the Spirit of truth . . . will guide you into all truth." [3]

Conflicting opinions between religion and science may and do exist, of course, just as opposing theories exist within the field of science. Both science and religion are constructive, and bitterness in controversy is not appropriate to either science or religion.

Often a teacher can help children to reconcile the seemingly conflicting views to which they are exposed. In one case a reading group in the second grade came to the statement that all human beings are animals.

Indignantly one girl said, "I'm no animal."

The teacher asked: "Can you name some animals?"

"Dogs, cats, rabbits, birds."

"Can you think of any others?"

"Lions, snakes, turtles, fish."

"Are they all the same?"

"No —, they're different," the child admitted.

A discussion of the differences followed. Snakes are much different from monkeys, yet both are classified as animals. Humans and monkeys are much different, yet both are animals.

"Do all these animals do things that humans do?" the teacher inquired.

After some hesitation: "My dog sleeps, and so do I. They all eat. They move around."

"Do we seem more like animals, or like plants, which stand still, and which have green leaves?"

"Well, I guess we're animals. I wonder if my mother knows she's an animal."

The theory of evolution conflicts with the beliefs of many people, although the number seems to be rapidly decreasing. That virtually all scientists believe that life has evolved upon the earth is a fact also. To insist that a child accept the prevailing view of scientists is scarcely good education; furthermore, it is not a scientific approach, but an authoritarian one. A child should be willing to examine the evidence and arrive at his own opinion. He has the right to reject the common interpretation of that evidence. The bones of dinosaurs have been found and can be seen in our museums, yet no dinosaur has been seen alive in our time. In the Grand Canyon only the simplest forms of life are found in the lower, older rocks. The remains of increasingly complex plants and animals are found in rocks closer to the surface. Whatever an individual's interpretation may be, there is evidence which to many people indicates that life on the earth has changed. In the past, however, individuals who have held a view in conflict with the prevailing one occasionally have been

[3] *Ibid.,* John xvi:12, 13.

proved right. Freedom to arrive at an independent opinion is of the utmost importance. By recognizing that right and even encouraging it, the teacher not only will develop good thinking but will help to maintain high morale and a vital spirit of inquiry in the class.

THE CARE OF LIVING THINGS

Establishing an aquarium

If the interrelationships of living things are to be taught, it may be advisable to set up a balanced aquarium, one in which there are sufficient plants to supply the animals with oxygen. On other occasions, when there is but one isolated animal to observe, and that for only a brief period, a simple tank may serve the purpose better than the more complex aquarium. In the simple tank of water with no plants to supply oxygen, the water must be aerated each day by dipping water out and pouring it back from a height of two or three feet. If the water is replaced, rather than aerated, sudden changes of temperature should be avoided by allowing the fresh water to stand and come to room temperature before use. The number of animals that can be accommodated in a particular tank varies with the size of the tank, the surface area, the temperature of the water, the number of plants, the kind and size of animals. One rule-of-thumb specifies that for each inch of fish there should be a gallon of water — in a six-gallon tank, $10'' \times 10'' \times 18''$, three fish each 2 inches long. Goldfish are suitable, but minnows and other small animals from a pond or a sluggish stream are of even more interest. Fish, tadpoles, and snails live well together, but fish are likely to eat smaller animals, even their own young.

The tank should be relatively broad in proportion to its depth; the greater surface area permits an exchange of gases between the water and the air. In the absence of a commercial tank, an enamel dishpan is serviceable. The tank should be clean before use; salt and water is usually preferable as a cleanser, but if soap is used care must be taken to rinse the tank well. If the tank is filled with water from the school faucet, the water should be aerated well or else allowed to stand for several days before use, since the water may contain chlorine. Clear water from a pond or stream is highly satisfactory.

One comparatively simple way to start a balanced aquarium is to fill the aquarium with clean sand to a depth of one or two inches. The sand may be conveniently rinsed by placing it in a pan under the faucet and stirring gently until the rinse water is clear. Before the tank is filled with water, it should be placed in its permanent location, a place where the children can see it easily.

Strong, indirect light is desirable for the plants; but long exposure to direct sunshine may overheat the aquarium. With a few inches of water in the tank, the plants can be anchored by covering the base of each plant with sand. If a block of wood or a sheet of cardboard is floated on the water, additional water can be poured onto the float, filling the aquarium without disturbing the plants. If possible, wait a few days for the water to clear and for the plants to become established before adding the animals. Perhaps the most common problem in establishing an aquarium is overcrowding the tank with animals. Underwater plants, such as Elodea and Cabomba, may be purchased from a supply house, a pet shop, or obtained from a pond or stream. Fish and pond snails likewise may be purchased, but a variety of animal life can be obtained with a dip net from a pond, if one is nearby. Children may be able to bring plants, crayfish, mussels, snails, aquatic insects, frogs' eggs, tadpoles, or minnows. To use a dip net, plunge it into the water quickly, sweep it through the water close to the bottom, and lift it out in one continuous motion. Examine the net to see if anything has been caught; then move to another spot and try again. Any disturbance is likely to frighten away some of the larger animals. It usually is advisable to dip without waiting to sight any particular animal.

Once a balanced aquarium is established, it is unnecessary to change the water in it, but water should be added occasionally to compensate for evaporation. The aquarium should be covered to reduce evaporation and to prevent the accumulation of a film of dust and oil on the surface. Placing a small sheet of copper inconspicuously at the back of the aquarium is said to retard the growth of algae. If excessive, the algae reduce visibility in the aquarium, but in other respects these simple plants, which ordinarily give the water a green color, are not harmful. In fact, they are a source of food for tadpoles and other animals; and the tiny plants may be of interest themselves.

Marine animals may be kept for a short while in a tank of the salt water from which they came. However, maintaining a salt-water aquarium for any great length of time is a more complex task than most teachers will care to undertake for school use.

Establishing a terrarium

A variety of habitats can be graphically portrayed with terraria; animals and plants can be maintained for observation, and interrelationships can be noted. Although there are certain well-defined habitats, the terrarium can be arranged according to the purpose of the class and adapted to whatever plants and animals are available. Small, slow-growing plants from the environment that is to be reproduced should be chosen for the terrarium. The terms are used loosely, but if an area for water is added the terrarium may be classified as a vivarium. A wide-mouthed gallon jar, an old fish bowl, or a leaky aquarium tank will serve adequately as a container, or one may be constructed from glass and adhesive tape.

A desert terrarium may consist of sand and a few stones, cacti, and a small pan of water embedded in the sand. A lizard or a horned toad may be added. If the teacher is willing, a nonpoisonous snake will be suitable, and some classes actually have had small alligators. The sand should be moistened slightly when the cacti are planted, and the terrarium can be located in partial sunlight, although overheating is possible. A reading lamp placed close to the terrarium may be used to protect against an extreme drop in temperature on week ends or in vacations during the winter. The terrarium may be covered with wire screen or with glass fitted loosely enough to provide for ventilation.

The materials for a woodland terrarium may be collected directly from the woods by the school children. On a base of coarse sand covered by a layer of humus may be placed a surface of moss, rock, pine needles, and humus, with native plants typical of the woodland from which they came. Lichens on the rocks, or a fungus on a "log" will add interest. The plants should be small enough to allow for growth in the container used, but ferns, a trillium, a Jack-in-the-pulpit, and smaller plants from shaded woodland areas may do well. The terrarium should be covered with glass and kept cool and moist, out of direct sunshine but in a strong light. A salamander, land snail, frog or toad, snake, or turtle may be included. Water for the animals may be provided by a "pond," a rustproof pan sunk in the dirt and filled with water.

A meadow may be simulated in a terrarium by simply filling the container with sod, preferably on a base of sand to provide drainage. A considerable number of plants and animals already may exist in the sod; others can be added. Turtles, grasshoppers, and other insects are suitable. The temperature and humidity should be moderate. Occasional sunshine is satisfactory. Water should be provided for the animals. Other possible terraria include the tropical, the bog, and the semi-aquatic — with a pool at one end and a moist shore at the other.

Feeding and caring for animals

A balanced commercial fish food is convenient to use and reasonably satisfactory for the aquarium animals. Bits of raw meat may be used to supplement the diet, and if possible a class may experiment to see what small water animals from a nearby pond will serve as a natural food for the larger aquarium animals. Cold-blooded animals, including fish, require little food. Feeding two or three times a week in small quantities that will be consumed immediately is recommended for aquarium animals. Any excess will decay at the bottom of the tank, fouling the water, although snails act as scavengers and will consume a limited amount of the excess food. The animals consume the plants to a certain extent, but if the aquarium is not overstocked with animals, and the plants are growing well, a balance will be maintained. Aquarium animals can do without food over vacation periods of moderate length.

Land snails and earthworms will subsist on the vegetation in a terrarium. Tadpoles will live on algae or can learn to eat commercial fish food. Toads and frogs are amphibians and should be kept in a container that includes both land and water. Live insects in the vivarium will be a source of food for the frogs or toads. Another method is feasible but may be time-consuming: these animals can be taught to eat bits of hamburger waved about on the end of a broom straw as if alive and in flight. If they do not eat, the frogs and toads should be released after a week or more of captivity. The care of a salamander is similar, though easier. Insects in the sod of a terrarium will supply them with food. Mosquito larvae and the maggots of flies are suitable. A jar filled with banana or other fruit on which fruit flies will multiply may be placed in the terrarium. The salamander will be able to eat the insects as they develop. The feeding habits of turtles vary. Commercially prepared turtle food (which has directions on the package) is satisfactory for some. Others will eat bits of meat dropped into shallow water, and some will subsist on lettuce or the vegetation of a terrarium. Lizards need live insects or a commerical lizard food. Alligators take raw meat in shallow water. The diet of snakes varies, but most can be fed live insects, or they can be released without feeding after a limited period of observation. Some experimentation with the diet may be informative.

Baby chicks need no food for 24 to 48 hours after hatching, but must be kept warm under a light bulb and perhaps a box for a hood. Fire hazard should be avoided in the brooder devised. Some experimentation will be profitable, but chickens may be fed worms, insects, leafy vegetables, a commercial mash, and of course — water. The grain should not be too coarse for the size of the bird. Table scraps may be used. Feeding instructions may be obtained from a poultry supply house where the grain is obtained; or for a short period, oatmeal and other household cereals may be used. Coarse sand for grit is essential, and laying hens need crushed oyster shell for the lime.

Rabbits are vegetarians. Food may be obtained from the cafeteria scraps, grass and hay, or commercial rabbit pellets. A salt brick should be within reach, and so should water. The diet of a guinea pig is similar, with emphasis on fresh green vegetables. Gray squirrels likewise eat green foods, seed, nuts, and fruit. The diets of chipmunks, hamsters, and woodchucks are similar to that of squirrels. The opossum eats seed, nuts, fruit, insects, and bits of meat. The raccoon has a varied appetite; it can eat table scraps, meat, and fish. A gopher will eat grain, potatoes, and even weeds. Moles need insects and worms. Bats eat insects, but should not be kept long in captivity. The diet of a mouse or rat is much like that of a dog or cat, with emphasis on meat and other protein food. Canned dog food, dog meal, table scraps, and grain are all satisfactory.

Chickens, rabbits, hamsters, and other relatively large animals should be kept in cages that are easy to clean. The cage should be so constructed that droppings will fall through onto a newspaper, which can be changed each morning, and the area should be dusted with slaked lime to neutralize possible odors. The use of bedding in the cage ordinarily should be avoided, for the bedding makes cleaning difficult. The bedding is unnecessary, except when an animal is about to bear young and needs to build a nest. At such a time the male animal should be moved to another cage for the protection of the young. Owing probably to nervousness or inadequate diet, even the female may destroy the young. A litter of rats, hamsters, or similar animals ordinarily would be born in some obscure crevice or burrow where it is silent and dark, rather than in a conspicuous cage in a relatively noisy classroom. Therefore it is advisable to remove the animals to the furnace room, or at least to a quiet corner, and cover the cage with an old blanket or two. Since the only justification for maintaining the animals is to provide for observation, the cover should be removed for brief periods for the children to see the animals and to feed and water them.

Plants in the classroom

In raising and caring for plants, experience is truly the best teacher. No hazard and little expense are involved. The best way for either the child or the teacher to learn is simply to begin and then profit by mistakes as well as successes. References can be found in libraries, and pamphlets are available at many seed stores.

Seed may be planted in flower pots, planting frames, or other boxes, or in tin cans with holes punched in the bottom. A few pebbles at the bottom of a flower pot or a tin can will provide for better drainage. If available, a shallow layer of sand and decayed vegetation may be added — or, even better, peat moss, or a coarse compost; then the pot may be filled with a loose, rich soil. Darker soils are usually richer in humus. Near the banks of a stream may be a good place to find rich soil. Potted plants may be purchased, brought from homes and gardens, or raised from bulbs or cuttings. A geranium, begonia, or coleus, for example, may be propagated by cutting several joints from a growing branch and placing the cut end in water or moist sand until roots and a new growth of leaves appear. Meanwhile any flowers and the larger leaves should be removed.

The simplest way to plant a bulb is merely to place it in a flower pot and cover it with dirt. Some bulbs, such as daffodils and hyacinths, are better adapted for indoor growth than others are. For the production of stronger plants it is commonly recommended that the potted bulbs be left in a cool, dark cellar or a similar place for a time so that the roots may become established before the tops develop.

The depth of planting for seed varies with the size of the seed. Beans may be covered with nearly an inch of fine soil, whereas radish or mustard seed should be covered with as little as possible. If a seed is planted too deep, the sprout may never reach the surface; on the other hand, if planted too near the surface the seed may dry out and die after having begun to germinate. Because plants kept indoors are watered artificially, they may well be planted at more shallow depths than outdoor directions indicate. Likewise, plants can be raised closer together indoors, but room for sunshine to reach the leaves is necessary, and overcrowding is one of the more common problems. Seedlings may be thinned by transplanting or otherwise removing the weaker plants.

Plants should be watered thoroughly at regular intervals; but to avoid an excess of water the upper surface of the dirt should be permitted to dry between waterings. The amount of moisture needed varies with the type of plant; a cactus, for example, thrives in a relatively dry soil. If mold appears, the watering may be excessive or the drainage poor. More sunshine will help, and in seed-sprouting experiments especially a few drops of carbolic acid added to the water will help somewhat to retard the growth of mold. If the mold appears in a humid terrarium, remove the glass cover to reduce the humidity.

Most potted plants thrive on considerable direct sunshine each day. Potted plants need to be fertilized occasionally, but an excess of fertilizer close to the plant may be harmful. It is well to water thoroughly after applying commercial fertilizer. Rinsing with soapy water may remove aphids and similar pests. If not, a spray will be needed.

Most of the conditions necessary for plant growth may profitably be determined in the classroom through experimentation.

STUDY GUIDE

1. Observe several animals, as children might be encouraged to do, and note how these observations could be used to develop meanings in science.
2. Where could you go within walking distance to show how plants grow, or to illustrate the great variety of living things? Specifically, what would you look for in each case?
3. Give a practical illustration of how work with animals could be introduced at a certain grade level. How would the work be organized and conducted?
4. Select one theme, such as cooperation among social animals, and see what references could be assembled for use with children of a given age. What direct investigations would be possible and appropriate?
5. Conduct an experiment with plants or animals, show it to your class, and explain how it could be used with children.
6. Assemble an aquarium, a terrarium, or an ant nest; or care for a caged animal in the classroom. Maintaining a caterpillar, a spider's egg sack, frog's eggs, or mosquito larvae can be equally rewarding. Keep a record of observations and note what value such an undertaking might have for children.
7. Specifically, how can work with plants and animals help to achieve the objectives recommended in Chapter 3?

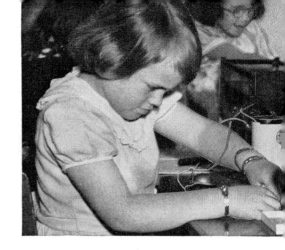

12

Experimenting with Magnetism and Electricity

"Where does electricity go when it goes off?" a third-grader wanted to know. Children are fascinated by electrical devices. Possibly for the same reason that children find electricity exciting as a field of study, some teachers fear to work with it. Although high-voltage electricity is truly dangerous, the voltage of a dry cell is a mere 1½, in contrast to approximately 110 for a house circuit and several thousand volts in the power lines out of doors. It is impossible to get a shock directly from a dry cell. Children should not experiment with the house circuit, but there is no hazard in working with dry cells as suggested in textbooks for children — even when mistakes are made. Surely there is far more danger in commonplace activities, such as walking along the sidewalk on the way home from school, or playing tag on the grounds at noon. People fear what they do not understand. Some who fear to touch a dry cell in the classroom will change the cells in a flashlight with no thought of danger, yet the voltage is the same. One reason for studying electricity is to overcome needless fears. Electricity is common in our way of life, and everyone should have some understanding of it.

Magnetism is closely related to electricity, and a study of magnetism ordinarily is a first step toward understanding electricity.

WORKING WITH MAGNETS

One of the boys in a second grade brought to school a magnet. He was allowed to show it to the class during their "news time" and then was told to put it away. But the interest persisted. Throughout the morning it seemed that the children were wasting their time, interrupting their work, as one after another would slip over to the boy's desk to see the magnet. So the teacher suggested that the magnet be placed on a table where everyone could see it. She added a variety of objects with which the children might experiment to see what a magnet will attract. Included were chalk, paper clips, thumbtacks, rubber bands, and bits of paper and wood. In a few days the children themselves brought a compass, a pair of magnetic toy dogs which would attract or repel each other, a magnetized tray from inside an automobile, a magnetized note-pad-and-pencil set, and a toy mummy which would lie in its case in only one direction and would rise mysteriously when placed in the opposite direction. Each child showed his contribution and explained it to the class. The teacher helped the children to find books with information about magnets. She also helped by suggesting experiments that might be tried, and by providing an opportunity to report whenever something new was discovered.

While children are experimenting to see what materials a magnet will attract, they may discover that a tin can is attracted by a magnet. Tin cans are mostly iron today, and it is the iron that is attracted, not the tin. Nickel is attracted by a magnet, but the United States nickel coin is made chiefly of copper and is not attracted. A Canadian nickel, if available, will show the attraction.

Making a compass

If a cork is pierced with a magnetized needle so that the needle will float horizontally in a pan of water, the needle will be free to turn in a north-south direction and will act as a compass. Glazed or oiled paper can be substituted for the cork. Glass, plastic, or earthenware containers should be used with this floating compass; enameled pans are iron beneath the surface, and the needle will be drawn to the sides of the pan.

An ordinary bar magnet suspended in the air so that it is free to turn will serve as a compass. A heavy thread or fine cord may be tied about the middle and the magnet hung from a yardstick between the backs of two wooden chairs. If there is iron near the suspended magnet, or if the cord used is heavy, the magnet may not be free to turn. The end which points north is designated as the north pole, the other end as south. If the magnet used is otherwise labeled, perhaps it has become remagnetized so that the poles marked on it are no longer correct.

Preparing magnets and determining the poles

In experimenting at the table, the children may discover that a magnet is stronger at the ends, which are called poles. A magnetized needle or any other magnet broken in two will have north and south poles on each segment.

Needles, knife blades, scissors, and other objects of steel will become magnetized when rubbed against one end of a strong magnet. A motion similar to that of whittling a stick of wood with a pocket knife is effective. Children are able to discover for themselves that magnetism can be so induced. They may find also that a nail and similar objects of relatively soft iron soon lose their magnetism, whereas an object made of steel will become a relatively permanent magnet. Magnets are made commercially of steel. Some of the stronger

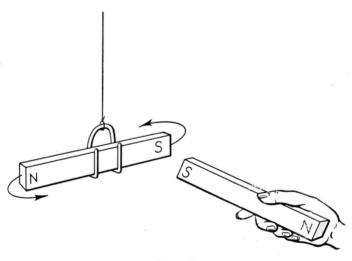

Fig. 70

A suspended magnet will act as a compass, will show which poles attract and which repel, and can be used to explain the action of the electric motor.

ones, however, are alloys, such as Alnico, an alloy of aluminum, nickel, copper, iron, and cobalt.

When one magnet is used to magnetize another, what determines the poles of the second magnet? Such a question may arise when the children make a compass and wish to magnetize a needle so that the sharp end will point north. To solve the problem they should note which end of the original magnet was used and how it was rubbed along the needle. Rubbing with the opposite end will reverse the poles.

While a bar magnet is suspended and free to turn, bring another magnet near. It will be seen that one end of the suspended magnet is attracted and the other end repelled. The children can make their own generalization, but the usual statement is that unlike poles attract and like poles repel.

Because like poles do repel, children can use one magnet to determine the poles of another. If the north pole of one magnet is known, the end of another which repels it is also a north pole.

To make a compass needle as sensitive as possible, both ends can be magnetized, one end with the north pole of the magnet and the other with the south. In a similar way old magnets can be remagnetized by rubbing them against a more powerful magnet. Care should be taken not to reverse the poles. The end marked N should be rubbed against the south pole of the stronger magnet.

Developing a concept of magnetism

By experimenting, children can become familiar with magnets. They can learn that the attraction of a magnet is greater when the magnet is closer to the object attracted. Anything attracted tends to be drawn toward the poles of the magnet. The magnetism will pass through water, glass, wood, and similar materials, though not through the sides of a tin can. A paper clip on a sheet of cardboard can be moved about by means of a magnet below the cardboard. The magnetism is unaffected by the cardboard.

Children can report what they have read about lodestones and other kinds of magnets and about the usefulness of magnets in everyday life. One girl, whose mother was a hairdresser, reported that her mother let her use a magnet to retrieve hairpins from the floor. The fact that the earth acts like a magnet may be discussed when the action of a compass is considered. The books read may offer an explanation of magnetism and may recommend activities, such as removing the magnetism from a needle by holding it with pliers and heating it at the tip of the flame from an alcohol burner until as hot as possible.

Magnetism itself is not something visible, but the attraction of a magnet can be shown indirectly by means of iron filings. If a cardboard is laid on top of a magnet and iron filings are scattered on the cardboard, the filings will be drawn into a pattern which reveals the direction of magnetism. Tapping the cardboard lightly will help to make the pattern clear. The area about a magnet so shown is known as the *magnetic field*. The magnetic field can also be shown by holding a compass in various positions near a magnet. The compass needle will point in the direction of the attraction.

ELECTROMAGNETS

When an insulated copper wire is wound around a nail and the bare ends of the wire are attached to a dry cell, the nail becomes an electromagnet. Through their own investigations children can learn that increasing the number of loops of wire makes a stronger magnet. The illustrations in books are often misleading. To keep the diagrams simple, only a few turns of wire are shown, but to be effective an electromagnet should have many turns of wire. Five to ten feet of wire wound onto a large nail will make a strong magnet. The ends of the wire should be left free so that the electromagnet can be connected to a dry cell. The wire should be insulated; no bare wire should be allowed to touch the nail. If more than one dry cell is available, it can be seen that increasing the current will strengthen the magnet. Children are apt to exhaust a dry cell by leaving it connected when it is not in use. A reasonable precaution is to remove the cap from one terminal so that the electromagnet will be attached firmly at only one terminal and is merely pressed against the other momentarily when in use. Another solution is to place a button switch in the line.

The magnetic field about a wire can be shown in several ways. If a copper wire about four to five feet long is attached to a dry cell and the middle portion of the wire is held vertically, a compass placed beside it will show that the direction of the magnetism is circular about the wire. A magnetized needle suspended by a fine thread about the middle will serve as a substitute for a compass if the compass is unobtainable. After the direction of the magnetic field has been determined, if the connections to the dry cell are reversed so that the end of the wire previously attached to the outer terminal is now connected to the inside one, and vice versa, it will be observed that the compass direction also is reversed. The direction of the magnetism depends upon the direction of the current.

Iron filings can be used to show the magnetic field about a wire. Punch a

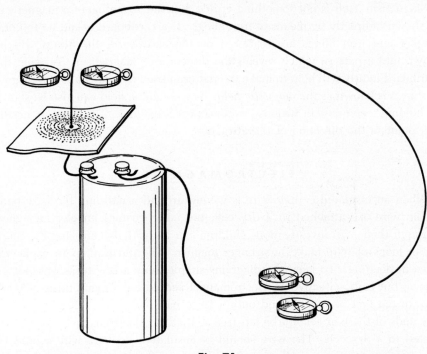

Fig. 71

The magnetism about a wire can be demonstrated with a compass or
with iron filings.

hole in the center of a cardboard and thread a wire through the hole. Attach
both ends of the wire to a dry cell. Hold the cardboard in a horizontal position
and the wire upright. Iron filings should then be scattered on the cardboard.
For the best effect the filings should be dusted onto the cardboard from a salt
shaker and, if necessary, the cardboard tapped gently until the pattern of lines
becomes clear.

Also to show the magnetic effect of an electric current, a pocket compass
may be placed on a table and a wire stretched above it in the same direction
as the compass needle.. When the wire is connected to a dry cell, note how the
compass needle is diverted by the magnetism of the current flowing in the
wire. This effect is used in electrical measuring instruments, such as the ammeter on the dashboard of an automobile. If the compass is held above the
wire, note that the direction of the compass needle is opposite its direction
when held below the wire; this also indicates that the magnetic field about a
wire is circular.

Although a single wire acts like a magnet, the magnetic effect is greater, the attraction or repulsion of a compass needle more pronounced, if the wire is wound to form a coil. In an electromagnet a nail or some other core is essential. If the nail is removed from an electromagnet, the coil alone is not as strong as it was with the core intact.

The children can determine the poles of their electromagnet — which end is north, which south. The end that repels the north end of a compass is also north. A magnet may attract one end of a compass without indicating the poles, for any bar of iron will be attracted. But only a magnet will be repelled by another magnet. After the poles are known, if the children reverse the connections to the dry cell they will find that the poles of the magnet are also reversed. This phenomenon is fundamental in the operation of an electric motor. The poles are determined by the direction of the current in the wire.

Electromagnets are very common and have many practical uses, often in very complex instruments. Some of the more simple, familiar applications include the electric motor, generator, telephone receiver, the loud-speaker of a radio or television set, and an electric doorbell; one of the most obvious applications is the electromagnet sometimes seen attached to a crane and used to lift scrap iron onto a railroad car. The usefulness of an electromagnet is due

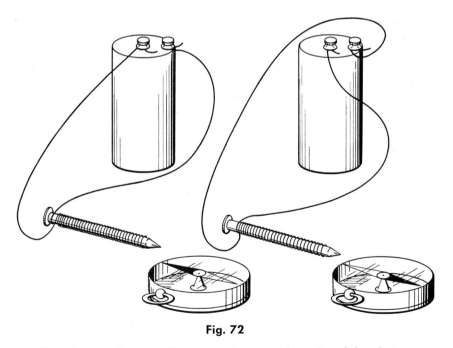

Fig. 72

Reversing the direction of current will reverse the poles of the electro-magnets.

Fig. 73

Electricity is common in our way of life, and everyone should have some understanding of it.

largely to the fact that its strength varies with the strength of the electric current; when the current ceases to flow, the attraction of the magnet is gone.

THE TELEGRAPH AND THE ELECTRIC BUZZER

The teletype has supplanted the telegraph for conveying messages in many cases, but the original instrument is more simple, illustrates well a practical use of the electromagnet, and has considerable historical significance. Children sometimes have telegraphs as toys, and sets can easily be made at home.

After a strong electromagnet has been made and has been used for awhile, it can be used in the construction of a telegraph set. Using the same magnet will save time and equipment, and — more important — the previous experience with an electromagnet will make the telegraph more easily understood.

To construct the sounder of a telegraph set, the nail of an electromagnet may be driven into a block of wood. The wood should be thick enough to give the nail firm support without having the point penetrate far enough to scratch the table or desk upon which the telegraph is to be used. From a tin can a strip of metal may be cut, about two inches wide and four inches longer than the electromagnet. Bend the metal into the shape of an L, the foot of the L being about two inches long. Tack the foot of the metal L firmly to the base of the telegraph, with the upright portion of the metal about an inch from the electromagnet. The nails at the base should be spaced as if at the corners of a square, so that the upright metal will be firm. The upper end of the metal should then be bent ninety degrees to extend out over the electromagnet, forming an armature to be drawn down when current flows through the electromagnet. The armature should be adjusted until it is close enough for the magnet to attract it, yet has resistance enough to spring back when the current ceases to flow.

The telegraph sounder may be tested by attaching one free end of the wire to a dry cell and then momentarily touching the other end to the second terminal. When the current flows, the magnet attracts the armature. A clicking sound results when the armature strikes the magnet. Messages are sent by means of dots and dashes. A dot is sounded when the armature is drawn down and then springs up almost immediately. A dash results from somewhat longer contact. So that dots and dashes can be distinguished by the sound, the armature should strike something when released. A board may be tacked to the side of the sounder, and into the board a nail may be driven to extend out over the armature, close enough that the armature will strike the nail when released by the magnet.

A telegraph key or switch to use with the sounder can be constructed from another block of wood and a short, broad strip of the metal from a can. One end of the metal should be attached securely to the block and the other end bent upwards above a round-headed screw located nearby in the block. The

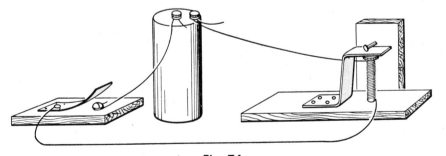

Fig. 74

A homemade telegraph set.

bare end of one wire from the sounder may then be nailed tightly to the base of the metal strip. The other wire from the sounder may be attached to a dry cell, and a wire from the dry cell may be wrapped about the round-headed screw and the screw driven down to hold the wire tightly against the wood. Current will flow to the sounder only when the metal strip is pressed tightly against the round-headed screw. The key as constructed here is equivalent to a button switch, such as is used at the front door of a house to ring the door-bell.

Sending messages with the completed set is interesting and helps to make clear the actual function of a telegraph. The Morse code for an S is three dots, and that for O is three dashes; so the children can easily send an SOS — three dots, three dashes, and three dots. With the complete code written on the blackboard, other simple messages can be worked out and sent slowly, one letter at a time, the child who receives the message writing down each letter as he receives it. Some children have practiced their spelling words in this way. To heighten interest, one child may sit in the cloakroom or the hall with the connecting wires running under the closed door. Some classes have dropped one end of their wires out the window to be drawn in by the class directly below so that messages can be sent from one floor to another. A similar arrangement has been made by adjoining classes on one floor, the wires running out the window from the back of one room to the front of another. Although more than one cell can be used, a much greater distance than that of adjoining rooms is likely to be impractical.

MORSE CODE

A	·—	J	·———	S	···
B	—···	K	—·—	T	—
C	—·—·	L	·—··	U	··—
D	—··	M	——	V	···—
E	·	N	—·	W	·——
F	·—·	O	———	X	—··—
G	——·	P	·——·	Y	—·——
H	····	Q	——·—	Z	——··
I	··	R	·—·		
1	·————	5	·····	9	————·
2	··———	6	—····	0	—————
3	···——	7	——···		
4	····—	8	———··		

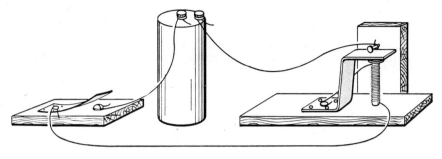

Fig. 75

A telegraph set converted to an electric buzzer

A visit to a telegraph office will serve to make the study meaningful and will help to modernize the information gained.

If the connections are changed, the homemade telegraph can be converted to an electric buzzer. Doing so helps to stress the significant features of each instrument. As in the diagram, connect the wires so that the current from the dry cell flows into the contact point — the nail above the armature — through the armature, and from there to the electromagnet and on through the circuit. With the wires connected in this manner, the current is interrupted automatically at the contact point. While the switch is held down, the armature is pulled back and forth, making a continuous buzz instead of a single click. When the magnet pulls the armature away from the contact point, the current ceases to flow, the magnet releases the armature, the armature springs back to the contact point, and the whole cycle is then repeated, producing a buzzing sound as the armature continues to strike the head of the magnet and the contact point. The only distinction between a buzzer and a doorbell is that the latter has a bell which is struck by the armature, or clapper, as it moves back and forth.

The key from the telegraph set may be used as a button switch for the buzzer — or an actual button switch, if available, may be used. Using the more realistic switch will help children to understand that their equipment is equivalent to what is found on doors everywhere. The relationship should be stressed, for it is possible to construct and operate improvised equipment without understanding the relationship to articles in actual, common use. Classroom experiences should serve to interpret experience outside the school. While electric bells are being studied, it is helpful to examine a real bell, perhaps the fire bell on the wall in the corridor, and if possible another bell should be kept on the table for the children to use.

Fig. 76

With a transmitter, a receiver, a dry cell, and some wire, children can learn how a telephone works.

THE ELECTRIC MOTOR

A bar magnet suspended horizontally by a fine cord about the middle will turn when approached by another magnet, one end attracted and the other repelled. As the suspended magnet begins to turn, if the poles of the magnet in hand are reversed, and the reversals are timed properly, the suspended magnet can be made to rotate, much as does the rotor of an electric motor. Reversing the poles of a magnet by hand is obviously impractical. In an alternating-current motor the poles change automatically each time the direction of the current is reversed. In direct-current motors the direction of the current is reversed by means of a device called a *commutator*. The children may practice making a suspended magnet rotate, and they may experiment with an electromagnet, reversing the connections to a dry cell to see how the poles of the magnet are thereby changed.

A real motor should be examined. Perhaps the motor on the blower of an oil-burning furnace will serve as an example — or one from the locomotive of a toy train or some household appliance. Instructions for building motors are found in many books, and the construction can be a worthwhile undertaking for a child who has the skill and likes to build. If the school has one, a St. Louis motor, or other demonstration motor, if left on the work table for the children to examine and use, will provide a valuable experience. A toy motor that will run is likewise useful.

THE TELEPHONE

A telephone is a familiar instrument of interest to children. To help the children understand how it works, the teacher may have them speak into the

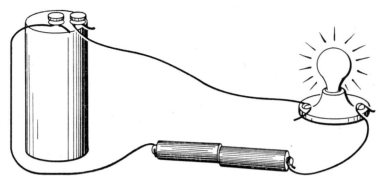

Fig. 77

Illustrating the variable current in a telephone line

open end of a cardboard box, such as the round box in which cornmeal is sold. The vibrations can be detected by placing the finger tips lightly on the bottom of the box. The diaphragm in a telephone transmitter vibrates in a similar manner when a person speaks into it. The diaphragm is a thin sheet located behind the perforations into which a person speaks. A view of the diaphragm can be obtained by unscrewing the mouthpiece of a telephone. Carbon particles behind the diaphragm are compressed with varying degrees of pressure as the diaphragm vibrates. Because of the changing pressure, electricity from the telephone exchange can flow along the line and through the carbon in the transmitter more readily at one moment than another; so the transmitter is a device to control the flow of electricity along the line.

Contrary to a common assumption of children, no sound passes along a telephone line, but rather a variable electric current. The concept of a variable current and how it is controlled can be clarified graphically. First the children may remove the carbon rods from inside two old dry cells. The flashlight size will do, but the larger ones are more convenient. One of the carbon rods may then be attached to one terminal of a dry cell. In the same manner the second carbon rod may be attached to a miniature lamp and the lamp to the second terminal of the dry cell. As the carbon rods are pressed together with varying degrees of pressure a variable current will pass along the wire from the dry cell, and the brightness of the light will vary accordingly. The transmitter of the telephone, like the carbon rods, does not generate the current but does control the amount of current flowing in the line.

If the cap is removed from an old-fashioned telephone receiver a metal diaphragm is revealed, and beneath that a permanent magnet with an electromagnet. The two magnets attract the metal and control the way it vibrates. When the variable current passes through the coils of the electromagnet, the strength of attraction varies in accordance with the strength of the current, and the diaphragm moves back and forth accordingly. That motion is the sound. The vibrations of the receiver correspond to the variations in the current, and those variations are controlled by the vibrations in the transmitter, which in turn correspond to the vibrations of the voice itself. Therefore essentially the same sound is reproduced. Just as the tone of a violin cannot be reproduced on a trumpet, even when both instruments play the same notes, so the vibrations of the metal diaphragm are not identical with the original voice, because metal will not vibrate in exactly the same manner, and therefore the sounds differ somewhat. We say that the telephone has a "metallic" sound.

If the school lacks the equipment, a telephone may be borrowed from the local telephone company so that direct observation and use by the children will be possible. Perhaps the earphones designed for use with a radio crystal set can be obtained from someone. If so, the children may connect one of the wires from it to one terminal of a dry cell and then touch the other wire to the second terminal; a click will be heard. When the current flows, the metal diaphragm is drawn inward; when it is released, another click can be heard. If a transmitter is available, wires may be connected from it to those from the receiver; and with a dry cell in the circuit somewhere it is possible to talk into the transmitter and be heard at the receiver. Visiting a telephone exchange also is a worthwhile experience for the older children. Although there is much that is complex about a telephone exchange, the general understanding gained can be rewarding.

ELECTRIC CIRCUITS

At Christmastime a first grade prepared an embellished cardboard figure of a snowman and fitted it with a miniature light bulb for a nose. The report dictated by the children provides an adequate explanation of the circumstances:

Frosty the Snowman

Frosty is a jolly snowman.
First Miss Johnson painted a snowman on a piece of cardboard.
We mixed soap flakes with a little water.
We put the sticky soap on the snowman.
We decided to call him Frosty.
We put a dry cell in back of Frosty.
A dry cell is full of electricity.
Jimmy wound the copper wire around the screw.
Then Jimmy hooked the other ends to the tiny bulb.
Then the light turned on.
We put the tiny bulb in Frosty's nose.
Frosty looks happy.

A six-year-old child in another class, while connecting lamps and doorbells with dry cells and button switches, found that a complete circuit is needed. She concluded: "That's why when a wire falls down in a storm all the lights go out."

Through direct experience in functional situations children can learn many of the facts about electric circuits. Suitable activities can begin at an early age, increasing in complexity as the child matures and gains experience. As soon as children are big enough to climb onto a chair, they are delighted by flipping the light switch on and off or by ringing the door bell. The activity is a form of investigation. Children in any one grade vary widely in their manual dexterity, but even in the nursery most enjoy ringing a bell or flashing a light, if the equipment is on a table ready for use. From such experience they learn some of the relationships among the switch, the bell, the wires, and the dry cell — relationships which are not apparent in the wiring at home. With increased skill the child will be able to make the connections himself; and as he matures, the skill and understanding can grow with him through use in situations in which the understanding is needed. The meaning of such terms as conductors, insulators, and terminals can be gained through experience, which provides a depth of insight that can be attained in no other way. When a short circuit occurs in the wiring, the experience will help children to understand the real purpose of insulation. Following the suggestions in their books, older children can arrange several miniature lamps in series and in parallel circuits, taking note of the differences. They can experiment with series and parallel arrangements of dry cells, lamps, bells, and whatever else is available.

Fig. 78

Series connection of dry cells: lamps connected in parallel

In elementary work, appliances are more often connected in series. A series circuit is one in which the wires lead from one appliance to another, much as if the appliances were located at various points along a circle. The term itself is suggestive of the meaning, for in any series one thing follows another, and the word *circuit* may be likened to a circle. Parallel connections, however, provide alternate paths for the current.

Short circuits, conductors, and non-conductors

With a doorbell, switch, and dry cell all in one circuit, children can bring about short circuits so that in one case the bell will not ring, and the wires will get hot; in another case the bell will ring and cannot be stopped, as sometimes happens to automobile horns. A short circuit can be made by removing the insulation and touching the bare wires together, or by bridging the space between the bare wires by means of another wire, a nail, a screw driver, or a pocket knife.

A device for testing the conductivity of various materials can be prepared by removing the switch from a circuit in which a lamp or a bell is connected to a dry cell. With the bare ends of the two wires in contact with a nail, the lamp will light or the bell ring, indicating that the current was conducted through the nail. But with the wires at opposite ends of a piece of chalk no current will flow, so the children may list chalk as a non-conductor. Lists of conductors and non-conductors may be prepared and reported. If there is disagreement, further tests should be made. Non-conductors are used as insulators.

Liquids also can be tested to see which will conduct electricity. With three or four dry cells and a lamp in series, salt water can be tested by dipping the bare ends of the wires into the water. Notice that the lamp is brighter when the ends of the wires are closer. Pure water, sugar solution, vinegar, alcohol, cleaning solvent, limewater, lemonade, and other familiar liquids likewise may be tested. If no miniature lamp socket is available for these tests, a flashlight bulb can be used merely by twisting the bare end of a wire tightly about the copper base of the bulb and touching another wire to the point at the center of the base.

Heating, resistance, and fuses

From experience children will learn that wires carrying electricity get hot, in some cases more than in others. By experimenting they can see that the wires get hotter when more dry cells are used. When the same current goes through

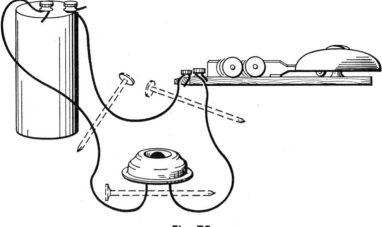

Fig. 79

Suggested points for intentional short circuits

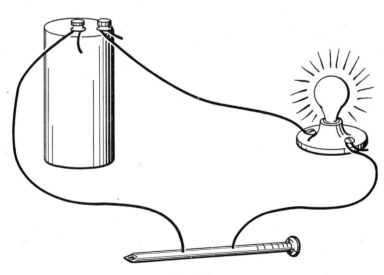

Fig. 80

Testing for conductivity.   Representative conductors are iron, aluminum,
carbon rod, copper, and silver coin.   Representative nonconductors are
chalk, rubber, paper, glass, wool, paint, and cloth.

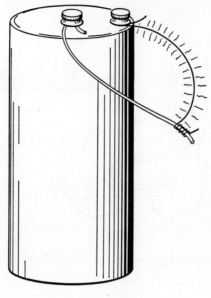

Fig. 81

When the same current goes through both, a small iron wire becomes
hotter than a large copper wire.

two wires attached in series, a small wire becomes hotter than a large one, an
iron wire hotter than a copper one; and short lengths of wire become hotter
than longer wires do. The filament in a lamp, toaster, electric stove, or other
heating device becomes hot while the wires leading to the lamp or heater may
remain quite cool. It is worthwhile to have a class examine heating appliances
and prepare a display with placards giving brief explanations.

To see the effect of increased resistance, connect one terminal of a dry cell to
a miniature lamp. To the second terminal of the dry cell attach a spool of fine
iron wire, or a long length of whatever wire can be obtained, preferably a
fine wire. When the second terminal of the lamp is connected to the fine
iron wire somewhere near the dry cell, the lamp will light. If the spool of iron
wire is unrolled and the connections are made farther and farther from
the dry cell, the lamp will become more and more dim. The longer
wire offers more resistance, so less current flows. The long wire here
is apt to be cumbersome, so for practical use it can be wound into
a more compact form. Such a device is called a rheostat. The volume
control on a radio is a rheostat. Other rheostats are found on electric fans and
mixers.

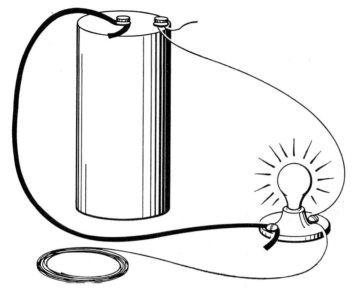

Fig. 82

The lamp grows dim as more of the fine iron wire is used.

To show how a fuse protects a house from overheated wires that may start a fire, a very narrow strip may be cut from the aluminum foil of a cigarette wrapper, the strip pinned to a block of wood, and the wires from one or more dry cells then touched to opposite ends of the foil. Heating the foil will cause it to melt before the copper wires become hot. Just as fuses are made in various capacities, so it may be noted that the narrower and thinner the foil the sooner it will melt. The practical use of a fuse can be clarified for the children by asking the janitor to show them the fuse box of the school. If a house under construction is visited at the appropriate time, a class will be able to see practical examples of parallel wiring, switch boxes, fuses, and insulators.

Common difficulties

Some of the more common difficulties that children encounter in working with electricity are due to loose connections or failure to remove the insulation where connections are made. Terminals should be tight enough that the wires will not pull out from under them or be held so loosely that they will make poor contact. Connections should be made with the ends of a wire, not the middle. A screw driver and pliers are helpful in making tight connections,

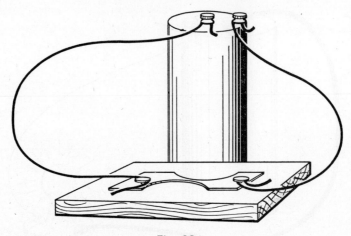

Fig. 83

As in a fuse, the narrow strip of metal foil will melt before the wires become hot.

and a dull paring knife is useful for scraping off the cloth, rubber, or enamel insulation. A common difficulty with electric bells is that the contact point gets pulled away, because children tug at the clapper to ring the bell by hand. A failure to ring may indicate that the contact should be adjusted. A confusion in the wiring so that a complete circuit is lacking, or perhaps a short circuit is made, is another source of difficulty. Often, however, the difficulties that arise provide excellent learning situations.

STATIC ELECTRICITY

Minor shocks from static electricity are common in everyday experience and require some interpretation. A great number of suitable experiments can be found in books for children. After running a comb briskly through his hair a child can lift bits of paper from the table with the comb or cause the hair on his own head to rise toward the comb. Such experiments are more successful on days when the air is dry, for otherwise the charge built up is carried away by the humid air. For the same reason that touching a light switch or an electrical appliance with wet hands is dangerous — because moisture will help to conduct electricity — the moisture in the air will carry away a charge built up by friction.

There are two kinds of static electricity. The charge acquired by a comb or a rubber rod is called *negative*, whereas the charge acquired by glass is called *positive.* Where suggested experiments call for a rubber rod and wool or cat's fur, ordinarily a pocket comb and the child's own hair can be used. For pith balls, puffed rice or a similar breakfast cereal that is light, smooth-surfaced, and more or less spherical can be substituted. Suspended by fine threads, two of the balls when approached by a charged pocket comb show the attraction and repulsion of electrical charges. The balls will be attracted to the comb, but when both have acquired the same charge from the comb they will repel each other and be repelled by the comb. It is more difficult to acquire a positive charge, but for this purpose a sheet of glass, or even a glass jar, when rubbed by silk or nylon will serve as a substitute for the usual glass rod. Pith balls which have become charged by a comb or rubber rod will be attracted by the positive charge on glass. Whenever two unlike materials are rubbed together, one is apt to lose electricity to the other. Of course static charges are not limited to rubber and glass rods; these are simply examples of materials which tend to acquire and hold a charge well. Many other examples of static charges are common in everyday experiences, and the children will be able to report some, such as walking across a rug and then touching a doorknob. Lightning is the product of static charges built up by friction of the air currents in a storm.

Benjamin Franklin and others before him knew of the two contrasting charges, such as that of the comb and the glass. Deciding that one charge represented the presence of electricity and the other a lack of it, Franklin designated one as positive and the other as negative. Unfortunately he named the wrong one positive; hence today the charge commonly referred to as negative is actually the one with an excess of electricity. With increased knowledge of atomic structure, we know today that because of friction electrons are rubbed off the outside of atoms and that the electrons which accumulate constitute an electrical charge. Owing to their structure, some atoms cling to electrons more tightly than others do, and thus acquire a negative charge.

An inflated balloon, rubbed against wool clothing and then placed on the wall or ceiling, will be held in that position for some time, attracted to the wall by the charge built up on the balloon. Some of the electrons in the material of the wall are repelled by the negative charge on the balloon and move away along the wall; therefore near the balloon the charge on the wall is opposite that of the balloon. Likewise, if a child will run a comb briskly through his hair and then bring the charged comb near a slender stream of water from a faucet, the stream will be drawn toward the comb.

It is interesting to have children comb their hair briskly while close to a radio receiver at home. If the hair is dry and free of oil — as after a shampoo — and if the humidity of the air is low, the combing will produce a good spark which can be seen in the dark and can be heard on the radio as static. Radio waves are produced by sparks and other electrical disturbances; if uncontrolled these waves are called static. In most parts of the country the air is likely to be drier during the cold days of winter, and static experiments are more successful then.

THE GALVANOMETER AND OTHER MEASURING INSTRUMENTS

Small amounts of current that will not light a lamp or ring a bell can be detected with a homemade galvanometer. A galvanometer can be improvised by suspending a magnetized needle from threads across the center of a coil of insulated copper wire. It may be convenient to prepare the coil by winding the wire about a glass jar of the desired size. In order for the coil to be as sensitive as possible, it should have as many loops of wire as possible, perhaps a hundred; and the inside diameter of the coil should be only slightly larger than the length of the needle. The closer the needle fits the coil, without striking it, the more sensitive the instrument will be. For convenience in use, the coil may be bound tightly with tape at three or four places and nailed to a small block of wood, care being taken not to break the insulation during the nailing. The wires leading to the coil should be a foot or more in length. With a thread through the eye of the needle, the needle can be suspended from the top of the coil. The weight of the needle will cause it to hang vertically, except when a current passes through the coil, causing the coil to become magnetized and the needle to be deflected. The amount of deflection will indicate the strength of the current. The needle can be magnetized by rubbing the ends against the ends of a strong permanent magnet or electromagnet. Strengthening the magnetism of the needle will make the instrument more sensitive.

Attach the instrument to a dry cell and notice that if the direction of the current passing through the coil is reversed — by reversing the connections to the dry cell — the needle will swing to the opposite side. A galvanometer will indicate both the direction and the strength of an electric current, but ordinarily it is suitable only for use with rather weak, direct currents. In some experiments the galvanometer can also be used with an alternating current — such as that produced by moving a magnet in and out of a coil — where the alternations are not too rapid for the needle to swing back and forth.

A similar instrument can be prepared by winding the insulated copper wire along the diameter of a pocket compass, but the wire across the face of the compass makes the compass needle difficult to see, and there is no spring to bring the compass needle back into line with the coil when no current is flow-

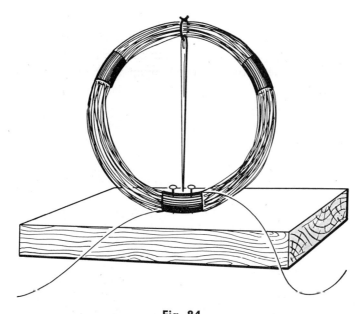

Fig. 84

An improvised galvanometer

ing. The latter difficulty can be corrected, however, by inserting a small magnetized needle under the compass, parallel with the wires of the coil. When the instrument is used, a stronger current will turn the needle of the compass farther than a weak current will.

In addition to its usefulness in the classroom, either galvanometer described will serve to illustrate the basic principles of other common electrical measuring instruments. An ammeter on the dashboard of an automobile is similar but provides an alternate path, a shunt, for the current so that only a certain fraction will go through the coil. The ammeter is suitable for use with larger amounts of current. With the additional path provided, an ammeter offers little resistance to the flow of current and so is used to measure the rate of flow, the amperage.

A voltmeter is a modification of the galvanometer. The voltmeter is provided with additional resistance, in the form of a resistor, through which the current must pass to reach the coil. Since voltage is equivalent to pressure, the ability to overcome resistance is indicative of voltage.

A watt-hour meter, used to measure the current entering a building, is somewhat different, being constructed much like a motor. The meter turns faster when more current is used, and so does an electric motor. In most houses the watt-hour meter is located either on the back porch or in the basement. A rotating disc, corresponding to the rotor which turns in a motor, can be seen in the instrument. In their own homes children can see that the rate at which the disc of a watt-hour meter turns depends upon what electrical equipment is being used. While a toaster or electric flatiron is heating the disc will turn more rapidly than when these and other appliances are disconnected. The children may note which household appliances draw more current through the meter and report their findings at school.

INDUCED CURRENT

When a magnet is moved near a wire, a current is induced to flow in the wire. In this way electricity is generated to operate motors, stoves, lamps, television sets, and countless other devices in our homes and places of business.

To demonstrate the way current can be induced, prepare a coil of insulated copper wire and attach the ends to the wires from the homemade galvanometer. When a strong magnet is thrust into the coil, note that the needle of the galvanometer moves; this indicates that a current is flowing in the wire. The coil

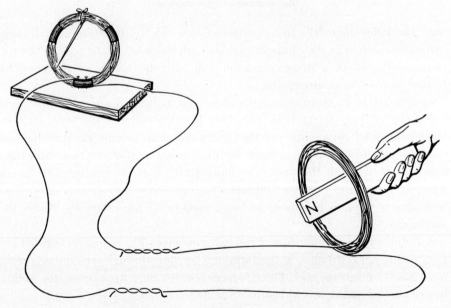

Fig. 85

The galvanometer will show that a current flows when the magnet moves in or out of the coil.

should be kept as far from the galvanometer as possible so that the magnet will have no direct effect on the needle of the galvanometer. Children can experiment with the apparatus to see what determines the strength of the current induced. They will find that the strength of the current depends upon the strength of the magnet, how rapidly the magnet is moved, how close the magnet and coil are, and the number of loops in the coil. If the galvanometer is sensitive it will show that a current flows when a strong magnet is moved past even a single loop of the wire, but with the entire coil the current induced is much stronger. Someone may discover that even though the magnet be near the coil there is no current unless the magnet is in motion. Or the magnet can be stationary and the coil can be moved to induce a current.

Testing the galvanometer with a dry cell — by reversing the terminals connected to the galvanometer — will show that the direction in which the needle moves in the galvanometer depends upon the direction of the current. Therefore a galvanometer can be used to show that the direction of an induced current depends upon the direction in which the magnet is moving and also upon which end of the magnet is used. As a magnet is thrust into the coil and then out, the needle of the galvanometer will swing back and forth, indicating that the current is flowing first in one direction and then another. Such a current is called an alternating current. In contrast, the current from a dry cell is a direct current, flowing only in one direction. The current commonly used in homes and factories is an alternating current.

The electric generator

In an electric generator the magnets used are electromagnets, and the coils are on a shaft whirling past the magnets, instead of having an in-and-out motion. The work of moving the magnet obviously is not done by hand; it is often done by means of a steam engine. Because coal is used to heat the water to form steam and run the engine, the energy which reaches us as electricity actually comes from the coal. In regions where there is plenty of water running down from mountains, a dam may be built to insure a steady supply and the weight of the falling water used to turn the generators. After the initial expense of construction, there are only the maintenance charges, no expensive fuel being necessary, and the cost of electricity accordingly is less. Factories now tend to locate where electricity is inexpensive.

The electric generator of an automobile will provide a common and convenient example of the way electricity is produced. With the hood of the car raised and the engine running, a class can watch the generator in operation.

The generator is turned by the engine, and a current is induced in the moving coils, much as it is induced in the classroom when a coil is moved past a magnet by hand.

For another illustration of how electricity is produced, a class may visit the generating plant which supplies the local community with electricity. In addition to the generators themselves a class should see the steam engines or turbines that turn the generators, the large switches, the power lines, the insulators, and the transformers. The huge piles of coal ordinarily held in readiness for the steam engines are spectacular and when observed will dramatize the need for a source of energy. If water power is used, the dam and the reservoir behind it will be even more spectacular.

Induction coil and transformer

An electromagnet can be used to induce a current in a coil, moving the magnet in and out, just as the permanent magnet was used. All that the children learned with a bar magnet will be found to be true with the electromagnet also. A current can be generated by inserting the magnet into the coil and then removing it; but with the electromagnet the magnetism can be removed simply by disconnecting one of the wires from the magnet to the dry cell, and can be restored by completing the circuit once more. Thus instead of moving the magnet in and out, a current can be induced merely by momentarily touching the wire to the terminal of the dry cell — or a button switch can be inserted in the line to provide a convenient way of making and breaking the circuit. Even better, a doorbell or a buzzer inserted in the line will make and break the circuit automatically in the process of ringing. This last arrangement will serve as an illustration of an induction coil. Someone familiar with automobiles can point out an induction coil under the hood with the engine. Induction coils are used to increase the voltage. An automobile needs the greater voltage to produce a spark in the spark plugs. Induction coils consist principally of two coils, one wound tightly upon the other — for the closer the two coils are, the greater the current induced. The second coil, into which the current is induced, has more turns of wire in it than the first, and because of the greater number of turns in the second coil the voltage is increased. The circuit is made and broken automatically by means of a buzzer. The sound of the buzzer can be heard while an induction coil is in use.

A transformer serves essentially the same purpose as an induction coil, but is used with alternating current. The two are much alike, except that the transformer needs no buzzer to interrupt the current, for alternating current flows first in one direction, then in another, and therefore is halted automatically in the process of reversing directions. Some transformers have fewer coils in the secondary than in the primary coil, so the voltage drops instead of increasing. Such are referred to as step-down transformers. Some common examples include the transformers used with toy trains and the one that is used in a house to reduce the voltage for a doorbell. Transformers also can be seen along many city streets on the poles just below the power lines. Their purpose is to reduce the voltage before the current is carried into the buildings. All that is visible is a black container, much like a bucket with wires leading from it. Larger transformers can be seen at a substation, often located near the edge of town.

CELLS AND BATTERIES

Two or more cells connected form a battery. The usual storage battery in an automobile is made of three cells. Because of the acid inside, storage batteries must be handled with care, but dry cells are harmless and children can be permitted to work with them without fear of injury.

An old dry cell that is no longer serviceable may be torn open by the children to see what is inside. The chemicals inside a dry cell are not dangerous to handle, but tearing the cell open is a messy job, and it may be advisable to spread newspapers on the table so that the remnants may afterwards be gathered up and discarded. The dry cell consists essentially of a zinc container with a carbon rod in the center and chemicals in paste form between. The action of the chemicals — principally ammonium chloride — on the zinc permits electrons to flow out of the cell from the zinc case and back to the carbon rod. A dead cell actually may be dry, but a good one is moist inside, not dry, as the term *dry cell* implies. The chemistry of a cell is too complex for most elementary-school children to understand, but examination of the contents will help provide insight appropriate to the maturity of the child.

The principles of any voltaic cell can be studied with simple materials. A large silver coin and the aluminum foil from some package can be used as the equivalent of the carbon rod and the zinc of a dry cell. The larger the coin and the sheet of aluminum, the greater will be the amperage of the cell. The voltage is determined by the two metals used — that is, by the difference in strength with which each kind of metal attracts electricity. A single sheet of paper toweling may be dampened with water and then sprinkled with table salt, folded, and inserted between the two metals. If one wire from an improvised galvanometer is pressed against the aluminum and the other wire against the silver, the galvanometer should indicate that a current is flowing. If for

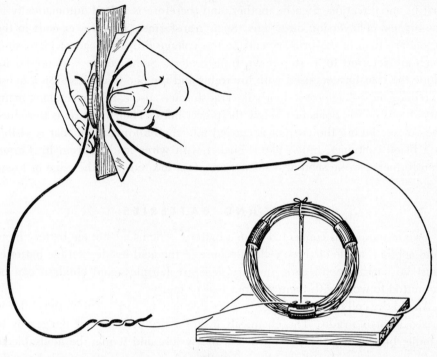

Fig. 86

A silver coin and a sheet of aluminum foil, with a paper towel moistened
with salt water placed between them, will produce an electric current.

some reason the galvanometer is not sensitive enough to detect the current, another means of identifying the current can be used. Have a child place the ends of two wires a short distance apart on his tongue; then have a second person touch the other ends of the wires to the aluminum and silver as before. A metallic taste should be noted, but only while the circuit from the cell is complete.

The children may repeat the experiment using other metals, such as iron and copper, or gold and the zinc from an old dry cell. The closer together the two metals are, without touching, the less the resistance, and so more current will flow; hence the advice to separate them with but a thin sheet of paper toweling. Care should be taken that the metals do not touch at some point beyond the paper. Instead of table salt in water, vinegar can be used, or baking soda in water. In fact, the children may experiment to see what solutions will serve the purpose, and also what metals will provide a strong current.

To make a cell that closely resembles a dry cell, tear a considerable amount of zinc from old dry cells and scrape it as clean as possible. With a hammer flatten the zinc into one big sheet; then attach a copper wire firmly to the zinc. If a nail is driven through the zinc to make a hole, the bare end of a copper wire inserted, and the wire then twisted back upon itself, a firm connection will be provided. The zinc may be placed on the bottom of a soup bowl or other nonmetallic container of convenient size. Next the zinc may be covered with a paper towel and several carbon rods from old dry cells placed on the paper. Heat the carbon rods in the flame of an alcohol burner to remove impurities. All the carbon rods should be attached to one end of a copper wire, and it may be convenient to tie the rods together, side by side. Attach the two copper wires to the terminals of a miniature lamp, flashlight size — or, if that is not available, to an electric bell. The lamp is likely to be more sensitive to a feeble current and is desirable in case the cell is not working effectively. Into a scant pint of warm water stir a heaping tablespoonful of ammonium chloride; then pour the solution into the bowl to cover the carbon rods. The lamp should light or the bell ring. If not, remove the carbon rods and rinse them in warm water. Whenever the cell fails, remove the carbon rods before trying again, for continued use weakens the cell, owing to what is called polarization. Test the bell or lamp with a dry cell to see if the lamp or bell is in working order. Before

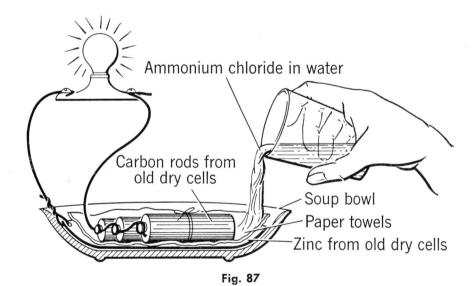

Ammonium chloride in water

Carbon rods from old dry cells

Soup bowl
Paper towels
Zinc from old dry cells

Fig. 87

When the ammonium chloride solution is added, the lamp should light, as it would if attached to a dry cell.

replacing the carbon rods to try the cell again, check to see that all connections are tight with insulation removed, scrape the carbon and the zinc, warm the solution again and heat the carbon rods, and make sure that the zinc is covered by the paper so that the zinc will not touch the carbon rods. If the difficulty is not corrected, attach the wires from the cell to an improvised galvanometer instead. The galvanometer should detect even a feeble current. A sheet of copper or some broad object made of copper can be used as a substitute for the carbon rods. Both the copper and the zinc should be in sheets as large as possible. The larger the surface exposed, the greater the current will be.

ORGANIZING AND CONDUCTING INVESTIGATIONS OF ELECTRICITY

Introducing the work

The subject of magnetism and electricity can be introduced in many ways. One second grade began as the result of a discussion on Columbus Day. The children wanted to know how sailors in early times used compasses, how a compass works, and why the needle points north. To aid in answering the questions, the effect of a magnet on a compass was demonstrated. "Is it sticky?" one child asked, and another said, "Can I do it?" Finding the answer to one question led to another, and thus the investigation was launched.

In another case a first grade began working with electricity when someone suggested that the house they had just built should have a doorbell. A fourth grade simply listed on the board what they would like to know and what they would like to do. While the planning was going on, the children in this class were looking through books for suggestions, and so the planning carried with it some help regarding sources of information. The planning served as a stimulus; the children were eager to get started.

The instructor of a sixth grade introduced the work with a demonstration, showing how a fine iron wire shorted across the terminals of a dry cell will glow. (A single strand of thin copper wire from an old lamp cord will do.) About a foot of the wire was held taut by the ends, and then the middle portion of the wire was pressed tightly across the two terminals of the dry cell. The wire glowed brightly for a moment and then "burned out" like the filament of an old light bulb. "What happened?" the instructor inquired. "How is the idea useful?"

Various heating devices and electric lamps were mentioned as applications. After examining the burnt wire, and after repeating the process a few times, the

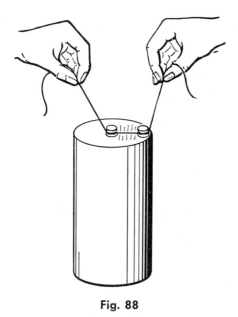

Fig. 88

Wires become heated by electricity.

class decided that the wire had melted and perhaps to some extent burned.

"But a lamp that would last for only a moment would be of little value. How could it be made more practical, last longer?"

In their social studies this class had been discussing the lives of Edison and other inventors. Therefore someone suggested that a better filament should be found, something that would not melt quickly, and Edison's search was recalled. Another person said Edison had taken the air out of bulbs to keep the metal from burning. The instructor questioned whether or not bulbs now are vacuums, and after some discussion it was decided that the best way to find out would be to break an old bulb to see if it would make a noise as the air rushed in — the bulb could be covered with cloth for safety while being broken. It also was decided that a hammer and a nail could be used to punch a small hole in a bulb. If a bulb is broken under water, no cloth will be necessary, and bubbles will form if the bulb contains a gas. Because scientists check their results many times, the children planned to open as many light bulbs as possible, and a number of pupils volunteered to bring old ones from home.

The class found that the bulbs they opened were not vacuums. One of the girls located a book which explained that bulbs today are filled with nitrogen, a gas that will not burn. The book also explained why worn-out bulbs are so often blackened at the end. The book said that vaporized metal from the filament has been deposited on the glass, and that with no gas at all in the bulb the filament would vaporize more rapidly.

As the work of the class continued, the study broadened to include questions of resistance and electric circuits, the way electricity is generated and brought to us along wires, and the importance of electricity in our way of life. In this case, work began with a problem presented by the instructor, a problem that proved challenging to the children themselves.

An experimental approach

Experimentation and reference work followed by student demonstrations, reports, and discussions can provide an ideal method of working with electricity. Opportunities for learning are abundant, and since electrical equipment is prominent in our way of life, there is much to stimulate interest. Experimentation appeals to children, and children of divergent abilities can work together profitably.

An organization which stressed experimentation and reporting was found successful in one class, for example, in which the sixth, seventh, and eighth grades were combined. The organization was flexible enough to permit one girl to make her own radio crystal set, from a commercial kit, while a group of other girls were working on a much more elementary level with magnets. Several boys who had brought a toy electric motor dismantled it to show the parts and explain how a motor works. In one of the more ingenious undertakings a sixth-grade boy devised a water heater by running a coil of wire from a dry cell through the water in a paper plate. The idea actually worked, but a number of problems were raised when he reported to the class, for someone pointed out that if current from the house circuit were sent along a wire running directly through water, the higher voltage would be dangerous. Accordingly, at the next opportunity the child set his plate of water in a second paper plate and arranged the wire to run between the two plates. This time the water heater was considered more practical, though not as efficient as before. Learning through experimentation can encourage initiative and permits each individual to work to his own capacity.

Often the experimentation is conducted with equipment left on a work table somewhere in the classroom. For three days, whenever they had an opportunity, the children in a third grade, for example, experimented with magnets, dry cells, wire, bells, and similar equipment. After three days of experimentation the class gathered together to talk about what they had done. When questions arose, the equipment was used to show what was meant. One child was selected to record what the class judged were the main points reported. Reporting provided the children with renewed incentive, new questions, and ideas they were eager to try. Experimentation was resumed, and further reporting followed.

For coherence, similar reports should be grouped together, whether prepared together or not. In a sixth grade, for example, several individuals had worked with voltaic cells, and all reported at the same meeting. The boys who had ripped open a dry cell showed the parts and explained the function of each one. The girls who had prepared a lemon cell, as directed in one of the books, collaborated in demonstrating and explaining it. The girl who had revived a dry cell by punching holes in the case and soaking it in water showed that it would ring a bell momentarily. With the teacher's supervision and assistance, one of the boys explained the storage battery. Caution was necessary because of the acid used. Previously two sheets of lead had been placed in a jar of dilute sulfuric acid, and a thin piece of wood had been inserted between the sheets to keep them from touching. Before the time for reporting, the lead sheets had been attached to several dry cells connected in series and left there for almost half an hour to charge the lead storage cell. When the report was made the dry cells were removed and the lead cell was attached to a doorbell. The bell rang briskly at first, indicating that the cell had been charged.

Although the demonstrations were presented and explained separately, the discussion of cells was carried on together, and the teacher helped the class to develop broad meanings from the reports.

Obtaining essential equipment

In some situations the amount of equipment available is a limiting factor, but often it is surprising what the children themselves can obtain when experimentation is proposed and the problem of equipment is considered with them. In one combined fifth and sixth grade, for example, the teacher brought magnets, iron filings, and a lodestone from the high school and placed them on the work table. The next day several other magnets were added by the children. Carmen brought his small brother's toy fish pond. At Edward's suggestion all the children contributed from their pockets a variety of small items that could be used to see what a magnet will attract. The children also obtained several dry cells, some insulated copper wire, and some nails so that electromagnets could be constructed. Someone brought a doorbell, someone else a button switch. The toys that came in included an electric motor, a locomotive and the transformer used with it, and a child's telegraph set. Several pliers and screw drivers were obtained, and one hammer came in. Other tools were borrowed from the janitor.

Electricity is an area which can be explored readily through direct experimentation — work that is both fascinating and meaningful for the children. Whether the resources are limited to worn-out toasters, light bulbs, and fuses that children can bring in for examination, or enriched with ample equipment supplied by the school, electricity is a delightful field for children to explore, provided they can work with it themselves and show others in the class what they have discovered.

STUDY GUIDE

1. Try some of the investigations suggested in this chapter, point out what a child could learn from similar investigations, and explain how the work might be conducted in a designated classroom.

2. Note several experiments with electricity that you would consider suitable for the children of a certain class. Describe several situations in which a teacher demonstration would be more desirable, and give your reasons.

3. List some of your own activities during the past twenty-four hours which have been dependent upon the use of electricity. What experiences with electricity are common for the children in the class you have designated? What experiences in the classroom will help the children to interpret their surroundings?

4. Give a teaching illustration to show how a study of magnetism and electricity can be used to answer the serious questions of children, and how the study can be closely related to work in other areas of the curriculum.

5. Give a teaching illustration to show how an investigation of electricity and electrical equipment can serve to develop scientific attitudes and ways of working.

6. Observe some children working with electricity, record your observations, and attempt to analyze the learning process.

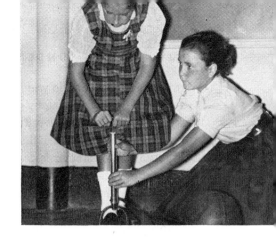

13

Understanding Air and the Weather

Atmospheric phenomena are important in the adult world. Children become interested in adult discussions and activities. News bulletins tell of rockets rising into the upper atmosphere. Automobiles and airplanes are streamlined to reduce air resistance. Food is sealed in airtight packages. We use vacuum cleaners in homes and air hoses at the service station. We use fans to move air in the summer. Air conditioners are becoming increasingly common. Anyone who makes a trip into the mountains is conscious of changes due to air pressure. Our ears may pop on an elevator ride. The atmosphere is also an important part of the child's environment. Children get balloons on occasion, and they sometimes make paper darts to sail through the air. Breathing is a problem in learning to swim, and after a strenuous game a child may be short of breath. On a cold winter day the condensation from a child's breath may attract his attention. There is much for any child to investigate.

Changes in the weather influence children as well as adults. The weather helps to determine how children must dress and whether or not they may play outdoors. Picnics, field trips, and sporting events sometimes have to be cancelled because of the weather. In the winter children may see snow on the

353

ground and frost on the windowpanes, and vision is often obscured by mist on the windshield of the family automobile. Clouds are prominent features of the sky. The weather is a favorite topic of conversation, and the radio carries forecasts for all to hear. When the wind blows in the winter we are apt to shiver, but a breeze in the summer is comfortable. Thunderstorms, tornadoes, hurricanes, snowstorms, and even rainstorms are exciting events. Farming is influenced by the weather, both at planting and at harvesting. Construction work is sometimes halted by the weather, and fishing boats are often in danger because of storms at sea. Airplanes may be grounded. The family wash may have to be dried indoors. In humid weather lumps sometimes form in table salt and crackers may lose their crispness. Houses must be repainted because of weathering. Roller skates left outdoors may be found rusted. As frost nips the last blossoms in our gardens we are urged by salesmen to equip our houses with storm windows, and children must begin to wear heavier clothing with the approach of colder weather.

The sidewalks were icy one morning as the children came to school. A first-grader said to the teacher, "Miss Wheeler, we had to be careful because it was so slippery." Someone else explained, "It's so cold the water freezes, and it turns to ice." Hopefully, another added, "When we go home, we can go ice skating." But someone else was less optimistic: "Maybe so, and maybe not." An argument developed, and the teacher suggested an experiment. Two pans of water were left outside the classroom window, one containing very little water and the other almost full. The day was cold, and the shallow water was soon frozen, but the other pan took much longer. A discussion helped to interpret the results and emphasize the hazards of skating on thin ice.

Investigations of air and the weather are interesting to children, easy to conduct, and meaningful in terms of everyday experience. Fortunately, a great variety of experiments can be found in books to aid children in their investigations, and for most of the experiments the equipment is simple and is easily obtained.

AWARENESS OF AIR AS A REAL SUBSTANCE

Children have confused impressions of the air about us. Commenting on the weather, one child said, "Clouds make the wind blow and make it rain." Another added, "Cold breezes make cold air." While watching the aquarium, one boy asked, "Why do the fish blow bubbles?" In another case a child opposed the placing of a cover on a balanced aquarium for fear the fish would be smothered. Children often lack an adequate conception of air.

Making the invisible apparent

Under ordinary circumstances we consider air invisible, yet in one sense the air can be seen. The blue of the sky is due to the air above us. The ethereal quality of air does make it somewhat difficult for children to understand.

Demonstration of the handkerchief that remains dry. A fifth grade studying weather included a number of experiments which helped to show that air is something real. None brought more excited comments than the following: A dry handkerchief was pressed firmly into the bottom of a drinking glass; the glass was inverted and then immersed in water. When the glass was lifted out, the handkerchief was still dry.

The demonstration of the handkerchief in a glass was shown to a first grade, and they too understood that the water did not enter to wet the handkerchief because of the air that was trapped in the glass, filling the space. At the P.T.A. meeting a few days later, some of the parents asked how it is possible for a handkerchief to remain dry under water, and the entire P.T.A. wanted to be shown. It seems that one of the children had performed the demonstration at home to impress his parents, and was so delighted by knowing more than they did that even though they begged for an explanation he would not tell. Simple demonstrations, if unfamiliar, can appeal to all ages, including adults.

The fifth grade used other demonstrations to make the point that air is real and occupies space; and when the idea was established, it was added to the list of learnings on the chart that the class entitled "The Truth about the Weather."

Experimenting with air in a tub of water. A number of additional experiments can be performed in water to reveal the presence of air. A large container — such as a wash tub, dish pan, or aquarium tank — is suitable for the experiments.

If a drinking glass or fruit jar is inverted and pressed down into the water, it can be seen that the water does not rise into the tumbler or jar — except to a slight extent, owing to compression of the air in the container. A cork or a bit of waxed paper floating on the water will help to make the surface of the water visible where the jar is inverted over it. When the jar is tipped a bit, bubbles of air will escape, and water will rise in the jar.

If two jars are immersed in the water, one jar filled with water and the other with air, the air from the one jar can be poured upward into the other. The jar of air must be held below the jar of water and then tipped so that the bubbles of air rise into the jar of water, and the air will displace the water in the upper jar. At the same time the lower jar will fill with water.

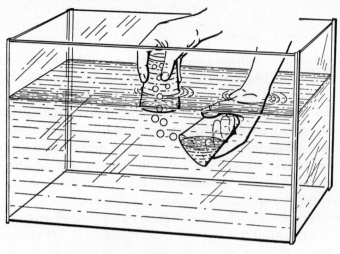

Fig. 89

In a tank or tub of water, air can be poured upward from one glass
to another.

By thrusting one end of a rubber tube into an inverted jar of water, such as
was described above, a child can blow air into the jar and cause the water level
to drop. The rubber tubing from an old bicycle pump, a shower-bath attach-
ment, or hot-water-bottle accessories will do. If the end of the tube is above
the water in the jar, the air in the jar can be sucked out, and this will cause the
water to rise again into the jar. When a funnel is inverted and pressed down
into water, air can be felt escaping through the stem of the funnel. If a finger is
placed over the opening the water will not rise in the funnel. With a glass
funnel the water level will be visible, but even an inverted tin can with a hole
punched in the bottom will serve for detecting the escaping air.

Using a jug to reveal the presence of air. A glass bottle or jug full of water
when inverted will show the bubbles of air rising into the jug as the water
escapes. If an empty jug is fitted with a two-hole stopper and the stem of a
funnel is inserted through one of the holes, another device will be provided to
reveal the presence of air. When the funnel is filled with water the water will
spill into the jug, but can be stopped merely by placing a finger tightly over the
second hole to prevent the escape of air. The device must be airtight to be
successful, and the stem of the funnel must be of small diameter; otherwise
bubbles of air may escape through the stem. The stem of a funnel may be
inserted more readily into the stopper if the stopper is moist and if a twisting

motion is used. Even glazed paper can be shaped into a satisfactory funnel, and a milk bottle with a tightly-fitting cap can be used as a jug and stopper. A second hole can be punched in the cap, and if need be, the cap may be sealed with petrolatum. Any bottle with a tightly-fitting cap through which two holes can be punched may do as well. In addition, a satisfactory stopper to fit any bottle can be shaped from modeling clay.

More evidence of air. During a discussion in the first grade one day, Gerard asked, "What is air?" Linda was ready with an answer: "It's something that is left when we die." Sandra said, "Air is wind blowing." David said, "It's something we can feel but can't see." Someone suggested blowing on their hands to feel the wind, and for a while they all did. The air was warm and moist. Several of the boys made gliders to show how the gliders would sail through the air. Some of the girls moved the door back and forth rapidly so that the air could be felt, and others used sheets of paper as fans to feel the air in their faces. At recess they had a race across the field to see if they could feel the air about them, and they noticed that the air was moving the leaves of the bushes. By now the children were beginning to realize that air is all about us.

Back inside the classroom, one of the boys discovered that if he covered his mouth and nose he was unable to breathe. All who tried this found it true. They decided that other animals must need air, because many have noses and mouths as we do. A few days later one of the boys came in with a sad story: one of his little chicks had smothered, because it was unable to break the shell of the egg and get air to breathe. Many of the children had never seen a baby chick hatch, so there were many questions, and from that point on the class was concerned with learning how chickens and other animals develop.

There are many ways to help children understand that air is real. A first-grade girl explained, "If I run fast, a piece of paper will stick to my 'tummy,' because air holds it there." And then she showed the others what she meant. Other ways included blowing up a balloon, bursting a paper bag to note the sound of the escaping air, constructing and using a pinwheel or other windmill, sailing a boat, and making a parachute by tying short lengths of string to the four corners of a handkerchief and attaching the remaining ends of the string to an eraser or other small weight. If a book is placed on a paper bag and air is blown into the bag, the air will lift the book. A sheet of paper falls slowly, but if it is crumpled the same paper will fall more rapidly. A feather or a bit of paper placed on the lid of a tin can will fall rapidly, for the lid displaces the air, but by itself a feather is supported by the air and falls slowly. If a glass containing dirt is filled with water, bubbles will show that even the soil contains much air. If a glass of water is placed in the direct sunshine or over a radiator to be warmed, some of the air dissolved in the water will become visible, escaping as bubbles.

By providing the facilities and giving an occasional suggestion here and there, a teacher who recognizes the possibilities can help children make their own discoveries and report them. The results will be meaningful and stimulating.

Air is necessary to keep a fire burning

Smothering a flame. When Richard told the second grade about a fire he had seen during the week end and asked why the men had been beating it with bags and blankets, the teacher suggested doing an experiment that would help to answer the question. The necessary glass jars were already on hand, and the class across the hall was having a birthday party; so after the party was over the candles from the cake were borrowed for the experiment. When glass jars were placed over lighted candles it was possible to see that fires will not burn without air. The candles in the larger jars, which contained more air, burned longer. When someone suggested that it might be the longer candle, rather than the larger jar, that was responsible for one flame's lasting longer, the smaller jars were placed over the longer candles to test that suggestion. How to extinguish a fire is worth learning. Even the children in a combined fifth and sixth grade, when they saw that fires can be extinguished by smothering, were surprised and said they would have run for water if their clothing had caught fire. The results could have been fatal.

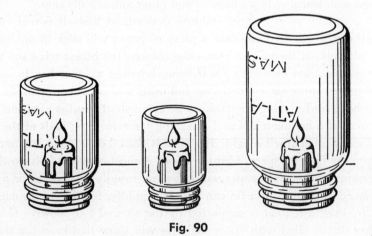

Fig. 90

Fires must have air to burn.

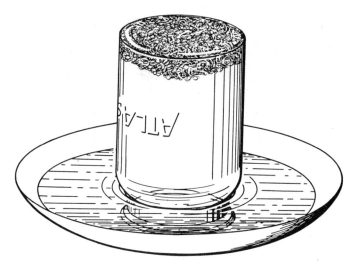

Fig. 91

As the moistened steel wool rusts, oxygen is removed from the air, and water will rise in the jar.

Oxygen, carbon dioxide, and nitrogen from the air. A combined fifth and sixth grade performed and reported a great variety of experiments with air. The work of one group included experiments showing that fire must have air, and Elizabeth showed that rusting, like burning, takes oxygen from the air. She moistened some steel wool and placed it in a glass jar; she then inverted the jar over water and waited for the steel to rust. Gail produced carbon dioxide by mixing baking soda and sour milk. Eva did much the same thing with vinegar and baking soda, and David told what he had read about plants using carbon dioxide from the air, and how the gas is given off by chimneys, how it comes from our breath, is used in soda water and in fire extinguishers. Hollis said that he had learned that the air which remains after oxygen is removed in rusting, as Elizabeth had shown, is mostly nitrogen. With a match he demonstrated that nitrogen will not burn; he then explained that he had seen clumps of bacteria on the roots of clover, which take nitrogen from the air and transform it into a compound that plants can use. Marjorie added that she had learned from a farmer friend that fertilizer has nitrogen for plants and that plants must have it for growth. Joseph said he had learned the same thing on the Farm and Home Hour radio program. George said that dynamite, such as had been used along the highway recently, is made of nitrogen and other things; Paul added that his father had used dynamite to blast out the stumps in a new field last spring. Nancy explained she had read that some of our nitrates come from the desert of Chile.

A fire extinguisher. By melting the base of a candle in the flame of a match, Martha was able to set the candle upright on the base of a glass jar. She poured into the jar about an inch of water in which baking soda had been dissolved, and then she was ready to demonstrate to the class. When her turn came, she lighted the candle and explained that oxygen is necessary to keep the fire burning. Then she poured vinegar into the soda solution, and as bubbles rose from the liquid the flame went out. At the teacher's suggestion she asked other children to relight the candle, but as their attempts failed the reason became clear. The candle would not burn in the carbon dioxide released by the soda and vinegar, and neither would a match.

Arthur and Marvin had made a fire extinguisher by partially filling a bottle with a solution of baking soda in water and then filling a test tube with vinegar and hanging the tube by a string inside the bottle. The bottle had been fitted with a tight stopper through which a hole had been drilled; a glass tube had

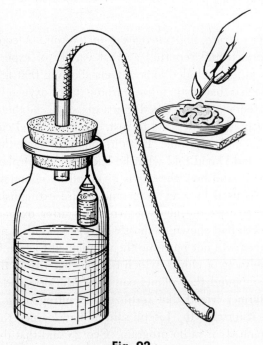

Fig. 92

An improvised fire extinguisher

been moistened and inserted into the hole. The boys tried their extinguisher once, and it worked well. When it was time for the demonstration, a fire was built in a dish pan and the extinguisher was inverted. As the vinegar spilled into the soda solution, carbon dioxide was formed, and bubbles of gas and water were forced out of the tube onto the fire — but unfortunately the stopper had not been inserted firmly enough, and the pressure forced it out of the bottle, spilling the contents, mostly into the dish pan. After the mess had been cleared away the demonstration was repeated, and this time it was a huge success.

For this fire extinguisher a heaping tablespoonful of baking soda dissolved in water should be sufficient. If the pressure is inadequate it may be that the stopper is not airtight. If the inside bottle of vinegar is small or the vinegar is weak, more vinegar can be added by suspending a second bottle of vinegar beside the first.

Experimenting with fire in the classroom is essential if children are to learn the necessary precautions. Without such closely supervised experiences many children are likely to make their own investigations surreptitiously.

There is water in the air

Evaporation and condensation are common in everyday experience and require some explanation. The vapor is invisible, yet washing dries, the bread in the kitchen becomes hard, and water somehow comes from the sky; dew appears on the grass, frost on the windowpanes. Children hear the relative humidity noted on radio or television, and they soon learn there is some relationship between clouds and the weather we have. Snow and ice are apparent even to the younger children, yet such a subject as adiabatic cooling is complex enough for older students. Truly, there is something of potential interest for everyone.

Evidence of evaporation. When Davey came to school he saw there was a puddle in the school yard. He anticipated playing in it later that morning. But when the kindergarten went outside, much to Davey's surprise the puddle was gone. He asked the teacher where it went, and she helped him to arrange an experiment. A small amount of water was placed in a saucer and left outside in the sunshine. In a little while it had disappeared. The teacher then explained evaporation to him and to the others, whose attention had been attracted by the experiment.

When a similar problem came up in a first grade, one child said the sun made the puddle dry up, another that the wind dried it up. One of the girls was eager to explain that some of the water evaporated into the air and the ground "drank it up" too. The word *evaporate* was new to the other children, and so there was a discussion of it. The teacher had one of the children wash the blackboard with a damp cloth, and everyone watched while the moisture disappeared. Later some of the girls while outside stood peering at their wet hands, trying to see the water evaporate from them. Soon they began to understand that water vapor is invisible. At the teacher's suggestion some of them moistened a piece of cloth and spread it on a bush to watch it dry. Back in the classroom, a group of the children filled three containers with water: a shallow pan, a bowl, and a shampoo bottle. The containers were left on the window sill for three days. By that time the shallow pan was dry, and the bowl had less water than did the shampoo bottle. The empty pan caused great excitement. One child asked, "Why didn't the water in the other things dry up too?"

Jane was able to answer that: "Because the pan has the biggest hole at the top for the air to get through."

Then someone wanted to know what would happen if the pan were covered so that no air would circulate. The teacher suggested they try that also, and the class accepted the idea with enthusiasm. The experiments were successful, and a number of parents reported that their children had repeated the experiments at home and had explained how water gets into the air to fall eventually as rain or snow. After such experiments with evaporation a seventh-grade girl said, "This must be what happened to the water in the pan I burned at home yesterday."

In another situation a third grade compared the drying times of two wet cloths, one crumpled into a ball and the other spread out wide. Likewise, a cloth in the sun was compared with one in the shade, one on the radiator with another on a table. Each experiment was repeated several times to be sure of the results. "That one looks like my mamma's sheets when they're on the line," said one of the girls; and the teacher agreed that it was about the same idea. This class continued with experiments which show that plants also give off water into the air.

How clouds and rain are formed. Before school one day, Billy noticed that drops of water had gathered on the glass cover of the terrarium in his combined second- and third-grade room. He thought the water looked like raindrops but wondered how they got there on the under side of the glass. Explanations were proposed by some of his classmates, and soon an argument developed regarding the cause of rain. Some of the children said that clouds bump together; others thought that clouds burst open to let water pour out. Finally the teacher suggested doing some experiments to help answer the question. Equal amounts of water were placed in several saucers, and a few of the saucers were covered with sheets of glass. All the saucers were placed on the radiator. In a few hours the saucers without covers were dry. The covered ones still held water, and some of the water had gathered on the under side of the covers. By tapping one of the covers the children made drops of water fall from the glass in a manner similar to rain falling from the sky. It was decided that rain forms in the air much as water from the saucer had gathered on the sheet of glass. It was decided also that the woodland terrarium was much like the woods outdoors, and that the water which gathered on the cover came from the plants, the moist soil, and the miniature pond.

In the eighth grade a teacher held a wide-mouthed gallon jar over the spout of a teakettle; the vapor from the teakettle condensed inside the cool jar, demonstrating how a cloud is formed. Through the glass the children could see the drops grow larger until eventually water began dripping from the jar, much as rain falls from a cloud. Had the water condensed close to the ground it would have been called fog, rather than a cloud. Or if the warm moist air had come in contact with the cold ground, the condensation would have occurred on the ground, just as here it condensed on the glass, and the drops of water would have been dew. Comparison was made with the condensation that occurs on the coils of a refrigerator. The coils are below the freezing point; hence the vapor freezes as it condenses, and frost is formed. In the air it would have been snow. When falling raindrops are frozen on the way down, the particles of ice are called sleet. In a thunderstorm the winds may be violent enough to toss the sleet upwards, and after more moisture has gathered on the particle of sleet, that moisture freezes as it falls again, and the larger particle is called hail. Large hailstones may consist of many layers of ice, one frozen upon another as the particle is tossed about by the wind. Essentially the different forms of precipitation depend upon the temperature — whether it is freezing or above — and on whether the condensation occurs in the air or on the ground.

CIRCULATION OF THE AIR

Wind is the air in motion. Children become aware of the wind at an early age, but may not understand it. The wind we feel may be part of a larger circulation that is due to unequal heating of the atmosphere. Near the equator the air becomes heated and rises; cold air from the north sinks and moves along the ground, setting up a circulation similar to that in a room or a con-

vection box. The warm air tends to move northward aloft. By using a globe or
large ball as a model of the earth it can be shown that air moving northward
from the broad equator is much like traffic along the highways pouring from
all directions into the heart of a large city: congestion results. The simple
pattern of circulating air is not possible; much of the warm air sinks to the
ground and moves northward along the surface. The changeable weather which
is common in most of the United States is due largely to the fact that at one
time we may be in the warm air that is moving north and later in the cold
air that is moving south. The front between the masses of cold and warm air is
likely to be stormy. The rotation of the earth gives the winds a whirling
motion, and hence the cold winds tend to come from the northeast and the
warm winds from the southwest.

Thus our prevailing winds are due to unequal heating and to the spinning
motion of the earth. Mountains influence the direction of the wind, and local
winds often are due to the fact that land fluctuates in temperature more than
do large bodies of water. In the summer the land becomes warmer than
the water, whereas in the winter the water is warmer. There is likely to be
a similar fluctuation in day and night temperatures; this produces on-shore and
off-shore winds, for the air becomes heated or cooled by the land or water
beneath it, and the difference in temperature results in a wind. The greater
the difference in temperature, the greater the wind.

A child's understanding of the winds must of necessity develop gradually
with increasing maturity and experience. Knowing the cause of winds involves
a variety of understandings, such as the concepts of air pressure and of expansion due to heating — meanings that the school can help to develop.

Expansion with heat

A simple thermometer. A thermometer can be improvised from simple
materials to show how a real thermometer works. In one case the children in a
fourth grade used a "coke" bottle, found a cork to fit it, drilled a hole in the
stopper, and inserted a plastic drinking straw. Glass tubing is good if available.
The bottle was filled to the top with water colored with red ink; then the
stopper was inserted, forcing the liquid part way up the tube. The hole in the
stopper had been drilled with a pocket knife and hence did not fit tightly,
so melted wax from a lighted candle was dripped onto the stopper to seal it.
An adequate stopper also can be shaped from modeling clay. The children
experimented with the improvised thermometer in various ways. It was placed
in the sunshine at the window for a while, then on a table at the far side of the

room, then above a warm radiator, and later in a pan of cool water. The height of the liquid in the tube was marked with a rubber band so that as the device was moved from one location to another the changed height of the column could be seen. The children found that just by holding the bottle in their hands for a while they could get the liquid to rise.

The bottle is equivalent to the bulb of a thermometer. As the liquid expands, the excess is forced up the narrow tube. When assembled, the bottle should be completely full of water, for any air remaining will expand more rapidly than water and will exaggerate the fluctuations of the apparent temperature. Evaporation from the open end of the tube, any change in the tightness of the stopper, variations in the diameter of the tube, and inadequacy of water as the fluid are among the features that limit the usefulness and accuracy of the apparatus — but as a learning device it serves the purpose well, and has been used successfully by children of all ages throughout the elementary schools.

The fourth grade prepared a scale for their thermometer by comparing it with the readings of a real thermometer. A narrow strip of white cardboard was glued to the tube and the device was placed first in a cold spot, then in a warm one; in each case the temperature indicated on the commercial thermometer was marked on the improvised one. With these two points located, the remainder of the scale could be interpolated.

The same bottle, with stopper and tube but without the water, will serve as an air thermometer. The stopper should be sealed as before, the bottle inverted, and the end of the tube placed in a glass of colored water. To prepare it for use, warm the bottle a bit by placing it in the sunlight, or by other means. If the empty bottle is heated with an alcohol burner, it should be heated gently and should be rotated to avoid breaking the glass. The air inside the bottle will expand, and the excess will bubble out. Then, if the air is allowed to cool, it will contract; and with the end of the tube still under water, the water will rise in the tube. Thereafter, as the air expands or contracts, the height of the liquid will vary accordingly, indicating the temperature. Some adjustment may be necessary to ensure that the variations take place within the length of the tube and that the liquid does not rise all the way into the flask or fall entirely out of the tube. In the air thermometer the liquid rises as the temperature decreases, whereas in an ordinary thermometer the fluid falls with the temperature. The contrast can provide a challenging problem for children, and lead them to consider what really happens in a thermometer as the temperature changes.

The expansion of air. That heat causes air to expand can be observed in other ways. For example, two children in a combined fourth and fifth grade brought Pyrex nursing bottles, and another brought balloons, which were put on the bottles. The bottles were put on the radiator, which was quite hot, and in about fifteen minutes enough air had entered the balloons to make each stand upright above the neck of the bottle. The air in the bottles had expanded into the balloons. For contrast, the bottles were then set by the cold windows, and the balloons soon fell limp.

With balloons the expansion of the air is limited by the resistance of the rubber to stretching. A bottle fitted with a stopper and glass tube, such as was used for an air thermometer, provides an even more effective way to observe the expansion. In this case the bottle, if possible, should be a Pyrex flask, nursing bottle, or test tube, as Pyrex is less apt to break when heated. A rubber tube fitted to the end of the glass tube is helpful. The free end of the tube should be placed in a glass of water, and can be held there with a clothespin or by other means. When the heat of an alcohol burner is applied to the "empty" flask, the air inside expands and bubbles out through the water. The amount of bubbling shows the amount of expansion. The flask may be set on the table then and allowed to cool, with the free end of the tube still under water. As the air in the flask cools and contracts, water flows back into the flask — as in a Silex percolator. Once the water enters, it helps to cool the flask and the process continues rapidly. When the temperature is back to normal, the amount of water in the flask indicates the amount of air removed.

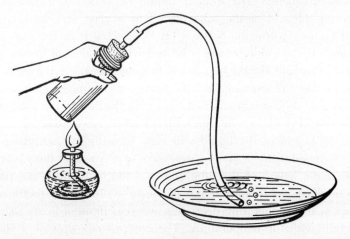

Fig. 93

The air in the pyrex bottle expands when heated and bubbles out through the water.

Though not as extreme, some expansion can be seen merely by inverting a bottle which has a hole punched in its metal cap and placing the neck of the bottle under water. The heat of a child's hands will be enough to produce a few bubbles. A thin glass bottle will heat more rapidly than a thick one, and hence is preferable.

The expansion of liquids and solids. If a narrow-necked bottle is nearly filled with cold water and set in the direct sunlight, as the water becomes warm and expands it will rise somewhat in the neck of the bottle, and if already to the tip, will spill. The amount of expansion shown will depend upon the proportions of the bottle and the amount of change in temperature. A white paper behind the bottle to serve as a reflector will help to heat the water.

Solids also expand or contract when heated or cooled. The metal cap of a glass jar can be tightened until the children find it difficult to loosen; then if the cap is held for a minute in hot water, the expansion should make the cap easy to remove. For another commonplace that can be used to illustrate expansion, place some ice or snow on one end of a glass sheet and pour hot water on the other end. The contraction at one end and expansion at the other puts the glass under a strain that causes it to crack.

Why the wind blows. Unequal heating by the sun is involved in explanations of why the wind blows. While the sun is shining, the temperature of the land rises more rapidly than that of the water nearby, and the result is an on-shore breeze. In either winter or summer, temperatures along the coast are usually milder than those inland. Both conditions can be explained. To gain one of the basic understandings involved, the children may place a stone, a jar of water, and perhaps an iron bar or other metal object somewhere in the room for an hour or more until all have come to the same temperature. The objects used should be approximately equal in weight. When the temperatures are about equal the objects should be placed in direct sunlight and the changes in temperature noted. Merely touching the objects before and after a short period of heating should indicate the temperature well enough for the purpose. Learning that water changes its temperature slowly should help the children to understand why temperature changes inland are more extreme than those along the coast. In cold weather the objects may be placed outside, in a similar way, to see how rapidly the temperature of each will drop.

A convection box provides an excellent means of making the circulation of air graphic.[1] As the air above the candle is heated, it expands and therefore is less dense — lighter. The cool air above the other chimney is more dense and therefore sinks, forcing the warm air to rise. In a similar way, when a rock

[1] See pp. 172–73.

is dropped into a jar of water, the water is forced to rise. If a glass jar is used, the rising water level can readily be seen and is quite revealing to children. Through such means children can begin to understand why air circulates and why the wind blows.

The pressure of the air

The concept of air pressure is abstract and is rather difficult to teach with real meaning. Explanations of the siphon, the egg-and-bottle demonstration, and the collapsing tin can, for example, are complex and often are used with children who lack the background and maturity to comprehend what is involved. Nevertheless, certain practical manifestations of air pressure can be learned at a comparatively early age, and out of these the mature concept can be developed.

Becoming aware of air pressure. A logical first step is to learn that there is such a thing as air pressure. Toby, in the third grade, said she understood the word pressure, because at home her mother uses a pressure cooker. When automobile tires are inflated at the filling station, a gauge is used to measure the pressure. Bicycle tires and playground balls also are filled with compressed air. Anyone from the class who has traveled into the mountains high enough to note a difference in pressure may report his impressions. News reports about airplanes equipped with pressurized cabins for cruising in the stratosphere or about pilots equipped with oxygen masks may be noted. In their daily weather reports newspapers and radios note the air pressure, and even small children sometimes hear the radio reports.

While observing a hamster in the third-grade room, Mary Ann was puzzled by the water fountain with which the cage was equipped. She asked why the water didn't all run out of the inverted jar. The teacher helped her to work out her own answer. They found a jar with a tight cap, punched a hole in the metal cap, filled the jar with water, and replaced the cap. The girl inverted it over the sink. Only a single drop of water came out. For contrast, a hole was punched in the bottom of a tin can. When the can was filled with water, the water ran out freely. They found, however, that as with the jar, when the upper end of the tin can was covered tightly, the flow of water was halted. A damp sheet of cardboard proved to be the best cover they could find. After experimenting for themselves, the girl and her teacher showed the entire class what happens and explained why. In a similar situation a fifth-grade teacher used a can of tomato juice that she was planning to have for lunch. With two holes the juice ran out easily. One of the holes should be located at the top where the air can enter. In fact, the children can try punching both holes at the bottom to see what happens and thus learn the significant point is concerned with air, not specifically the number of holes in the can. If the hole is large enough, a bottle can be emptied through but one hole. In such a case the air and the water move past each other in the opening.

In a fountain pen the ink is held inside the pen by the pressure of air on the outside. In other words, the pressure of the air is greater than the weight of the ink. If there were a hole at the top of the pen so that air could press on all sides equally, the weight of the ink would cause it to spill. The point can be illustrated with a length of glass tubing or a drinking straw. If one end of the tube or straw is dipped into water and the top end is covered tightly with a thumb or finger, the tube can be lifted without spilling the water inside. But when the finger is removed, the water will fall. Dip tubes are used in this way to remove waste particles from the bottoms of aquaria. A syringe or a medicine dropper will serve to illustrate the same principle. Drinking milk with a straw is similar. Any suction is merely a difference in air pressure. A plumber's force cup or a suction cup when moistened and pressed against a wall has a portion of the air removed from the cup while the outside pressure remains normal. Inverting a glass filled with water and covered with paper is another illustration. If one door of a cupboard is standing ajar and a second door is opened abruptly, the first will be pulled shut. Or shutting one may cause the other to open. A coat closet — or even the classroom — if there are two doors, not latched, and no open windows, may be used in this way to make air pressure apparent.

Understanding the barometer. Using an aneroid barometer is an excellent way for children to become aware of air pressure and to learn its relationship to weather changes. Records may be kept of the pressure and of weather conditions. When comparisons are made a relationship should become apparent. If mercury and a long glass tube are available, constructing a mercurial barometer will provide a basis for understanding how the barometer itself works. The older children can well prepare their own mercurial barometer; for the younger ones it may be preferable to begin with a barometer someone else has prepared, concentrating on the use of a barometer and letting other questions develop from that use.

A convenient way to assemble the barometer is to tip the long tube at a slight angle from the horizontal — otherwise the heavy mercury in falling may break the glass — and insert the mercury with a medicine dropper, tapping the tube a bit when bubbles of air are trapped by the mercury. When the tube is completely full it can be inverted slowly and placed with the open end below the surface of mercury in a small glass or cup. One finger should be placed tightly over the open end while the tube is inverted. The tube can be held upright by fastening it to the wall, a chair, an iron stand, or whatever else may be convenient. A yardstick may be fastened beside it or tied to the tube, the lower end of the yardstick just touching the surface of the mercury.

Any pockets of air left in the tube will lessen the accuracy of the barometer. Because of impurities in the mercury and the lack of means of correcting for altitude or temperature, discrepancies will be noted when the readings are compared to those reported in the news, but as a learning device the home-made barometer is excellent. Barometer tubes can be purchased, or a glass tube at least 32 inches long can be sealed at one end by melting the glass in the heat of a flame, such as that from a Bunsen burner. Even an alcohol burner or other source of heat may do, but the amount of heat needed depends upon the thickness of glass. The tube should be rotated while being heated, and the heating should continue until no air can be blown through the tube.

To understand how a barometer works, it is helpful to invert a tall jar or bottle under water and then lift the bottle until only the neck is below the surface. Previous experiences may help the children to explain that the air pressure outside holds the water in the bottle. The tallest bottle available can be used. Although water is heavy, its weight is not as great as the pressure of the air. If the children are allowed to lift the mercury, to see how very heavy it is, before it is used in the barometer, they will see that air pressure must be great to hold mercury in a tube. As the air pressure increases, more of the mercury will be forced up into the tube — or if the pressure is less the level of the mercury will fall. Thus changes in pressure are revealed by the height of the mercury. Cold-air masses are areas of high pressure and clear weather. As bad weather approaches, the barometer falls. The pressure is low in a storm, but as the pressure increases, the trend is toward fair weather.

The aneroid barometer operates somewhat like spring scales to weigh the air. The spring is inside a vacuum box, and the air on the outside presses against the sides of the box. If an old barometer is available, it can be opened and the mechanism examined. Aneroid barometers are more convenient to use than those with a long tube of mercury, and even though individual instruments vary, they are likely to be more accurate than one which can be constructed in a classroom. A good mercurial barometer, however, is more accurate than the aneroid type; where exact readings are needed, mercurial barometers are used.

The milk-bottle barometer which is sometimes recommended is of doubtful value. Some fluctuation in temperature is unavoidable, and the consequent expansion and contraction of the air inside the bottle is apt to be a larger factor than the changes in pressure.

An altimeter, used in aviation, is actually an aneroid barometer, the dial of which is marked to indicate altitude rather than pressure. Like any barometer, the altimeter responds to changes in pressure, and the pressure decreases with increasing altitude. Corrections must be made for weather conditions, just as in the weather instrument corrections must be made for altitude. Air pressure is merely the weight of the air. At higher altitudes there is less air pressing down upon the instrument, or upon people. When two boys are scuffling on the ground, other boys sometimes jump on top, one upon another, making a deep pile of boys. By analogy, the idea involved may help to explain what pressure is. The boy at the bottom feels the most pressure, which is the weight of boys above him. The pressure is less nearer the top of the pile — and so it is with our atmosphere.

Ventilation and human comfort

A thermometer is an instrument that is likely to be familiar, and even before children understand the number concepts involved they can begin to use a

Fig. 94

The principle of a barom-
eter can be demonstrated
with simple equipment.

Fig. 95

Air pressure holds the water up in the bottle.

thermometer themselves and become familiar with differences in temperature. In fact, the thermometer can be used as one means of learning to read and interpret numbers. A third-grade boy had learned to use a thermometer, and one day when the room became uncomfortably hot, he noticed that the thermometer on his desk read 78° but the one on the wall registered 80°. The discovery led to further investigation, and as a result he learned that warm air rises. "No wonder!" he concluded. "It would be hotter up there than down on my desk." A sixth-grade boy, to show that warm air rises, got a tall stepladder from the janitor and placed a thermometer as near the ceiling as he could. After several minutes he reported that the thermometer registered 82°. Then he set the thermometer on the floor and there got a reading of 74°, a difference of 8°. He later explained to the class that his results show warm air rises and the cooler, heavier air sinks to the floor. He showed the class the book that had given him the idea, and he explained how air circulates in a room. The class found also that the books recommend lower temperatures, and as a result the situation was corrected.

Movement of air in the classroom. With a smudge pot to produce a small amount of smoke it is possible to trace the warm air as it rises above the radiators and drifts across the room. A tin can with a few slightly damp paper towels — from a waste basket, perhaps — will provide a suitable smudge. The tin can should be placed on an asbestos pad, a plate, a brick, or some other suitable surface, for otherwise the heat of the can may damage a desk top. Merely covering the can tightly with a saucer, or perhaps another tin can, will cut off the air supply if the flame burns too freely or the smoke becomes excessive.

If the room is ventilated at the windows, streamers taped just above to hang down over the opening will show the direction and strength of the air currents. A bit of loose cotton suspended by a thread will serve the purpose. One combined fifth and sixth grade, while studying the weather, built a ventilation box, but at first it did not work properly. The children were disappointed, but then discovered that the box was not airtight. After taping up the edges the children experimented with various ways of ventilating a room and were so excited about the results that they begged to show their work to the other classes in the school. They did, explaining in detail how and why air circulates and how a room should be ventilated. Commonly rooms are ventilated by raising the bottom sash. With a ventilation box it is easy to see that warm, stale air is trapped above the openings. The effect is convincing. On the other hand, it can be shown that a window opened slightly at the top provides a complete, gradual change of air. A larger opening or a window opened at both top and bottom provides a more rapid circulation. A cross draft is stronger yet and is suitable for warm weather. A ventilation box will help children see how air circulates in a room, and help them to learn how a room should be ventilated.

Keeping warm in winter and cool in summer. To show the advantage of storm windows or other insulation that provides a "dead-air space," two jars may be filled with hot water, the water being equally hot in both jars. The two jars may be set together on some convenient desk or table, but one should be covered by inverting another larger glass jar over it. In about fifteen minutes the jars may be checked and the temperatures compared. The experiment may be repeated a number of times. Longer intervals of time can be used for some of the tests, and records should be kept so that accurate comparisons can be made. Experiments may be conducted with ice water instead of hot water. In a similar way the warmth of different kinds and amounts of clothing can be evaluated by wrapping the jars in different materials. One rewarding test is to compare a heavy wrapping with a number of light ones.

The reason that white clothing is more comfortable than black during the summer will become apparent if two cans are filled with equal amounts of equally cool water, one can wrapped in black paper and the other in white, and both placed in the direct sunlight. In a few minutes the temperatures may be determined again and comparisons made. The results may be checked by repeating the experiment, and similar tests may be made with other colors. After experimenting, the children should realize why some colors seem warmer than others in the winter, or in the summer.

The cooling effect of damp clothing is often taken for granted on the assumption that the water itself is cold. By experimenting with the cooling effects of various liquids the children may be induced to re-examine the situation. Among the suitable liquids commonly available are rubbing alcohol, various cleaning solvents, household ammonia, nail-polish remover, glycerin, and mineral oil. All should be left for an hour or more until they have reached room temperature. If a thermometer is available the temperatures can be checked to see that all are alike. Then a little of one liquid may be dropped or rubbed onto the back of someone's hand and water likewise applied to the other hand for comparison. A number of children should check the cooling effect, and a record may be kept on the blackboard to show which has the greater cooling effect in each case. It will be noted that some evaporate faster and feel cooler than others, though all are at room temperature. The explanation is that the heat required for evaporation is supplied by the body, hence the cooling effect. A child's feet may be warmer while he is actually wading in the water than later when his shoes begin to dry. Perspiration helps to keep us cool, instead of making us warmer, as some may suppose.

Parenthetically it may be noted that some things feel hotter or colder than others when touched, because some conduct heat better than others. A leather or metal chair, for example, feels cooler than a chair upholstered with cloth. To see how some materials compare in the way they conduct heat, place in a cup a sterling silver spoon, a plastic spoon, a spoon of chrome or silver plate, and one of paper or wood, and then pour very hot water into the cup. Note how long it is until the upper end of each becomes warm.

Even though both may be at the same low temperature, an iron bar will feel colder than a stick of wood. The iron will conduct heat rapidly from a person's hand and will give an impression of coldness. Because some objects conduct heat more readily than others, when touched they give an impression of being hotter or colder than they really are.

OBSERVATIONS OF THE WEATHER

A study of weather may be considered the culmination of previous undertakings that began with questions about the atmosphere. Children who have studied air pressure and the circulation of air, for example, can use their knowledge to interpret a weather map. Learning also may begin with some of the more obvious aspects of weather, as observed, and progress may then be made toward interpretations of wind, air pressure, and even maps and fronts. Whenever it seems desirable, weather experiences may be tied in with studies of seasonal changes, aviation, living things, health, or geography. A study of weather is complex enough for even the most advanced and capable pupils, and simple enough for even the youngest children in the schools.

Awareness of the weather

As various aspects of the weather become apparent to children, curiosity is aroused, and investigation begins. One day late in the autumn Walter noticed what he thought was glass on the nursery-school grounds, so he called the teacher's attention to it. He then got the brush and dustpan, swept up the pieces, and took them into the building. The fragments were left in a pan during the rest period. Afterwards the child was surprised to find nothing but muddy water in the jar.

While snow was on the grounds, the same children filled jars with the snow; and when the jars were brought inside for continued play, the snow melted. Deciding that the heat of the room was responsible, the children placed the jars of water outside, expecting the water to change back into snow. They were surprised when they found ice in the jars rather than snow. These children were learning some of the basic facts about weather.

Elementary-school children of all ages can observe the weather, make reports, and help to keep records. In so doing, they can develop an awareness of weather and changes in the weather. Becoming aware of the weather is a first step toward understanding it. There are numerous ways the teacher can help to stimulate observations. The observations in turn should raise worthwhile questions in the minds of the children. Seeking answers to real questions will lead to greater understanding of the weather.

Weather calendars and the bulletin board. Keeping a weather calendar is a common way to stimulate observations and to provide for recording and reporting those observations. To prepare the calendar, divide a large sheet of tag board into squares, five squares one way by seven the other; the days of the month may be numbered in the squares, and considerable space will be left for recording the weather. The records may be kept by individuals, but a group undertaking is likely to be stimulating, and the discussions of what is to be recorded can be profitable. A committee may do the observing for a given number of days. Merely recording that the day is cloudy and cold with a strong wind may be sufficient for small children, but as insight increases, the observations should become more detailed. The conditions recorded often are pictured in some way — for example, a bright yellow sun for a sunny day. If symbols are used, the children should develop their own.

A bulletin board maintained largely by the children themselves may include a calendar, or observations recorded in some other form. The readings may be listed each day as made — perhaps recorded on a chart, and older children may use the figures to prepare graphs. In one case the observations were merely tallied, showing the number of rainy days, windy days, and sunny days, for tallying was the mathematical process being taught at that time. A common practice with the younger children is to picture the weather conditions, and the bulletin board provides a suitable place to display these sketches. The bulletin board is versatile, for it may show forecasts, reports, and photographs of flood and wind damage, weather instruments, and cloud forms, in addition to the work of the children themselves. When either the teacher or one of the children brings in a clipping, it can be discussed and then posted. A bulletin board that is constantly being changed, and is used by the children to report what they have discovered, can help to develop an awareness of changing weather conditions. Problems regarding what makes rain, or why the wind blows harder one day than another, may be solved as they arise.

Increasing experience and insight. As observations continue, it will become apparent that all clouds do not look alike but vary with the kind of weather. Merely learning the names of various cloud forms has little value; but on the other hand, some of the names may be picked up as the children become familiar with the clouds and learn that certain kinds are seen only on clear days and others only before a storm. By watching the clouds it may be possible to note the direction of the winds aloft, and comparison may be made with the wind direction along the ground to determine how the air is circulating.

By following the news reports of relative humidity, the children may learn how comfort varies with humidity, and they may note other evidence of humid or dry air, such as salt clogging in the shaker on some days and crackers and even paper becoming limp. At other times, when the papers are crisp, static experiments are successful, and animals seem more alert and active.

In a storm the wind is whirling rapidly. By stirring the water in a bucket or large glass jar, a child can see how a vortex develops with increasing speed in water as in our atmosphere. The vortex in the water is like the "spout" or "funnel" of a hurricane or tornado. Whirlwinds and ordinary storms are less intense, but otherwise are similar. Lightning is like the spark from static electricity, and the basic idea can be demonstrated by running a pocket comb through hair to get a spark. The friction of the comb running through the hair builds up the charge, but in a storm the friction is due to currents of air moving past each other. When the charge of electricity is released, it heats the air, producing the flash. Just as a spark causes a snapping sound, the lightning makes thunder. Another way to explain thunder is by comparing it to the noise heard when a tire blows out or when a paper bag full of air is burst. In each case the noise is due to a sudden movement of the air.

In connection with the weather, children sometimes ask why antifreeze is added to the radiator of the family automobile. A graphic answer can be provided by placing outdoors in freezing weather several tin cans of equal size, the cans filled with equal amounts of various fluids to be tested, such as water, salt water, alcohol, antifreeze, and a cleaning solvent. A record of the temperature and condition of each liquid should be made at regular intervals. A discussion of the results will help the class to see how some liquids freeze at temperatures at which others will not.

A classroom weather station

Maintaining a weather station differs only in degree from keeping a weather calendar or bulletin board. The purpose is to stimulate observations and help make the interpretations that lead to increased understanding. Observations can be aided by using instruments. A small child may note that the weather is cold; an older child can record the number of degrees.

Barometer, thermometer, and rain gauge. A variety of instruments can be assembled at the school to aid in making the observations. Inexpensive aneroid barometers are on the market, but if the school has none perhaps a child can bring one from home. If the school has mercury and a long glass tube, a mercurial barometer can be assembled and used. In any case, the pressure as reported in the news can be recorded on the bulletin board, in the school newspaper, or in a record book.

Improvised thermometers are cumbersome, and commercial thermometers are comparatively easy to obtain. If diligent, the children may record the temperature at regular intervals throughout the day and thus obtain an approximation of the day's maximum. The weather bureau uses a special thermometer, like a fever thermometer in principle, to obtain the maximum. Owing to a constriction in the tube, the mercury rises but will not fall until the observer reads the temperature and then shakes the tube.

An ordinary tin can and a ruler will serve as a rain gauge. A large can is preferable, and if desired, it may be fitted with a funnel of the same diameter to reduce evaporation from the can. A sheet of metal from a large tin can may be used to prepare the funnel. The metal may be twisted into the shape of a cone and the uneven top cut to fit the can. It may be helpful to make a pattern of paper and trim the metal accordingly. Another way to prepare a funnel that will fit is to obtain a very thin aluminum pie pan and shape it like a lid to fit the top of the rain gauge. The pie-pan funnel should sag toward the center, and a hole can be punched in the middle where the rain water will drip into the can. To make the rain gauge more realistic, and also more accurate, a smaller tin can may be set inside the first, directly beneath the funnel, so that

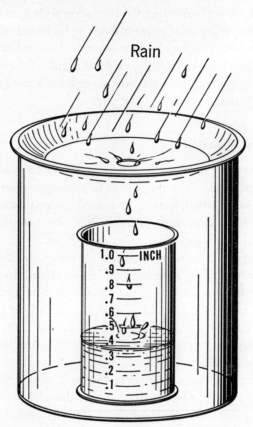

Fig. 96

Cross section of a rain gauge made from a gallon can, a baking-powder
can, and a thin aluminum pie pan to serve as a funnel.

all the water will run into the second can. In the smaller can the water will be
deeper, in effect magnified, and so can be measured more accurately. But
either a special measuring stick will have to be prepared, or the scale can be
marked on the small can. Water may be poured into the larger can until
exactly an inch deep and then emptied into the smaller can, with care taken not
to spill any. If the special measuring stick is then dipped into the water, the
height can be marked on the stick, and the mark will represent one inch of
rainfall. With that point determined, it may be divided into ten parts, each
equal to one-tenth inch of rain.

The cans should be painted to prevent rusting and then fixed in a convenient
place outdoors. In case of snow, the snow should be melted and measured as

water. It is advisable to remove the funnel and inside can whenever the snow-fall is heavy, and to use only the outer can. One-tenth inch of water from the snow is considered an inch of snow.

Determining the humidity. The dew point can be determined with a shiny tin can, a thermometer, and a bit of ice. An ordinary tin can with the label removed will do, and a thermometer that may be dipped into water will be needed. After filling the can with water at about room temperature, drop a cube of ice into the water and stir the water gently with the thermometer. As the ice melts, the water will be cooled. When moisture first begins to condense from the air onto the can, the temperature should be read. That temperature is the dew point, the temperature at which condensation will occur. The temper-ature of the air should be recorded also, and if the children think the tempera-ture will soon drop as low as the dew point, they may forecast rain, dew, or some other form of precipitation. The dew point should be determined out-doors, for the indoor air may differ somewhat. The dew point indicates the relative humidity, for both are concerned with the moisture in the air.

The relative humidity ordinarily is determined with a psychrometer. If two thermometers can be obtained, a psychrometer may be prepared with little difficulty. A porous cotton cloth to serve as a wick should be attached to the bulb of one thermometer. If the lower end of the wick is placed in a glass of water, water will soak up the wick; and as the water evaporates, the bulb of the thermometer will be cooled, much as wet clothing will cause a person to feel cold. Fanning the instrument before making a reading will increase its accu-racy, for otherwise the air about the wick may become saturated and retard evaporation. On the basis of the two thermometer readings, the relative humid-ity can be obtained from a table. The relative humidity is expressed as a per-centage, and it represents the amount of water vapor actually in the air as com-pared with the amount that would be in the air if the air were saturated. As the percentage approaches 100, rain or other precipitation becomes imminent. The children may note that the relative humidity is reported sometimes as less than a hundred, even though rain is falling. The reason may be that the air close to the ground is drier than the air above, where the condensation actually is oc-curring. Such a situation is rather common where warm moist air rises above a mass of cold dry air and is cooled as it rises.

For weather forecasting, the relative humidity should be determined out-doors. In the winter especially, the relative humidity inside is apt to be much lower, but it may be interesting to make a comparison. Such a comparison may help children to understand that unless water is added with a humidifier the air inside a house may become dry enough to damage furniture and woodwork,

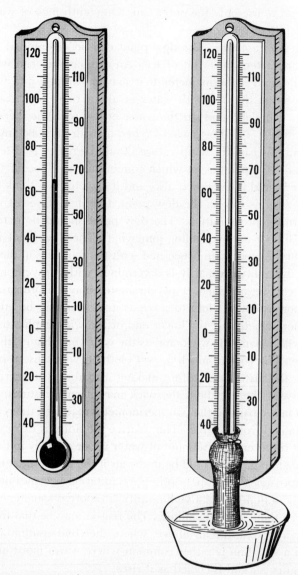

Fig. 97

A way to determine the relative humidity.   Evaporation cools the wet bulb.

and by drying the mucous membranes may encourage the spread of respiratory infections. Some child may recall that when he was sick the physician asked for water to be boiled on the stove to increase the amount of moisture in the air.

A psychrometer determines the relative humidity indirectly. The drier the air, the more rapid the evaporation, and the greater the cooling of the wet bulb. If the dry bulb registers 50° and the wet one reads 44°, the difference is 6°. On the table the 50° and the 6° may be used to locate the relative humidity, 61%. With readings of 60° and 55° the relative humidity would be 73%. The children may find it interesting to compare their figures with the reports that will appear later in the newspapers, yet in the school accuracy is secondary to the process of learning what is meant by relative humidity and how it affects people.

Table 1. RELATIVE HUMIDITY

Dry-Bulb
Temperature   Difference Between Wet and Dry-Bulb Temperatures, °F.

	1°	2°	4°	6°	8°	10°	12°	14°	16°	18°	20°
10°F.	78	56	13								
15°	82	64	29								
20°	85	70	40	12							
25°	87	74	49	25	1						
30°	89	78	56	36	16						
35°	91	81	63	45	27	10					
40°	92	83	68	52	37	22	7				
45°	93	86	71	57	44	31	18	6			
50°	93	87	74	61	49	38	27	16	5		
55°	94	88	76	65	54	43	33	23	14	5	
60°	94	89	78	68	58	48	39	30	21	13	5
65°	95	90	80	70	61	52	44	35	27	20	12
70°	95	90	81	72	64	55	48	40	33	25	19
75°	96	91	82	74	66	58	51	44	37	30	24
80°	96	91	83	75	68	61	54	47	41	35	29
85°	96	92	84	76	70	63	56	50	44	38	32
90°	96	92	85	78	71	65	58	52	47	41	36

Observations of the wind. Directions may be found for constructing an anemometer; or if the wind is not too strong, even a pinwheel can be used to estimate the speed of the wind. Marking one blade of a pinwheel in some way to distinguish it will help in counting the revolutions; and by counting the revolutions while riding in an automobile at a known speed, a person can calibrate the device. The use of such a device will help children to understand how the weather bureau determines wind speeds with an anemometer. But a less complex way to determine the approximate strength of the wind is merely to note the effect out of doors:

Table 2. WIND SPEEDS

Wind	Miles per Hour	Description
Calm	less than 1	Smoke rises almost vertically, and little evidence of any wind can be seen.
Light	1–7	Smoke drifts; leaves rustle gently, and the wind can be felt slightly.
Gentle	8–12	Leaves and twigs in motion; light flags extended.
Moderate to Fresh	13–24	Dust and loose paper raised by the wind; small branches in motion; small trees with leaves sway; crested wavelets form on ponds.
Strong	25–38	Large branches move; telephone and telegraph wires whistle; umbrellas difficult to use; whole trees sway; walking against wind is difficult.
Gale	39–75	Trees and property damaged; transportation impeded.
Hurricane or Tornado	above 75	

Keeping records and making forecasts. The observations that children report may include the direction and strength of the wind, the temperature, pressure, clouds, rainfall, dew point, and relative humidity. With the observations in, a forecast may be prepared. Newspaper weather maps that show the previous day's weather should help to develop an understanding of weather changes, if used regularly, and learning to read the maps has value in itself. The insight that goes into preparing the forecasts will vary according to the age and background of the chidlren. Increasing cloudiness toward the southwest, the direction of the wind and movement of the clouds, increasing humidity, a falling barometer, and rising temperatures all are apt to be indicative of an approaching storm, especially when combined in a familiar pattern. Shifting winds, a rising barometer, and drier air commonly mark a change to cool, clear weather. If weather maps or reports of weather conditions to the southwest or west can be obtained, it is usually safe to forecast similar weather locally, because of the easterly movement of storms. Forecasts are complex, but the real purpose of the work with children is more to learn the factors involved than to make accurate predictions. The experience should help children to arrive at their own meaningful generalizations and interpretations.

An actual case

The teacher of a combined fourth and fifth grade reported that during a language lesson the sky suddenly became dark and rain began to fall. Soon tiny white particles of ice began bounding off a low roof outside the schoolroom window. The attention of the children, and of the teacher as well, drifted from the language lesson to the storm. The eyes of the children became bright with excitement. They left their seats and moved to the window. As the sky darkened further, the sleet came down harder, in larger particles. Excitement ran high. When the storm was over, a barrage of questions followed:

What causes rain, snow, sleet, hail? Clouds, fog, dew, mist? What is a barometer? How does a thermometer work? How can they tell how fast the wind blows? Why doesn't the sun shine every day? What dries the sidewalks after a rain? Why does night come so much earlier in the winter than in the summer? What is air? Wind? Air pressure? How do they forecast weather?

The questions were organized to eliminate duplications; then all the books that discussed the topic of weather were gathered and placed on a convenient table. The children eagerly consulted the books for information. In a matter of minutes all were finding explanations of air, air pressure, wind, rain, snow, and the like. In one book a boy found directions for making a toy anemometer and a system for recording observations. Then plans were made not only for reading about the questions raised but also for conducting experiments and recording observations. It was decided to put the anemometer in the school yard. One of the fathers helped with the construction. Several children made plans together for constructing a weather vane. One child brought a thermometer, and the janitor placed it outside the classroom window. In their language work the class had begun to study the writing of reports; so the children chose weather topics for their reports. New words such as velocity, precipitation, temperature, instruments, measure, and bureau were included in the spelling practice. Plans were made to visit the weather station at the airport.

A degree of truth is involved in some weather sayings; others are false. This class prepared a list of the sayings that were familiar to them, and by tabulating the kinds of weather that actually occurred, helped to reveal the limitations of such omens. A record was kept of the weather-bureau forecasts and of those in an almanac. The forecasts of the almanac, like the weather sayings, occasionally came true; but the weather-bureau forecasts were far more frequently correct.

STUDY GUIDE

1. Conduct an experiment with air, demonstrate it to your class, and explain what it reveals. How could the experiment be used with children? What can be accomplished, and why do you think the experiment would be suitable for that purpose?
2. Prepare a weather instrument, or borrow one; then show how it works and explain its value in weather forecasting.
3. Observe the weather regularly for a week or more and prepare some form of record, as children might do. Explain what children might gain from such an undertaking.
4. Clip or copy a weather report from a newspaper, and point out several of the meanings that should be understood to follow the report; then for each meaning indicate briefly a suitable way to develop the desired insight.
5. Select two or three understandings children might gain from a study of air and the weather; then use these to show how such a study may be of value in the everyday experiences of common people.
6. Discuss the weather with some child; attempt to determine the extent of his insight and some of the questions he considers interesting. Show him a weather instrument or perform a simple demonstration related to a study of air and weather. How did the demonstration affect his attitude?

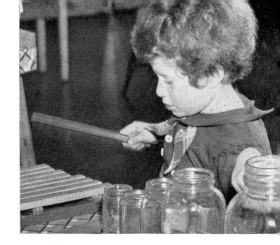

14

A Variety of
Experiences in Science

In this chapter three areas of the environment are considered. These areas are somewhat related, for they all deal with manifestations of energy. But all areas of science are somewhat related, and those relationships which are most pertinent to the problem at hand are the relationships which should be stressed in teaching.

EXPERIENCES WITH AVIATION

A miniature airport built of shoe boxes and using toy airplanes was the focal point for a fourth-grade study of aviation. The high point of the study was a visit to the commercial airport of the city. With arrangements made in advance, the children were escorted throughout the airport and were even permitted to inspect a large airliner.

Aviation is closely related to and is often included in a study of air and weather. Reversing the emphasis, some classes incorporate experiences with air and weather in a study of aviation. The environment as a child sees it is not precisely organized into fields of knowledge. A child may be interested in the jet aircraft he saw flash across the sky, or he may be concerned with the problems of supersonic flight about which he hears people talking. The child's knowledge is limited, but his interest is real, and with the teacher's help it can lead him to deeper insights. Interest in aircraft can lead to studies of machinery, transportation, communication, the stars, and navigation. Many phases of geography, including maps, longitude and latitude, and time differentials are likewise closely related to a study of aviation and often have bearing on the problems which fascinate children.

Considerable bulletin-board and reference material can be obtained by writing or visiting the office of a commercial airline, and libraries have numerous picturesque stories about the early days in aviation.

How an airplane flies

The force that lifts an airplane is easier to demonstrate than to explain. Hold a sheet of paper by two corners and allow the sheet to hang in a vertical position. Then blow air against the paper or move the paper rapidly forward so that it will tend to rise like a kite. Air moving under the wings in a similar

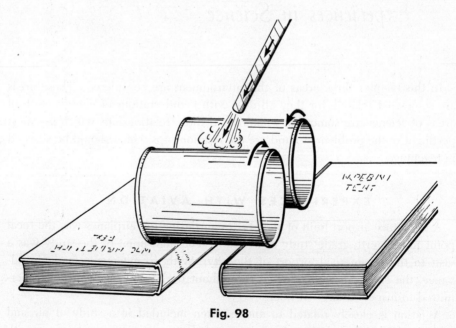

Fig. 98

Demonstrating how an airplane flies

manner tends to lift an airplane, but, surprisingly, a much greater lifting force is based upon a different principle. Lay two books a few inches apart on a desk and place a tin can on its side to span the interval between the books; place another can beside the first, the two about half an inch apart. Then roll a sheet of paper to form a tube. With the aid of the tube, blow downward between the cans. Ordinarily people expect the cans to be blown apart, but instead they come together. Each can moves toward the stream of air that blows across the curved surface of the can. In like fashion, the upper surface of an airplane wing is curved so that air moving rapidly across the wing causes the airplane to be lifted.

Another way to perform the experiment is to punch a hole at the center in the bottom of each can, pass a cord through the hole, knot the cord, and then with the free end suspend the two cans from a yardstick which has been placed across the backs of two chairs. Blowing between the cans as before should give the same effect. Still more variations can be devised by the children, using ping-pong balls, bottles, and other objects. Blowing between two sheets of paper will reveal the same phenomenon. It demonstrates Bernoulli's principle, which was named for the man who first formulated it. The principle applies to a stream of water as well as to a stream of air. A boat in a narrow stream, for example, tends to be drawn from the shore into the current.

Holding a sheet of paper by two corners, then turning down the near edge, will give approximately the contours of an airplane wing. Blowing horizontally across the curved surface will cause the sheet to rise, much as an airplane does. The propeller also works on this principle to draw an airplane forward. An aspirator or spray gun may be used as another illustration. A similar device can be prepared by cutting a drinking straw near one end so that the two segments

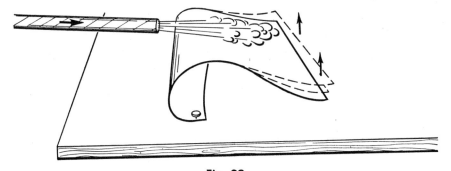

Fig. 99

The lifting force on an airplane wing

formed will remain attached, not completely severed, then bending the straw at the point where cut so that an L is formed. With the longer segment horizontal, and the shorter portion dipped into water, blowing through the horizontal segment will cause water to rise toward the stream of air, as in a spray gun.

A visit to an airport, or perhaps a museum, will provide opportunity for children to see not only the contours of an airplane but also the engine, the controls, and the instruments used. Pictures on the bulletin board will serve a similar purpose. Working with model airplanes and gliders, or even paper darts, will help children understand how the controls alter the direction of flight. How a jet plane is propelled by the exhaust gases can be demonstrated by allowing the compressed air to escape from a balloon as the balloon is released in midair.

Air resistance and gravity

A seventh-grade class came across a story of how Galileo dropped weights from a tower to show that objects of different weights will fall together — that the heavier ones do not strike first, as might be expected. The story was used in the book as an example of how scientists gain knowledge by experimenting rather than relying upon reasoning or authority alone. Instead of passively accepting the authority of the text, this class, in a truly scientific spirit, decided to try the experiment themselves. A large stone and a small one were dropped simultaneously from the second-floor classroom window. A portion of the class had been posted below as observers to note which stone hit the ground first. And the children were convinced when they found that what the book said was true: the stones fell approximately together, regardless of weight. For contrast, other objects of equal weight but different shapes were dropped together, and the class saw that air resistance can be a large factor. A paper crumpled into a ball, for example, fell much faster than a flat sheet of equal size.

Acceleration. At a one-room rural school in Wyoming, during recess, the children loosened boulders on the sides of a canyon and watched the stones bound down the slope, gain momentum, and finally tumble into the stream below. The teacher used the experience to teach that acceleration occurs as bodies fall, and to develop the concept of a center of gravity. Some of the stones already were teetering on the edge. A huge boulder, approximately the size of an automobile, needed but a slight push to start it rolling down the canyon wall. Yet it crashed to the bottom with impressive force, leaving a huge crater at one point where it struck on the way down. Other schools may not be able to duplicate this experience, but it does reveal how meaning can be drawn from situations that may be commonplace locally.

Wind resistance. To show the wind resistance that objects of various shapes may have, a number of articles may be suspended by threads, and it will be seen that some are affected more than others when the children blow upon them. If in each case a weight, such as an iron bolt, is hung from the one being tested, the weight of the bolt will tend to equalize any differences in the weights of the objects. To see how the air swirls about when it passes various objects, someone may blow against a milk bottle, the flat edge of a ruler, or other articles, and the direction of the air currents on the leeward side of the bottle or ruler can be detected by setting a lighted candle in various positions. The flame will show how the air is moving at that point. A plastic fish, a toy automobile, and similar objects may be tested to see how well streamlined they are.

A parachute will help to illustrate air resistance. One can be made by tying strings to the four corners of a handkerchief or similar cloth and attaching the four strings to a nail or other small weight.

Floating. Balloons float in air much as a cork does on water. Because the water is heavier, the cork is forced to rise. It is possible to float a drinking glass in a bucket of water by putting just enough water in the glass to keep it right side up. A tumbler floating in water is comparable to an iron ship, and will help to answer questions about how a metal ship can float. Adding a little water to the tumbler will cause it to float lower in the water, much as a ship does when cargo is loaded.

By adjusting the amount of water inside a small bottle with a tight cap, a bottle can be made to float in salt water but sink in fresh. The bottle may be floated also in kerosene, alcohol, or whatever fluids may be available. Some liquids are heavier, more dense, than others. Children who have swum in salt water may have noted that floating is easier there.

Even a rock tends to float in water. If a stone is held by a string tied about it and then immersed in water, the stone will feel lighter while in the water. The difference in weight can readily be measured with spring scales, if the scales can be obtained. The tendency to float is called *buoyancy,* and the volume of the stone determines how much the loss of weight in water will be. The children can determine for themselves why some objects, such as ice and cork, float above the surface of the water whereas a rubber stopper, for example, will sink, or why a small pebble will sink as readily as large ones do.

Fig. 100

A small bottle filled with just enough sand will float in salt water but will sink in fresh water.

EXPERIENCES WITH MACHINERY AND THE ENERGY TO DO WORK

Utilizing the interests of several "hot-rod" enthusiasts, an eighth-grade class launched a rather extensive investigation of machinery. Their study of centrifugal force helped them to see why a car should slow down when approaching a curve. The discussions and experiments involving stability and the center of gravity helped the farm children to understand why a tractor may be unstable on a hillside.

Machinery helps people do their work more easily. Today a basement can be dug more rapidly and easily with a power shovel or a bulldozer than was possible some years ago when such work was done with a team of horses pulling a scraper. Tools also may be considered machines, and digging a basement without even a shovel would be hard indeed. Physicists analyze machinery in terms of a few basic forms, called *simple machines,* but the analysis is not simple, and such an analytical approach seems inappropriate to the maturity of children, especially the smaller ones. Machinery nevertheless plays a prominent part in the child's environment and has a fascination for children. The schools can encourage children to observe automobiles, elevators, threshing machines, cream separators, vacuum cleaners, and refrigerators, and can help the children to learn how such equipment works. Field trips can be made to scenes of construction to observe a pile driver, a concrete mixer, a derrick, and similar equipment. Opportunity also can be provided for children to explain what they have seen individually. A study of machinery may overlap the study of other fields to whatever extent is desired. If someone sees scrap iron being loaded onto a railroad car by means of an electromagnet, a study of electricity may result, and the study may include machinery which is not electrical. The Industrial Revolution and the history of inventions are subjects closely related to a study of machinery. Machinery is increasingly common everywhere in our homes, on the farms, and in the factories. There has been some tendency to regard this area as typically of interest only to boys, but there seems to be little reason for such an inference. In any case, all our people live with machinery today, and everyone should have some understanding in this area as in others.

Tools and simple machinery

Many teachers encourage children to bring mechanical toys of various kinds to class. The child who brings in a toy is given an opportunity to demonstrate and explain how it works. Often a display is prepared. Grouping the various kinds of toys for the display helps to stress worthwhile generalizations, and further meaning can be brought out by preparing an explanatory placard for each item in the display. Thus the children gradually develop mature generalizations concerning the advantages of machines and how they function. Similar displays can be prepared of common tools, or of kitchen equipment, and sometimes all of these are included in one display.

Numerous meaningful questions arise when toys and common tools are shown, and further investigation will follow if the equipment is placed on a work table where children can handle it: What makes the bucking donkey buck? What happens when a spring is wound up, and how is the energy released a little at a time to keep the toy going? How does a top spin along the floor, and why does it move in larger circles at one time than another? How do the gears in an old clock turn the hands? And why are some of the gearwheels larger than others? What is the purpose of the balance wheel? How does the body tip up on a toy dump truck, and how does a toy power shovel move about to pick up sand or dirt? Which toys have roller bearings on the wheels, and how do the bearings help?

The teacher can supplement the resources brought by the children with equipment about the school. The seesaw on the playgrounds can be used to show how one child on the long end of a plank can lift several on the short end. Any plank can be arranged to illustrate the point if there is no playground equipment. A weight can be suspended by a string from a yardstick across the backs of two chairs to form a pendulum. By timing the oscillations the children can learn that whether the swings are large or small the number per minute is always the same. If the length of the string is increased, the number of oscillations will be less, and shortening the string will increase the rate; thus the children can learn how a pendulum clock is adjusted. The balance wheel in a watch serves the same purpose. If there are swings of different lengths on the playground, the oscillations of these may be timed and compared. The flagpole will illustrate how a pulley can be used merely for convenience. Putting up a flag could be quite difficult without the pulley.

The janitor may be able to show tools used about the school. The painter may have a block and tackle, which consists of several pulleys and is used to lift heavy objects. There may be a ramp or chute for loading and unloading supplies. In the building there may be other equipment that can be examined: a grindstone; the gears of a lawnmower; the screw that adjusts a wrench or the vise on a workbench; a chisel; a carpenter's plane, which is an adaptation of the chisel; a crowbar for prying; and the lever on the mop bucket, used for wringing out mops. A turnbuckle, a brace and bit, an automobile jack and other illustrations of levers and screws can be found about most schools to show how hard work is made easy. The children can learn how a pair of pliers should be held to get the firmest possible grip, or how snips must be used to cut through a heavy wire.

Over a period of time a teacher can collect many discarded items that are useful in teaching, such as an old clothesline pulley, an alarm clock that no longer runs accurately, a worn eggbeater, an abandoned meat grinder, a child's tow truck with a windlass for lifting the vehicle being towed. One school obtained an old automobile engine from a junk yard, and many classes after that were able to examine the gears, valves, cylinders, pistons, and other essential parts. Tinkertoy, Erector, and similar construction sets can be used to illustrate numerous mechanical principles. The pencil sharpener may be examined, including the handle that makes turning possible and the screw-type cutters inside. Bicycles can be examined conveniently either in the classroom or at the bicycle racks outside. A bicycle utilizes a number of mechanical principles, including the leverage gained by pedals, the chain drive, and the bearings. The gear ratio may be determined by counting the revolutions of the rear wheel and of the pedals. A bicycle with a gearshift is especially good for the purpose.

The teacher can encourage the children to examine and experiment with the equipment available and then demonstrate and explain what they have found. One third-grade group, for example, showed how they could arrange pulleys to drag a box across the floor, with one of the larger boys sitting in the box. As the children examine a variety of apparatus, they should come to realize that gears, wheels, pulleys, levers, screws, wedges, and similar devices are involved in complex equipment, and that some help by making slow work fast, others by making hard work easy.

A third-grader showed insight when he said: "A machine is something that makes work easier, faster, and more fun."

Water power and steam

Most of our heavy work today utilizes energy other than that of our own muscles or those of domestic animals. We use hydroelectric power, steam, diesel, and gasoline engines; and the industrial use of atomic energy is in its infancy.

In many regions today the generators that produce electricity are run by steam engines. The energy we use as electricity thus comes from the burning of coal in a steam engine. Steam engines also have been vital in the history of our railroads and the industrial development of our country. If a steam engine can be observed somewhere, the children will be able to understand such engines better.

The force of steam can be demonstrated readily in the classroom by placing about ¼ inch of water in a test tube and then closing the tube with a rubber stopper. Some corks will do, but others are porous and allow the steam to escape. When the test tube is heated over an alcohol burner or hot plate, steam is formed, and the pressure of the steam will eject the stopper. The force with which the stopper is ejected will depend upon how firmly it was inserted. There is little danger of breaking the glass, ordinarily, unless the stopper has been allowed to dry in the tube. While the test tube is being heated, however, care should be taken to point the stopper in a safe direction. If the tube is tipped while over the flame, it can be held near the top while the bottom is heated, for glass is a poor conductor of heat. In a steam engine the piston is moved by steam, just as the stopper is forced from a test tube by steam.

Wherever streams are swift there is abundant water power, and when dammed up the falling water can be made to turn a water wheel or turbine. The turbine is attached to an electric generator; the generator turns and electricity is produced.

It is possible to develop the idea of water power by constructing a water wheel that will turn when placed in the sink under the water faucet. The water wheel can be built by tacking rectangular sheets of metal to each side of a

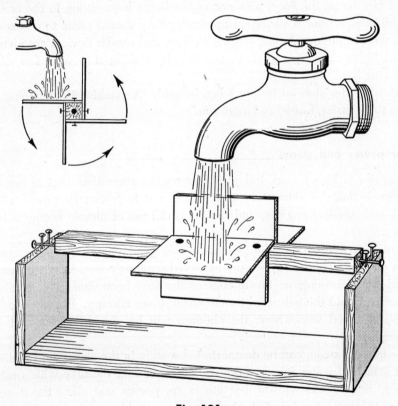

Fig. 101

A water wheel

stick, the stick being approximately an inch square and several inches long. If each strip of metal is flush on one edge and projects beyond the other, the strips attached to the four sides will form a paddle wheel. A nail may be driven into each end of the wood, and if one nail is held lightly in each hand the wheel will turn when placed under the water faucet. A convenient stand can be constructed to hold the water wheel. If one end of a string is tacked to the wooden shaft and the other end is run up over a pulley, the wheel can be made to lift a small weight.

In one class, an eighth grade, a very strong cylindrical magnet was attached crosswise near one end of the shaft. A coil of wire with many loops was fastened nearby so that as each end of the magnet moved past the coil a feeble current was generated in the coil. With the ends of the coil attached to a home-made galvanometer, it was possible to detect a slight current. The turning of

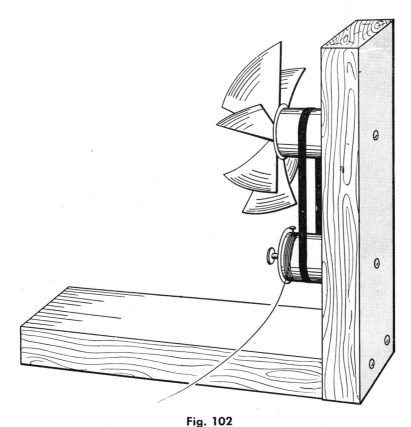

Fig. 102

A water turbine

the water wheel caused the magnet to turn past the coil, as in an electric generator, and electricity flowed in the line.

Another type of water wheel, more like a turbine, was constructed in a fifth grade. The top cut from a large tomato can was tacked to a wooden spool from which thread had been removed. The metal was then cut in pie-shaped sections and each section twisted more than sixty degrees. An L-shaped stand was made of wood, and a nail was driven horizontally into the top portion of the stand. The spool was placed on the nail, and when the apparatus was set in a dishpan and water poured down over it, the wheel would turn. Afterwards another spool was attached to the same stand, a few inches from the first, and a heavy rubber band was stretched over both spools to serve as a belt. A cord was tacked to the second spool, and a toy truck was fastened to the other end of the cord. The truck was loaded, and then as the turbine revolved, the cord began to wind onto the spool, and the loaded truck was drawn across the table.

That the pressure of water which moves a turbine, or the pressure from a

Fig. 103

The greater the height of the reservoir, the greater the water pressure.

faucet at home, is due to the weight of falling water can be demonstrated by punching three holes, one above the other, in the side of a tall juice can. Driving a nail into the side of the can is a convenient way to punch the holes. One hole should be placed a short distance from the top, one at the bottom, and the third halfway between. The holes may be covered while the can is being filled with water. When the water is free to run, the greater pressure will be apparent at the bottom hole. Other classes have illustrated the same point by punching a hole in the bottom of a tin can and inserting a one-hole rubber stopper with a long rubber tube attached. The higher the "reservoir" of water is lifted, the greater the pressure of the water emitted from the tube. Wherever possible cities locate their reservoirs on hilltops. Children often are puzzled because the pipes they see are running up from the basement, even in a tall apartment house, yet the books say water runs downhill. Bending the lower end of the tube upwards will help to explain how water from a reservoir runs mostly downhill yet up into a building.

Atomic energy

Because of its prominence in the news, atomic energy will receive incidental attention in many elementary classrooms. The subject is complex, and hence few will undertake a thorough study. When some happening attracts public attention, spontaneous discussions in the classrooms often follow, and news clippings may be posted as various events occur. Constructing wooden or cardboard models of nuclear reactors and other devices featured in the news in some cases may be undertaken by older children, working from the photographs and descriptions available. When one fifth-grade class became interested in atomic energy, questions were raised about atoms and molecules, and the investigations were directed into a study of chemical changes. Other possibilities would be to study various sources of energy, machinery, and the importance of science in the world today.

There is one interesting direct experience with atomic energy which can be arranged almost anywhere: Cover a luminous dial watch or clock and leave it for an hour or more in a dark closet. Then take a magnifying glass into the closet, and as soon as your eyes have become well adjusted to the darkness, look through the magnifying glass at the luminous dial. You will see tiny points of light — scintillations. Certain instruments used in nuclear research are similar in principle, and the various kinds are called scintillation counters, alpha counters, and spinthariscopes. The luminous dial contains a phosphorescent substance, material that glows when exposed to light; when placed in darkness, the glow gradually becomes weaker. The luminous paint also contains a small amount of some substance which, broadly speaking, is sometimes called "radium." When an atom of radium breaks down into a smaller atom, it emits an alpha or beta particle. The alpha particles are emitted with considerable force, which causes the luminous dial to glow at that point. Although atoms are far too small to be seen, it is possible to observe the point of light and thus detect the breaking down of a single atom. This deterioration of atoms is called *radioactivity,* and is used in hospitals to locate cancer or treat a goiter. Radioactivity has a multitude of other uses in medicine, research, and industry. In radioactivity an atom breaks down slowly. The atomic energy — often called nuclear energy — of a bomb, and also of industrial power, comes from a similar though more abrupt disintegration of atoms, which is called *fission.*

The heat we receive from the sun, like the force of a hydrogen bomb, comes from a similar process, called *fusion;* but in fusion small atoms of hydrogen join to form larger atoms and release energy. In any case, the sun is an example of nuclear energy that is familiar to everyone. If the sun were an ordinary fire, it would have been burned up long ago.

Inertia, friction, and direction of motion

A toy car with a flywheel instead of a spring to keep it running across the floor can be used to illustrate *inertia.* Or, try to stop a swing when someone is in it, and compare the difficulty with that of stopping an empty swing. Likewise an empty swing is easier to start than a full one. Both examples illustrate inertia. Another good way to clarify the idea is to have children push a piano or other heavy object along a level surface. They will see that keeping an object moving is easier than getting it started.

Centrifugal force can be illustrated by fastening a soft rubber ball to the end of a cord and then on the playground having a child whirl the ball about his head and suddenly release it. Another way is to fill a bucket perhaps half full of water and then at arm's length whirl it overhead without spilling any. This demonstration also is better conducted outdoors.

As objects move, *friction* tends to slow them down. Wheels help to reduce friction. To illustrate this, invert a child's wagon and have as many children climb onto it as possible; then have other children attempt to pull the wagon across the floor. Compare the difficulty with that encountered when the wagon is right side up and carrying the same weight. If the wheels are dry, oiling them may make a noticeable difference.

Another way to illustrate the same points is to attach a strong rope to an

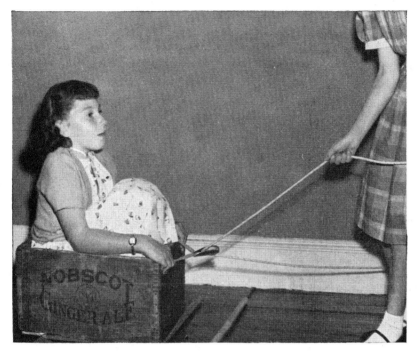

Fig. 104

The pulley and the rollers both help.

apple box, fill the box with books, and then note how hard it is to drag the box across the floor. For contrast, cut broomsticks into lengths that equal the width of the box and use the pieces as rollers under the box. If the janitor has a dolly, perhaps it can be borrowed and used under the box to see the purpose of such a device.

The energy of friction is converted into heat. By merely rubbing their hands along the tops of their desks, the children will find that considerable heat is produced, especially if it is done forcefully.

Rubbing two wooden blocks together before and after oiling the surface between them will reveal how oil reduces friction. If smooth blocks are compared with rough ones the difference will be apparent.

If two ropes are attached to an apple box that is loaded with books and the children pull in different directions, so that the ropes are at right angles to each other, it will be interesting to a class to note in what direction the box moves. If the children pull harder on one rope than another, does that change the direction?

If spring scales are available and the children are mature enough for more exact observations, the pull can be measured by attaching scales to each rope. In many of the experiments suggested, however, the load may have to be reduced to be within the range of the scales. Numerous other adaptations can be made according to the problems raised and the resources available. One variation, for example, may be to test how hard it is to pull objects up an incline, with rollers or without, and with the incline at various angles from the table or floor.

EXPERIENCES WITH SOUND

Some highly successful experimentation with sound has developed from an interest in music. Largely because many of the children were taking music lessons, the teacher of a fifth-and-sixth-grade class proposed that they begin a study of sound. Bernard brought his fife, played a composition on it, and then explained how the instrument makes sounds. Nancy and Mary Jane played their violins and then together explained how the music is produced by the vibration of the strings; how differences in length, thickness, and tightness of the strings determine how rapidly the strings vibrate, and thus set the pitch; and how a vigorous motion of the bow will cause the strings to swing farther from side to side and hence produce louder notes. Margaret showed with her trombone how the vibrations of her lips caused the metal of the instrument to vibrate and produce the sound, and how moving the slide changed the length of the air column and hence the pitch of the note. She showed also that tightening her lips would raise the pitch. William and John demonstrated their trumpets, indicating how the valves change the length of the air column, much as does the slide of a trombone. Three boys, Philip, Byron, and Joseph, were learning to play the drum, and they showed how the sound is really vibration, louder sounds being a greater motion. The children of the class felt the motion with their fingers. On the piano Shirley played a selection she was preparing for a recital. The top was lifted so that the children could see how the hammers struck the wires and caused them to vibrate. The different rates of vibration of high and low notes could be seen as well as felt by the children. They saw that the base strings were long and heavy and vibrated slowly, whereas the treble strings, being short and thin, moved more rapidly. It was pointed out that the pitch remained the same whether the wire was struck hard or softly, since the rate of vibration was unchanged. With the louder sounds the wires could be seen swinging farther from side to side — that is, the *amplitude* was greater.

Having begun with their musical instruments, this class continued their study of sound, doing reference work and whatever experiments they could find in the books they were reading.

Perhaps the first idea for children, one which can be developed early, is that sound is vibration. The children can feel their own throats while speaking and also note how a piano, a drum, and other instruments vibrate when played. By speaking into a cylindrical cardboard carton, such as an oatmeal box, and with fingers lightly touching the bottom of the box, a child can detect the vibrations which are the sound of his voice. The same carton can be used for showing differences in the pitch and loudness of sounds. With his fingers on the carton a child should be able to determine that a high-pitched sound is a rapid vibration, and that a sound is louder when the motion is more pronounced.

Pitch and loudness

The more rapid the vibrations, the higher the pitch of a sound. If a yardstick is placed on a desk with about half the length extending out over the edge, and if the end on the desk is held firmly in place, plucking the free end will cause that end to vibrate and produce a certain tone. Each time the stick is plucked the tone will be the same, but if plucked harder one time than another, the yardstick will swing farther back and forth, and the loudness will vary accordingly. Loudness depends upon the amplitude — how far the yardstick swings from side to side. But the pitch is always the same for a given length of yardstick. Drawing the yardstick back onto the desk so that a shorter length is free to vibrate will give a higher pitch. The pitch depends upon the frequency, the rapidity of the vibrations, which in turn depends upon the length of stick extending over the edge. Comparison may be made to a pendulum, for a pendulum of a given length will always swing the same number of times per minute. The concepts of pitch and volume can be reinforced by having children feel their own throats or some musical instrument while high and low notes are being sounded.

In stringed instruments it will be observed that higher notes are obtained by shortening the length of string that is free to vibrate. Each note can be played softly or with greater volume, and the explanation is the same as it was with the yardstick. The pitch depends upon the frequency, but the frequency depends upon more than length of string. Two strings on the same instrument may be of equal length, yet one may play low notes and the other high. The heavier strings vibrate more slowly and hence produce lower notes. The instrument is tuned by tightening or loosening the strings, changing the pitch. The kind of material the string is made of also will affect the pitch.

A stringed instrument with which the children may experiment freely can be constructed from a board, some rather fine wire, and several screw eyes. If four strings are desired, the four lengths of wire may be nailed to the end or to the reverse side of the board and then drawn up over the face of the board and attached to screw eyes in the opposite end of the board. To raise the wires off the board, a small strip of wood may be inserted under the strings at the first end and nailed to the board. Another strip may be placed at the opposite end if necessary. By tightening the screw eyes, the instrument can be tuned in any way desired. The children may experiment with various adjustments. Also the device may be used in a rhythm band of home-made instruments. Wires of different sizes may be used and instruments of different lengths constructed. A similar device may be improvised by stretching rubber bands of different sizes across a chalk box with the lid removed.

Many children know how to blow into the mouth of a bottle to produce a deep-throated whistling sound. By partially filling the bottle, the pitch can be raised. A number of soda-water bottles may be filled to certain different levels so that the notes they produce will harmonize, and when all are blown at once a chord will result. These too may be used in a rhythm band. In a pipe organ the longer tubes produce lower notes. In a slide trombone the length of pipe is increased to make lower notes, although the tightness of the lips is a factor too, just as tightness is a factor in the pitch of a violin string. A trumpet or other valved instrument uses extra tubing to lengthen the pipe for lower notes. If an old harmonica can be obtained and the cover removed, examining the reeds which produce the sound is worthwhile. A reed instrument may have valves along the side so that varying lengths of the tube are used. An "oboe" may be constructed from a drinking straw by flattening one end of the straw and snipping with scissors along each edge for about one-fourth of an inch to produce a double reed. With a little practice a single note can be obtained by blowing on the reed end. By snipping off the lower end, a little at a time, the pitch can be raised as in running the scales.

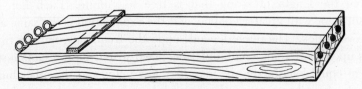

Fig. 105

A stringed instrument

Sound waves

The vibrations of sound are transmitted in the form of a wave motion. With a length of rope stretched across the room it is possible to show how a wave is transmitted, for the wave moves along the rope, yet the rope itself has only a back-and-forth motion. For the purpose, one end of the rope may be tied somewhere, or both ends may be held by children. By plucking, jerking, or striking one end, a wave can be made to pass along the rope. A child's toy, sometimes called a "Slinky," is actually a long, closely wound coil much like a spring. The coil provides an even better way of illustrating the wave motion of sound. If the coil is stretched across the room it can be compressed by striking it in a lengthwise direction, and a wave will move along the coil to the opposite end and there will be reflected back again. If one particular spot on the coil is watched, it will be noted that the coil moves back and forth in vibration yet the wave moves forward. When a sound is emitted, the source is vibrating, and the air is compressed momentarily as the coil was. That compression moves outward, much as the wave moved along the coil — except that in the air sound spreads in all directions, until reflected. If there is a pond nearby, the pond will be ideal for studying wave motion. Pebbles may be tossed into the water to show how the waves that are formed will spread. A cork on the surface will show the back-and-forth motion of the water itself. The children may note that the water in waves along a beach has a pronounced forward motion, but that is due to the manner in which a wave is tipped forward as it strikes the slope of the beach.

With so much talk about supersonic airplanes, the children may have a casual acquaintance with the speed of sound. But light travels much faster. We see lightning before we hear thunder, because the light travels faster and reaches us sooner than the sound. The idea can be demonstrated by having someone go to the far end of the playground and strike a tin can with a hammer or a rock while the class watches at a distance. The children should be able to report other examples they have noticed.

Sound travels through some materials even more rapidly than through air. With an ear to the railroad track, a person can hear a train while it is still far away. In the classroom, with one ear at the end of a baseball bat or yardstick, a child can plainly hear a watch held at the opposite end. Likewise, if there is a long table in the room, and if someone taps one end of it gently, a person at the other end can hear the tapping more plainly with his ear against the table than while standing erect. If several marbles are placed in the trough formed by two books tipped at an angle and another marble is shot against the first one in the line, the energy will be transmitted through the line of marbles much as the sound of the watch was transmitted along the yardstick.

As one way of learning that sounds can be reflected, teachers sometimes have children make and use megaphones of paper. In one second-grade class the children had no idea of what an echo is. The more the teacher explained, the more bewildered the class seemed to be. One said she couldn't see how the sound of her own voice could be heard again. So the class was taken for a walk to Echo Bridge. There, under the bridge, after they had called out and heard their voices come back to them, the children understood what an echo is. The next morning one child came in saying she had heard her voice echo in an empty room which her mother had cleared while house cleaning.

Harmony and resonance

To understand why the notes in a chord harmonize whereas other sounds often clash, children may experiment with water to see how waves behave. They may experiment in a large tub of water or, better yet, a quiet pool. The waves are easier to follow on the broader surface. A large puddle on the school grounds after a heavy rain may be satisfactory. By striking the water with a hand or a stick a person can make a wave pass across the pool, and if someone else will do likewise from another point, it will be observed that as the waves meet they either cancel each other or reinforce each other to form a higher wave. If the waves reinforce each other at one point and interfere at another, the result is similar to the effect noted when two instruments are not quite in tune and a pulsating sound results. The height of the wave — the amplitude — is equivalent to the loudness — or volume — of the sound; where sound waves reinforce each other the sound is loud, and where the waves clash the sound dies down, and pulsations result.

While the class is experimenting with the water, if a large wave is produced first and then a smaller, more frequent one, it is possible to see how one wave may be superimposed upon another yet each largely retain its own identity. Similar effects can be shown with a rope. Two waves can be made to pass along a rope at the same time. If one wave can be made just twice as frequent — half as long — as another, the effect will illustrate what happens when two notes harmonize. The two tend to reinforce each other.

A violin and a trumpet may play the same note, yet each instrument has its own distinctive sound, because a trumpet does not vibrate quite the way a violin does. Although the principal wave produced by either instrument is the same when the same note is played, each instrument produces additional waves which are superimposed upon the main note, and this gives the instrument its distinctive quality. The sound of a voice on a telephone differs from that in direct conversation because the metal diaphragm in the telephone will not vibrate exactly as the human throat does.

Anyone who has played a musical instrument may have noted that occasionally some object in the room will vibrate whenever a certain note is struck. To duplicate the effect, invert a metal pan or tray, put a dinner fork on it, and place both on top of a piano. By playing the scale it should be possible to find a certain note that will cause the fork and pan to rattle. Other equipment may be substituted for the pan and fork, and a brass instrument is excellent for use in the experiment. Each object will vibrate more freely at one frequency (pitch) than at another. Where the vibration was picked up from the piano or horn, the effect is called resonance.

Two small children were blowing on a tank of water to see how waves are formed. They soon learned that they could give the water a rocking motion by blowing at regular intervals. They had found that waves have a rhythmic quality. To keep a swing going, it must be given a push at the right moment each time, for otherwise the pushing will interfere with the swinging. The swing, or any other pendulum, will respond to but one frequency — and so it is with objects that vibrate when a particular note is played.

If the pedal of a piano is held down to free the wires, a note sung or played abruptly on some nearby instrument will cause certain strings of the piano to hum in resonance. For another illustration, a clock or watch may be held in the hand for all to hear the ticking and then placed on a table for comparison. The table acts as a sounding board, the board vibrating in resonance with the clock. If the clock is placed on a pillow or some child's coat, the sound will not be as loud. At home the draperies, rugs, and furniture tend to absorb the energy of the sounds and prevent echoes. Well-built schools have cork ceilings or other means of deadening unnecessary sounds. If a child speaks well before the class, so that his voice can be heard by all, his entire chest and head will vibrate in resonance with his throat as he speaks. It is possible to feel these vibrations with the finger tips.

The curiosity of a child has no bounds other than the limitations of his own environment. The investigations children make today reveal new opportunities for tomorrow. Science is the key to the future, and the future rests with children who are in the schools today.

STUDY GUIDE

1. Explain how a study of aviation could stimulate work in related areas of science and in other areas of the curriculum.
2. How could a study of machinery be organized to stress meanings? Outline some suitable activities in such a study, and indicate what you would consider a logical sequence of learning in the study.
3. How can a study of machinery and the energy to do work provide for individual initiative and varying backgrounds, interests, and abilities while also encouraging the children to work together cooperatively?
4. How would you determine whether or not a study of sounds was successful?
5. Show how the difference between chords and discords could be explained to a child. What would you do if a child asked why some sounds are loud and why some are shrill? What would you do if he asked what makes an automobile go, or what *radioactive* means?
6. If while children are reporting an experiment designed to show how an airplane flies the demonstration fails to work as expected, what should be done? Give an illustration.
7. How can books be used effectively in a study of aviation?

Science Books for Children

THE SKY

Adler, Irving. *Time in Your Life,* John Day, New York, 1955, 128 pp. Ages 11 and up.

Branley, Franklyn M. *Mars,* Crowell, New York, 1955, 148 pp. Upper elementary.

Coles, Robert R., and Frances Frost. *Star of Wonder,* McGraw-Hill, New York, 1953, 48 pp. Grades 4–6.

Freeman, Mae and Ira. *Fun with Astronomy,* Random House, New York, 1953, 57 pp. Grades 4–6.

Gallant, Roy. *Exploring the Moon,* Garden City Publishing Co., Garden City, New York, 1955, 63 pp. Grades 4–7.

Heuer, Kenneth. *Wonders of the Heavens,* Dodd, Mead, New York, 1954, 81 pp. Grades 5–8.

Lewellen, John B. *True Book of Moon, Sun and Stars,* Children's Press, Chicago, 1954, 43 pp. Primary.

———. *You and Space Neighbors,* Children's Press, Chicago, 1954, 58 pp. Ages 9–12.

Neurath, Marie. *Let's Look at the Sky,* Lothrop, Lee and Shepard, New York, 1953, 36 pp. For young readers.

Podendorf, Illa. *True Book of Seasons,* Children's Press, Chicago, 1955, 47 pp. Primary.

Rey, Hans A. *Find the Constellations,* Houghton Mifflin, Boston, 1954, 72 pp. Grades 4 and up. An aid to observation.

Schneider, Herman and Nina. *You Among the Stars,* W. R. Scott, New York, 1951, 56 pp. Grades 3 and up.

Sootin, Harry. *Isaac Newton,* Messner, New York, 1955, 191 pp. Upper elementary.

White, Anne T. *All About the Stars,* Random House, New York, 1953, 144 pp. Grades 5–8.

Wyler, Rose, and Gerald Ames. *Golden Book of Astronomy,* Simon and Schuster, New York, 1955, 97 pp. Upper elementary.

Wylie, Charles C. *Our Starland,* Lyons and Carnahan, Chicago, 1953, 378 pp. Upper elementary. An aid to observation.

Zim, Herbert S. *The Sun,* Morrow, New York, 1953, 51 pp. Ages 6 and up.

CHEMICAL CHANGES

Freeman, Ira M. *All About the Wonders of Chemistry,* Random House, New York, 1954, 148 pp. Grades 6–8.

Morgan, Alfred. *First Chemistry Book for Boys and Girls,* Scribner, New York, 1950, 179 pp. Grades 4–6.

White, Anne T. *George Washington Carver,* Random House, New York, 1953, 182 pp. Upper elementary.

THE EARTH'S SURFACE

Fenton, Carroll L. and Mildred A. *Riches From the Earth,* John Day, New York, 1953, 159 pp. Ages 8–11.

Fisher, James. *Wonderful World; the Adventure of the Earth We Live On,* Garden City Publishing Co., Garden City, New York, 1954, 65 pp. Upper elementary.

Goetz, Delia. *Deserts,* Morrow, New York, 1956, 64 pp. Ages 8–12.

Pough, Frederick H. *All About Volcanoes and Earthquakes,* Random House, New York, 1953, 150 pp. Grades 4–6.

Shannon, Terry. *Among the Rocks,* Sterling, New York, 1956. Upper elementary.

Twitchell, K. S., and R. Wyndham. *Keith Arnold in Mining Engineering,* Dodd, Mead, New York, 1956, 183 pp. Vocational novel for ages 12–16.

White, Anne T. *All About Our Changing Rocks,* Random House, New York, 1955, 142 pp. Upper elementary.

Wyler, Rose, and Gerald Ames. *Restless Earth,* Abelard-Schuman, New York, 1954, 156 pp. Upper elementary.

———. *The Story of the Ice Age,* Harper, New York, 1956, 81 pp. Ages 8–12.

Zim, Herbert S. *What's Inside the Earth?* Morrow, New York, 1953, 30 pp. Grades 3 and up.

PREHISTORIC ANIMALS

Andrews, Roy C. *All About Dinosaurs,* Random House, New York, 1953, 146 pp. Ages 9–12.

Bloch, Marie Hahn. *Dinosaurs,* Coward-McCann, New York, 1955, 43 pp. Grades 3–6.

Clark, Mary Lou. *True Book of Dinosaurs,* Children's Press, Chicago, 1955, 47 pp. Grades 2–4.

Dickinson, Alice Hoke. *First Book of Prehistoric Animals,* Watts, New York, 1954, 92 pp. Grades 4–7.

Fenton, Carroll L. *Prehistoric World; Stories of Animals in Past Ages,* John Day, New York, 1954, 126 pp. Upper elementary.

Neurath, Marie. *Wonder World of Long Ago,* Lothrop, Lee and Shepard, New York, 1955, 36 pp. Ages 6–10.

Scheele, William E. *First Mammals,* World Pub. Co., Cleveland, 1955, 128 pp. Ages 10 and up.

———. *Prehistoric Animals,* World Pub. Co., Cleveland, 1954, 125 pp. Ages 12 and up.

Zim, Herbert S. *Dinosaurs,* Morrow, New York, 1954, 64 pp. Grades 4–7.

LIVING THINGS

Blough, Glenn O. *Lookout for the Forest,* McGraw-Hill, New York, 1955, 48 pp. A conservation story for grades 3 and up.

———. *Wait for the Sunshine,* McGraw-Hill, New York, 1954, 47 pp. Seasons and growing things; ages 7–9.

Candy, Robert. *Nature Notebook,* Houghton Mifflin, Boston, 1953, 120 pp. Ages 8–12.

Jauss, Anne Marie. *Discovering Nature the Year Round,* Aladdin, New York, 1955, 64 pp. Upper elementary.

Moore, Alma C. *Friendly Forests,* Viking, New York, 1954, 96 pp. Conservation; ages 9–13.

Plants

Blough, Glenn O. *Tree on the Road to Turntown,* McGraw-Hill, New York, 1953, 48 pp. Ages 5–9.

Dickinson, Alice Hoke. *First Book of Plants,* Watts, New York, 1953, 93 pp. Grades 4–7.

Fenton, Carroll L., and Hermine B. Kitchen. *Plants That Feed Us,* John Day, New York, 1956, 96 pp. Ages 9 and up.

Kieran, John. *An Introduction to Trees,* Doubleday, Garden City, New York, 1954, 77 pp. Upper elementary.

King, Julius. *Telling Trees,* Sloane, New York, 1953, 127 pp. Upper elementary.

Kirkus, Virginia. *First Book of Gardening,* Watts, New York, 1956, 69 pp. Upper elementary.

Podendorf, Illa. *True Book of Trees,* Children's Press, Chicago, 1954, 43 pp. Primary.

———. *True Book of Weeds and Wild Flowers,* Children's Press, Chicago, 1955, 47 pp. Ages 4–8.

Selsam, Millicent. *Plants We Eat,* Morrow, New York, 1955, 123 pp. Grades 4–8. Includes experiments.

———. *See Through the Forest,* Harper, New York, 1956, 48 pp. Ages 7–11.

Stefferud, Alfred. *Wonders of Seeds,* Harcourt, Brace, New York, 1956, 119 pp. Ages 10–14.

Sterling, Dorothy. *Story of Mosses, Ferns, and Mushrooms,* Doubleday, Garden City, New York, 1955, 159 pp. Grades 5–8.

————. *Trees and Their Story,* Doubleday, Garden City, New York, 1953, 119 pp. Upper elementary.

How Animals Live

Adelson, Leone. *All Ready for Summer,* McKay, New York, 1956, 24 pp. Primary.

Earle, Olive L. *Paws, Hoofs, and Flippers,* Morrow, New York, 1954, 192 pp. Grades 5–8.

Gray, James. *How Animals Move,* Cambridge, New York, 1953, 114 pp. Upper elementary.

Green, Ivan E. *Animal Masquerade,* Coward-McCann, New York, 1955, 64 pp. Grades 3 and up.

Green, Mary M. *Everybody Has a House,* W. R. Scott, New York, 1953, 20 pp. Primary.

Hogan, Inez. *Little Ones,* Dutton, New York, 1956, 45 pp. Ages 4–7. Self-protection of forest creatures.

Hylander, Clarence J. *Animals in Armour,* Macmillan, New York, 1954, 203 pp. Grades 6 and up.

Mason, George F. *Animal Clothing,* Morrow, New York, 1955, 94 pp. Ages 10–14.

Selsam, Millicent. *How the Animals Eat,* W. R. Scott, New York, 1954, 91 pp. Ages 9–12.

————. *Time for Sleep,* W. R. Scott, New York, 1953, 56 pp. Grades 1–3.

Growth and Development

Berrill, Jacquelyn. *Strange Nurseries,* Dodd, Mead, New York, 1954, 96 pp. Upper elementary. How animals care for their young.

Bridges, William. *Zoo Babies,* Morrow, New York, 1953, 94 pp. Grades 3–6.

Buck, Pearl S. *Johnny Jack and His Beginnings,* John Day, New York, 1954, 47 pp. Sex education for younger children.

Darling, Louis. *Chickens and How to Raise Them,* Morrow, New York, 1955, 62 pp. Ages 8 and up.

Garelick, May. *What's Inside?* W. R. Scott, New York, 1955, 61 pp. Ages 3–7. The hatching of an egg.

Hussey, Lois, and Catherine Pessino. *Collecting Cocoons,* Crowell, New York, 1953, 73 pp. Grades 4–6.

O'Brien, Esse F. *Animal Tots,* Steck, Austin, Texas, 1956. Primary.

Podendorf, Illa. *True Book of Animal Babies,* Children's Press, Chicago, 1955, 44 pp. Primary.

Selsam, Millicent. *All About Eggs and How They Change Into Animals,* W. R. Scott, New York, 1952, 60 pp. Ages 4–8.

————. *All Kinds of Babies and How They Grow,* W. R. Scott, New York, 1952, 40 pp. Primary.

Strain, Frances. *Being Born,* Appleton-Century-Crofts, New York, 1954, 134 pp. Grades 6–8. Sex education.

Birds

Cruickshank, Helen Gere. *Wonders of the Bird World*, Dodd, Mead, New York, 1956. Ages 8 and up.

Fenton, Carroll, and Dorothy Pallas. *Birds and Their World*, John Day, New York, 1954, 95 pp. Grades 4–7.

Friskey, Margaret R. *True Book of Birds We Know*, Children's Press, Chicago, 1954, 47 pp. Primary.

Lemmon, Robert S. *All About Birds*, Random House, New York, 1955, 142 pp. Ages 10 and up.

McClung, Robert M. *Vulcan: the Story of a Bald Eagle*, Morrow, New York, 1955, 63 pp. Grades 3 and up.

Neurath, Marie. *Wonder World of Birds*, Lothrop, Lee and Shepard, New York, 1953, 36 pp. Grades 3 and up.

Ripper, Charles L. *Hawks*, Morrow, New York, 1956, 64 pp. Ages 8–12.

Sears, Paul M. *Barn Swallow*, Holiday House, New York, 1955, 45 pp. Ages 6–9.

Insects and Spiders

Hogner, Dorothy C. *Spiders*, Crowell, New York, 1955, 56 pp. Grades 3 and up.

Lane, Ferdinand C. *All About the Insect World*, Random House, New York, 1954, 141 pp. Upper elementary.

Lewellen, John B. *True Book of Honeybees*, Children's Press, Chicago, 1953, 45 pp. Ages 8–12.

Marcher, Marion W. *Monarch Butterfly*, Holiday House, New York, 1954, 42 pp. Grades 3 and up.

McClung, Robert M. *Tiger, the Story of a Swallow-tail Butterfly*, Morrow, New York, 1953, 44 pp. Grades 1–3.

Neurath, Marie. *Wonder World of Insects*, Lothrop, Lee and Shepard, New York, 1953, 36 pp. Ages 6 and up.

Podendorf, Illa. *True Book of Insects*, Children's Press, Chicago, 1954, 47 pp. Primary.

Sears, Paul M. *Firefly*, Holiday House, New York, 1956, 37 pp. Ages 6–9.

Sterling, Dorothy. *Insects and the Homes They Build*, Doubleday, Garden City, New York, 1954, 125 pp. Grades 5–8.

Swain, S. N. *Insects in Their World*, Garden City Publishing Co., Garden City, New York, 1955, 53 pp. Grades 5 and up.

Teale, Edwin W. *Insect Friends*, Dodd, Mead, New York, 1955, 96 pp. Ages 9–14.

———. *Junior Book of Insects*, Dutton, New York, 1953, 249 pp. Upper elementary.

Tibbets, Albert B. *First Book of Bees*, Watts, New York, 1952, 68 pp. For young readers.

Reptiles and Amphibians

Harris, Louise and Norman. *Slim Green*, Little, Brown, Boston, 1955, 52 pp. Ages 5–8. Story about a snake.

McClung, Robert M. *Bufo; the Story of a Toad,* Morrow, New York, 1954, 40 pp. Ages 6–8.

Sears, Paul M. *Tree Frog,* Holiday House, New York, 1954, 45 pp. Ages 7–9.

Sherman, Jane. *Real Book About Snakes,* Garden City Publishing Co., Garden City, New York, 1955, 224 pp. Upper elementary.

Zim, Herbert S., and Hobart M. Smith. *Reptiles and Amphibians,* Simon and Schuster, New York, 1953, 157 pp. Upper elementary and older.

Animals of the Zoo

Blough, Glenn O., and Marjorie H. Campbell. *When You Go to the Zoo,* McGraw-Hill, New York, 1955, 128 pp. Upper elementary.

Bridges, William. *Zoo Pets,* Morrow, New York, 1955, 94 pp. Grades 1–5.

Darling, Louis. *Seals and Walruses,* Morrow, New York, 1955, 63 pp. Upper elementary.

Goudey, Alice E. *Here Come the Bears,* Scribners, New York, 1954, 92 pp. Primary.

———. *Here Come the Deer,* Scribners, New York, 1955, 92 pp. Primary.

———. *Here Come the Elephants,* Scribners, New York, 1955, 93 pp. Primary.

———. *Here Come the Lions,* Scribners, New York, 1954, 92 pp. Primary.

Hogner, Dorothy Childs. *Cat Family,* Oxford, New York, 1956. Ages 9 and up.

Hylander, Clarence J. *Animals in Fur,* Macmillan, New York, 1956. Ages 10–16.

Leyson, Burr W., and Ruth Manecke. *Zoo Comes to You,* Dutton, New York, 1954, 88 pp. Ages 6–10.

McClung, Robert M. *Major, the Story of a Black Bear,* Morrow, New York, 1956, 64 pp. Ages 8–12.

Osmond, Edward. *Animals of the World,* Oxford, New York, 1956, 31 pp. Ages 8–12.

Schlein, Miriam. *Deer in the Snow,* Abelard-Schuman, New York, 1956. Ages 5–8.

Zim, Herbert S. *Big Cats,* Morrow, New York, 1955, 64 pp. Ages 8–12.

———. *Monkeys,* Morrow, New York, 1955, 64 pp. Grades 4–7.

Miscellaneous Animals

Adrian, Mary. *Gray Squirrel,* Holiday House, New York, 1955, 46 pp. Grades 3–5.

Alstrop, Jack Bentley. *Enjoying Pets,* Vanguard Press, New York, 1955, 240 pp. Ages 8 and up.

Aulaire, Ingri M. *Animals Everywhere,* Doubleday, Garden City, New York, 1954, 24 pp. Ages 3–6.

Berrill, Jacquelyn. *Wonders of the Woodland Animals,* Dodd, Mead, New York, 1953, 77 pp. Ages 8 and up.

Dudley, Ruth M. *At the Museum,* Melmont: leibel, Los Angeles, 1956. Primary.

Garland, Joseph. *All Creatures Here Below,* Houghton Mifflin, Boston, 1954, 86 pp. Grades 6–8.

Green, Ivan E. *Animals Under Your Feet,* Laurel, Scranton, Pennsylvania, 1953, 129 pp. Ages 7–10.

Hogner, Dorothy C. *Earthworms,* Crowell, New York, 1953, 51 pp. Ages 7–10.

Lewellen, John B. *True Book of Farm Animals,* Children's Press, Chicago, 1954, 44 pp. Primary.

Malter, Morton S. *Our Tiniest Animals in Real Life Size,* Whitman, Chicago, 1955, 32 pp. Primary.

Ripper, Charles L. *Bats,* Morrow, New York, 1954, 63 pp. Ages 9–12.

Stevenson, Elmo N. *Pets, Wild and Western,* Scribners, New York, 1953, 163 pp. Grades 4–6.

Weil, Ann. *Animal Families,* Children's Press, Chicago, 1956. Primary.

Zim, Herbert S., and Donald H. Offmeister. *Mammals: A Guide to Familiar American Species,* Simon and Schuster, New York, 1955, 160 pp. Upper elementary.

Seashore and Pond

Adrian, Mary Eleanor Venn. *Fiddler Crab,* Holiday House, New York, 1953, 40 pp. Grades 3 and up.

Broekel, Ray. *True Book of Tropical Fishes,* Children's Press, Chicago, 1956. Primary.

Buck, Margaret W. *In Ponds and Streams,* Abingdon-Cokesbury, Nashville, Tennessee, 1955, 72 pp. Upper elementary.

Cavanna, Elizabeth. *First Book of Sea Shells,* Watts, New York, 1955, 39 pp. Upper elementary.

Dudley, Ruth H. *Sea Shells,* Crowell, New York, 1953, 149 pp. Upper elementary.

Earle, Olive L. *Octopus,* Morrow, New York, 1955, 64 pp. Grades 4–7.

Evans, Eva. *Adventure Book of Shells,* Capitol, Irvington-on-Hudson, New York, 1955, 93 pp. Ages 10–14.

Gaul, Albro T. *Pond Book,* Coward-McCann, New York, 1955, 136 pp. Grades 4–7.

Goaman, Muriel. *Judy's and Andrew's Book of the Seashore,* Transatlantic Arts, Hollywood-by-the-Sea, Florida, 1956. Primary.

Lane, Ferdinand C. *All About the Sea,* Random House, New York, 1953, 148 pp. Ages 9–12.

Neurath, Marie. *Wonder World of the Seashore,* Lothrop, Lee and Shepard, New York, 1954, 36 pp. Ages 10 and up.

Pels, Gertrude J. *Care of Water Pets,* Crowell, New York, 1954, 119 pp. Upper elementary.

Podendorf, Illa. *True Book of Animals of the Sea and Shore,* Children's Press, Chicago, 1956. Primary.

———. *True Book of Pebbles and Shells,* Children's Press, Chicago, 1954, 47 pp. Ages 6–9.

Poole, Lynn. *Diving for Science,* McGraw-Hill, New York, 1955, 160 pp. Ages 10–16.

Selsam, Millicent. *See Through the Sea,* Harper, New York, 1954, 44 pp. Ages 7–10.

Health

Cosgrove, Margaret L. *Wonders Inside You,* Dodd, Mead, New York, 1955, 84 pp. Upper elementary.

Higgins, Helen Boyd. *Walter Reed; Boy Who Wanted to Know*, Bobbs-Merrill, Indianapolis, 1956, 192 pp. Ages 7 and up.

Lewis, Lucia Z. *First Book of Microbes*, Watts, New York, 1955, 64 pp. Upper elementary and older.

Malkus, Alida S. *Story of Louis Pasteur*, Grosset and Dunlap, New York, 1952, 178 pp. Upper elementary.

Perry, John. *Our Wonderful Eyes*, McGraw-Hill, New York, 1955, 159 pp. Upper elementary.

Ravielli, Anthony. *Wonders of the Human Body*, Viking, New York, 1954, 125 pp. Upper elementary.

Schneider, Leo. *You and Your Senses*, Harcourt, Brace, New York, 1956, 137 pp. Ages 10–14.

Selsam, Millicent E. *Microbes at Work*, Morrow, New York, 1953, 95 pp. Upper elementary.

Williams, Beryl, and Samuel Epstein. *William Crawford Gorgas*, Messner, New York, 1953, 184 pp. Grades 6–9.

Zim, Herbert S. *Our Senses and How They Work*, Morrow, New York, 1956, 64 pp. Ages 8–12.

————. *What's Inside of Me*, Morrow, New York, 1952, 32 pp. Grades 3 and up.

MAGNETISM AND ELECTRICITY

Bendick, Jeanne. *Electronics for Young People*, McGraw-Hill, New York, 1955, 187 pp. Ages 12 and up.

Bendick, Jeanne and Robert. *Television Works Like This*, McGraw-Hill, New York, 1954, 64 pp. Grades 6–9.

Epstein, Sam and Beryl. *First Book of Electricity*, Watts, New York, 1953, 63 pp. Grades 4–6. Includes experiments.

Gould, Jack. *All About Radio and Television*, Random House, New York, 1953, 143 pp. Upper elementary.

Meyer, Jerome S. *Picture Book of Electricity*, Lothrop, Lee and Shepard, New York, 1953, 39 pp. Ages 9 and up.

Neurath, Marie. *Around the World in a Flash*, Lothrop, Lee and Shepard, New York, 1954, 36 pp. Upper elementary.

Stoddard, Edward. *First Book of Television*, Watts, New York, 1955. Grades 6–8.

AIR AND THE WEATHER

Adler, Irving. *Hurricanes and Twisters*, Knopf, New York, 1955, 143 pp. Grades 4–8.

Blough, Glenn O. *Not Only for Ducks*, McGraw-Hill, New York, 1953, 48 pp. Ages 6–10.

Fenton, Carroll and Mildred. *Our Changing Weather*, Doubleday, Garden City, New York, 1954, 110 pp. Upper elementary.

Friskey, Margaret. *True Book of Air Around Us*, Children's Press, Chicago, 1953, 47 pp. Primary.

Larrick, Nancy. *See for Yourself; a First Book of Science Experiments,* Aladdin, New York, 1952, 48 pp. Ages 6–9.

Sandman, Howard E. *Who's Afraid of Thunder?* Sterling, New York, 1953, 61 pp. Grades 3–5.

Schloat, G. Warren. *Magic of Water,* Scribners, New York, 1955, 44 pp. Ages 7–11.

Tannehill, Ivan R. *Hurricane Hunters,* Dodd, Mead, New York, 1956, 271 pp. Ages 12–16.

Zim, Herbert S. *Lightning and Thunder,* Morrow, New York, 1952, 64 pp. Grades 4–6.

AVIATION

Beeler, Nelson, and Franklyn Branley. *Experiments with Airplane Instruments,* Crowell, New York, 1953, 115 pp. Upper elementary and older.

Bendick, Jeanne. *First Book of Space Travel,* Watts, New York, 1953, 69 pp. Ages 8–12.

Branley, Franklyn. *Experiments in the Principles of Space Travel,* Crowell, New York, 1955, 119 pp. Upper elementary.

Brown, Slater. *Spaceward Bound,* Prentice-Hall, Englewood Cliffs, New Jersey, 1955, 213 pp. Upper elementary. Fiction.

Frost, Frances. *Rocket Away,* McGraw-Hill, New York, 1953, 48 pp. Upper elementary. Fiction.

Goodwin, Harold L. *Real Book About Space Travel,* Garden City Publishing Co., Garden City, New York, 1952, 192 pp. Upper elementary.

Hurst, Earl O. *Big Book of Space,* Grosset and Dunlap, New York, 1954, 24 pp. Upper elementary.

Hyde, Margaret O. *Flight Today and Tomorrow,* McGraw-Hill, New York, 1953, 140 pp. Upper elementary and older.

Lewellen, John. *True Book of Airports and Airplanes,* Children's Press, Chicago, 1956, 47 pp. Grades 2 and up.

Moore, Patrick. *Boy's Book of Space,* Roy, New York, 1956, 144 pp. Upper elementary.

Pratt, Fletcher. *All About Rockets and Jets,* Random House, New York, 1956, 139 pp. Grades 5–8.

Ross, Frank, Jr. *Space Ships and Space Travel,* Lothrop, Lee and Shepard, New York, 1953, 166 pp. Upper elementary.

MACHINERY AND ENERGY

Adler, Irving. *Tools in Your Life,* John Day, New York, 1956, 128 pp. Ages 11 and up.

Barrow, George. *Your World in Motion,* Harcourt, Brace, New York, 1956, 181 pp. Ages 12 and up. Includes experiments.

Bendick, Jeanne. *First Book of Automobiles,* Watts, New York, 1955, 64 pp. Upper elementary.

Burns, William A. *Man and His Tools,* McGraw-Hill, New York, 1956, 160 pp. Ages 10 and up.

Doorly, Eleanor. *Radium Woman: A Life of Marie Curie,* Roy, New York, 1954, 181 pp. Upper elementary and older.

Elting, Mary. *Machines at Work,* Garden City Publishing Co., Garden City, New York, 1953, 90 pp. Ages 8–12.

Huey, Edward G. *What Makes the Wheels Go Round,* Harcourt, Brace, New York, 1952, 176 pp. Grades 5–8.

Lewellen, John B. *Mighty Atom,* Knopf, New York, 1955, 58 pp. Grades 2–4.

———. *True Book of Toys at Work,* Children's Press, Chicago, 1953, 45 pp. Primary.

Pearl, Carleton. *Tenth Wonder: Atomic Energy,* Little, Brown, Boston, 1956, 129 pp. Upper elementary and older.

Schneider, Herman and Nina. *More Power to You,* W. R. Scott, New York, 1953, 128 pp. Upper elementary.

Zim, Herbert S. *What's Inside of Engines,* Morrow, New York, 1953, 32 pp. Ages 7–10.

MISCELLANEOUS

Adler, Irving. *Fire in Your Life,* John Day, New York, 1955. Upper elementary.

Baer, Marian E. *Sound, an Experiment Book,* Holiday House, New York, 1952, 127 pp. Grades 3 and up.

Beeler, Nelson, and Franklyn Branley. *Experiments in Science,* Crowell, New York, 1955, 154 pp. Upper elementary.

Epstein, Samuel, and Beryl Williams. *Real Book About the Sea,* Garden City Publishing Co., Garden City, New York, 1954, 223 pp. Ages 8–14.

Holden, Raymond P. *Famous Scientific Expeditions,* Random House, New York, 1955, 143 pp. Ages 10–14.

Larson, Egon. *Radar Works Like This,* Roy, New York, 1953, 64 pp. Upper elementary.

Leeming, Joseph. *Real Book of Science Experiments,* Garden City Publishing Co., Garden City, New York, 1954, 222 pp. Upper elementary.

Levinger, Elma. *Galileo; First Observer of Marvelous Things,* Messner, New York, 1952, 180 pp. Ages 12 and up.

Lewellen, John. *Boy Scientist,* Popular Mechanics, Simon and Schuster, New York, 1955. Grades 6 and up. Received Edison award.

Parker, Bertha. *Golden Book of Science,* Simon and Schuster, New York, 1956, 97 pp. Grades 3 and up.

———. *Golden Treasury of Natural History,* Simon and Schuster, New York, 1952, 216 pp. Grades 3 and up.

Podendorf, Ila. *True Book of Science Experiments,* Children's Press, Chicago, 1954, 45 pp. Primary.

———. *True Book of Sounds We Hear,* Children's Press, Chicago, 1955, 46 pp. Primary.

Ross, Frank. *Ben Franklin–Scientist,* Lothrop, Lee and Shepard, New York, 1952, 128 pp. Ages 9–14.

Scheib, Ida. *What Happened?* McKay, New York, 1955, 117 pp. Upper elementary. Science behind the news.

Schneider, Herman and Nina. *Let's Look Under the City,* W. R. Scott, New York, 1954, 70 pp. Grades 3–5.

Schwartz, Julius. *Now I Know,* McGraw-Hill, New York, 1955, 32 pp. Grades 2–5.

———. *Through the Magnifying Glass,* McGraw-Hill, New York, 1954, 142 pp. Ages 10 and up.

Smith, Frances C. *First Book of Conservation,* Watts, New York, 1954, 63 pp. Ages 9–13.

Somerville, John. *Way of Science; Its Growth and Method,* Schuman, New York, 1953, 172 pp. Ages 11–14.

Stevens, William Oliver. *Famous Men of Science,* Dodd, Mead, New York, 1952, 164 pp. Upper elementary and older.

Wyler, Rose. *First Book of Science Experiments,* Watts, New York, 1952, 69 pp. Grades 5–8.

Zim, Herbert S. *Things Around the House,* Morrow, New York, 1954, 32 pp. Ages 6–10.

Publications for the Teacher

American Medical Association. *Publications About Your Health,* The Association, Chicago, 1955. Pamphlets which can be obtained free are described.

Avery, Madalyn. *Household Physics,* Macmillan, New York, 1955, 472 pp. Stresses practical explanations of common household equipment, such as vacuum cleaners, refrigerators, and thermostats.

Beuschlein, Muriel. *Free and Inexpensive Materials for Teaching Conservation and Resource-Use,* National Association of Biology Teachers, no date, 10¢, distributed by Richard L. Weaver, P.O. Box #2073, Ann Arbor, Michigan.

Blough, Glenn O., and Marjorie H. Campbell. *Making and Using Classroom Science Materials in the Elementary School,* Dryden, New York, 1954, 229 pp.

Blough, Glenn O., and Albert J. Huggett. *Methods and Activities in Elementary-School Science,* Dryden, New York, 1951, 310 pp.

———. *Elementary-School Science and How to Teach It,* Dryden, New York, 1951, 532 pp. The larger edition includes a survey of subject matter.

Bruce, Guy V. *Science Teaching Today,* National Science Teachers Association, 1201 Sixteenth St., N.W., Washington 6, D.C. Experiments with water, air, fuels and fire, heat, magnetism and electricity, sound, light and color. In seven volumes, 30 to 72 pages each, at 75¢, or $4.50 for set. Upper elementary.

Burnett, R. Will. *Teaching Science in the Elementary School,* Rinehart, New York, 1953, 541 pp.

Burt, William Henry, and Richard Philip. *A Field Guide to the Mammals,* Houghton Mifflin, Boston, 1952, 200 pp.

Chaney, Margaret S. *Nutrition,* Houghton Mifflin, Boston, 1954, 484 pp.

Craig, Gerald S. *Science for the Elementary-School Teacher,* Ginn, Boston, 1947, 561 pp.

———. *Science in Childhood Education,* Bureau of Publications, Teachers College, Columbia University, New York, 1944, 86 pp.

Fisher, James, and Peter Scott. *Sea Birds,* Houghton Mifflin, Boston, 1954, 320 pp.

418

Forbush, Edward Howe. *Natural History of the Birds of Eastern and Central North America,* Houghton Mifflin, Boston, 1939, 400 pp.

Freeman, Kenneth. *Helping Children Understand Science,* Winston, Philadelphia, 1954, 314 pp.

Gaddum, Leonard W., and Harold L. Knowles. *Our Physical Environment,* Houghton Mifflin, Boston, 1953, 625 pp.

George Peabody College for Teachers. *Free and Inexpensive Learning Materials,* The College, Nashville, Tennessee, 1956, 244 pp., $1.00.

Grant, Charlotte L., H. Keith Cady, and Nathan A. Neal. *High School Biology,* McGraw-Hill, New York, 1952, 812 pp.

Greenlee, Julian. *Better Teaching Through Elementary Science,* Wm. C. Brown, Dubuque, Iowa, 1954, 216 pp.

———. *Teaching Science to Children,* Wm. C. Brown, Dubuque, Iowa, 1955, 185 pp. Activities for small children.

Hoffman, Ralph. *Birds of the Pacific States,* Houghton Mifflin, Boston, 1938, 353 pp.

Hudspeth, Jack and Frances. *Handbook for Teachers of Elementary Science,* Steck, Austin, Texas, 1949, 77 pp.

Klots, Alexander B. *A Field Guide to the Butterflies of North America, East of the Great Plains,* Houghton Mifflin, Boston, 1951, 368 pp.

Mallinson, George Greisen and Lois Marion. *A Bibliography of Reference Books for Elementary Science,* National Science Teachers Association, 1201 Sixteenth St., N.W., Washington 6, D.C., 1953, 42 pp. Mimeographed, 50¢.

Mallinson, George Greisen, and Jacqueline Buck. *Science Bibliography,* National Science Teachers Association, Washington, D.C., 1954, 11 pp. Mimeographed, 50¢. A listing of textbooks.

McCorkle, Paul. *Physical World,* McGraw-Hill, New York, 1956, 465 pp.

McKay, Herbert. *Easy Experiments With Plants,* Oxford, New York, no date, 98 pp.

Morris, Percy A. *A Field Guide to the Shells of Our Atlantic and Gulf Coasts,* Houghton Mifflin, Boston, 1951, 236 pp.

———. *A Field Guide to the Shells of the Pacific Coast and Hawaii,* Houghton Mifflin, Boston, 1952, 220 pp.

National Education Association, Department of Elementary School Principals. *National Elementary Principal,* Bulletin "Featuring Science in the Elementary School," vol. XXIX, No. 4, The Association, 1201 Sixteenth St., N.W., Washington 6, D.C., February 1950, 48 pp.

———. *Science for Today's Children,* The Association, 1201 Sixteenth St., N.W., Washington 6, D.C., 1953, 311 pp. Thirty-second Yearbook, Bulletin vol. XXXIII, No. 1.

National Science Teachers Association. *Elementary School Science Bulletin,* The Association, 1201 Sixteenth St., N.W., Washington 6, D.C. Published six times a year; a subscription ($5.00 a year) provides 10 copies of each issue of the Bulletin, 8 issues of *The Science Teacher,* and other services and materials.

Palmer, E. Laurence. *Fieldbook of Natural History,* McGraw-Hill, New York, 1949, 664 pp. An encyclopedia of plants, animals, minerals, and stars.

Parker, Bertha M. *Science Experiences, Elementary School,* Row, Peterson, Evanston, Illinois, 1952, 272 pp. For teachers of grades 4 and up; suggested experiences in a variety of fields.

Peattie, Donald Culross. *A Natural History of Western Trees,* Houghton Mifflin, Boston, 1953, 751 pp.

Peterson, Roger Tory. *A Field Guide to the Birds,* Houghton Mifflin, Boston, 1947, 320 pp. For species east of the Rockies.

———. *A Field Guide to Western Birds,* Houghton Mifflin, Boston, 1941.

———. *Wildlife in Color,* Houghton Mifflin, Boston, 1952, 192 pp.

Pough, Frederick H. *A Field Guide to Rocks and Minerals,* Houghton Mifflin, Boston, 1952, 333 pp.

Rey, H. A. *The Stars,* Houghton Mifflin, Boston, 1952, 144 pp.

United States Office of Education. *Teaching Nutrition in the Elementary School,* Washington, 1955, 33 pp. For sale by Superintendent of Documents, U.S. Government Printing Office, Washington 25, D.C., 25¢.

Walker, Ernest P. *First Aid and Care of Small Animals,* Animal Welfare Institute, 270 Park Avenue, New York 17, 1955, 46 pp., 25¢.

Zim, Herbert S. *Science for Children and Teachers,* Association for Childhood Education International, 1200 Fifteenth St., N.W., Washington 5, D.C., 1953, 55 pp.

Index

Aardvark, 147–48, 150
Acceleration, 388–89
Acid-base test, 245–46
Aims, 71–88, 152–53
Air: demonstrating presence of, 75, 353–58; in water, 32–33; pressure of, 34, 40–41; resistance of, 388, 389; materials for a study of, 191
Airplanes, 42, 385–89
Ammeter, 341
Anemometer, 381
Animal life, 276–317; teaching examples, 2–3, 15–16, 49–50, 60, 61, 62, 80, 100–01, 102, 127, 130–34, 138, 142; materials for a study of, 165–71, 173, 189–90
Answering children's questions. *See* questions
Ants, 126; nests for, 168. *See also* animal life
Aphids: preparation of spray to control, 250
Apparatus. *See* materials for teaching
Aquarium: observations in, 15, 32, 38, 135–36, 277, 287–88; feeding animals in, 314–15; stocking of, 131–32, 312–13; tank for, 173, 189–90; condensation in, 3
Arithmetic: as related to science, 140
Art: as related to science, 136–37
Atmosphere, 353–83
Atomic energy, 397–98

Attitudes. *See* scientific attitudes; cooperation in science
Audio-visual aids, 18, 158, 273–74, 295
Aviation, 42, 385–89

Background: of the teacher, 14, 19–21, 23–24; of the child, 29–30, 120
Bacon, Francis, 145
Bacteria cultures, 21, 75–76, 305
Balance: construction of, 173–75
Ball and ring apparatus, 173
Barometer, 34, 369–71, 377
Basalt, 264, 272–73
Batteries, 345–48, 351
Behavior of living things, 42–43, 300–04
Bell, Alexander Graham, 17
Bells and buzzers, electric, 329, 348
Biographies of scientists, 93–95
Bird feeder: construction of, 169–71
Birds, 63, 78, 281–82. *See also* animal life
Books, selection of, 56, 98–100, 160; use of, 22–23, 103–05, 125–27, 135
Bruno, Giordano, 69
Buoyancy, 389

Cages: construction of, 164, 165–68
Capillarity, 41, 304
Carbon dioxide: test for, 243, 244
Catalyst, 243
Caterpillars, 2–3. *See also* animal life
Cells, voltaic, 345–48, 351